Chemical Reaction Analysis

PRENTICE-HALL INTERNATIONAL SERIES
IN THE PHYSICAL AND CHEMICAL ENGINEERING SCIENCES

NEAL R. AMUNDSON, EDITOR, *University of Minnesota*

ADVISORY EDITORS

ANDREAS ACRIVOS, *Stanford University*
THOMAS J. HANRATTY, *University of Illinois*
DAVID E. LAMB, *University of Delaware*
JOHN M. PRAUSNITZ, *University of California*
L. E. SCRIVEN, *University of Minnesota*

ARIS   *Introduction to the Analysis of Chemical Reactors*
ARIS   *Vectors, Tensors, and the Basic Equations of Fluid Mechanics*
FREDRICKSON   *Principles and Applications of Rheology*
HAPPEL AND BRENNER   *Low Reynolds Number Hydrodynamics in Particulate Media*
HOLLAND   *Multicomponent Distillation*
LEVICH   *Physicochemical Hydrodynamics*
LYKOV AND MIKHAYLOV   *Theory of Energy and Mass Transfer*
PETERSEN   *Chemical Reaction Analysis*
WILDE   *Optimum Seeking Methods*

PRENTICE-HALL, INC.
PRENTICE-HALL INTERNATIONAL, UNITED KINGDOM AND EIRE
PRENTICE-HALL OF CANADA, LTD., CANADA

Chemical Reaction Analysis

EUGENE E. PETERSEN

Department of
Chemical Engineering
University of California at Berkeley

PRENTICE-HALL, INC.

Englewood Cliffs, New Jersey

PRENTICE-HALL INTERNATIONAL, INC., *London*
PRENTICE-HALL OF AUSTRALIA, PTY, LTD., *Sydney*
PRENTICE-HALL OF CANADA, LTD., *Toronto*
PRENTICE-HALL OF INDIA (PRIVATE) LTD., *New Delhi*
PRENTICE-HALL OF JAPAN, INC., *Tokyo*

Library of Congress Catalog Card Number: 64—66084

Printed in the United States of America

C—12872

To
K. R. E. R. - F. M.

I am grateful to the following authors and publishers for permission to reprint the epigrams.

To The Public Trustee and the Society of Authors for the quotation from Episode I of George Bernard Shaw's play, *Misalliance*.

To Harcourt, Brace & World, Inc., Publishers for the quotation from *The Middle Kingdom* by Christopher Morley.

To the Liveright Publishing Corporation for the quotation from the poem "Observation" by Samuel Hoffenstein taken from the book entitled *Poems in Praise of Practically Nothing*.

Preface

Under the generic title "Chemical Reaction Analysis" this book deals with chemical kinetic processes and physical rate processes, and the manner in which these processes interact to govern the apparent overall behavior of chemically reactive systems. Although systems of this type are evident in many branches of science and engineering, the study and development of the field has remained largely within the sphere of chemical engineering; as a result, emphasis has been placed on serving the needs of the chemical industry. To an extent, such emphasis is justified. On the other hand, we cannot overlook the importance of many systems which lie outside the usual realm of chemical engineering, such as those supplying nutrients to the living cell or igniting solid propellants, all of which can be analyzed from a common set of principles. Accordingly, it seemed appropriate to shape this book to serve the needs of those interested in chemically reactive systems in general: to emphasize the chemical reaction itself and show how the behavior of the reaction system is modified when resistance to energy and material transport is large. By following this more general approach, I hope to have made the book valuable to a greater audience, who can adapt the principles and methods to fit specific cases rather than depend upon recipes.

Manifestly, this small book cannot cover all the topics which are concerned with heterogeneous chemical reactions and transport processes. The subject is too broad for this. However, the problem of what to select was quite naturally resolved for me: I could best deal with those topics which reflected my own interest and experience. Perhaps no one will completely agree with my selection of subject material; but I do not view this with any great alarm, because the subject matter is reasonably diverse and is developed from a unified point of view, thereby giving a perspective from which the vast and rich literature in this field can be evaluated. In fact, if the book stimulates the reader to probe deeper into this fascinating area, it will have served its purpose.

Certain prerequisite knowledge is assumed as part of the reader's background. He should have some familiarity with kinetics, and in particular with catalysis, because the treatment of the latter topic in this book is probably insufficient for the application of these methods to a specific problem. He must have had some experience with the theory of transport processes, and should have a working knowledge of ordinary differential equations. To understand the treatment of complex reactions, familiarity with vector and matrix operators is needed. The discussions in the two appendices should be sufficient for this purpose; however, to work confidently with these methods the suggested references should be consulted.

Many people have encouraged me and helped me in the writing of this book and to these people, many of whom must remain anonymous, I am indebted. I take pleasure in acknowledging the helpful comments of my colleagues Professors R. Aris, J. M. Prausnitz and T. Vermeulen on various parts of the book. I am sincerely grateful to two other colleagues, Professors A. Acrivos and M. Boudart, for helping me to shape ideas during the course of this project and for their comments on the finished manuscript. Their influence is evident in many parts of this book. I owe a great debt to Dr. J. C. Friedly who patiently and critically read the original manuscript. His comments and suggestions for improvement are too numerous to list in detail. To Mrs. Edith Taylor and Mrs. Jerilyn Schricker, who contributed far more to the final form of the manuscript than typing, I express my sincere thanks. Finally, this book would not have been possible without the efforts of my wife, Kay, who saw to it that large blocks of uninterrupted time were available to me for meditation.

E. E. PETERSEN

Berkeley, California

Contents

Chemical Reaction Analysis

Introduction

I

He who would bring home the wealth of the Indies
Must carry the wealth of the Indies with him.

Spanish Proverb

The first aphorism of Sir Francis Bacon's *Novum Organum*, "Man, who is the servant and interpreter of nature, *can act and understand no further than he has observed*, either in operation or in contemplation, of the method and order of nature" [emphasis added], is almost a prophetic warning of special significance to the kineticist. He depends upon experimental measurements perhaps even more than does his counterpart in other areas of chemistry and chemical engineering. The rate of a chemical reaction *must* be measured experimentally. And yet, curiously, without theoretical interpretation, a set of measurements is often virtually useless. The bridge between theory and experiment is chemical reaction analysis: a subject concerned with the interaction of chemical kinetic and physical rate phenomena and having for its objective the resolution and evaluation of the importance of each of the individual processes in the over-all rate process.

Very few real systems involving chemical reactions can be analyzed, even in principle, with rigor, whereas certain systems, some of which have little practical importance, can be analyzed in a sophisticated fashion. While at first it may seem strange to be concerned with systems of little practical value, the real purpose of analysis is to find out which features of a reaction system are important. Can we neglect certain features which greatly complicate the analysis of the system and obtain a meaningful result? Unfortunately no unique answer can be given to this question because the importance of a particular effect often depends upon how the information is to be used as well as upon what property is being assessed. Intuition is often unreliable in making this decision. Thus, the systematic survey of the influence of certain coupled processes in modifying the over-all rate of chemical reactions

I

combined with the development of techniques for analyzing such systems become the avowed objectives of chemical reaction analysis.

The task of the chemical reaction analyst may be rather idealistically divided into two phases: to measure and evaluate the chemical kinetic behavior of the particular system of interest, and to use this information to design equipment in which this reaction can be carried out economically on a commercial scale. Without minimizing the importance and difficulty of the latter phase, the former is by far the more difficult and important. Moreover, the first phase *should be* completed before the latter phase begins. It is for this reason that this book deals almost exclusively with the evaluation of chemical kinetic behavior.

Difficulties arise, however, when we endeavor to deal exclusively with chemical kinetics. A given chemical reaction will often occur only over a rather narrow range of conditions, and everywhere within this range other processes, such as transport of mass and energy, may influence the over-all rate. In these cases we are forced to analyze all of the processes simultaneously if we are to learn about the kinetics. Finally, chemical reaction rates are measured in reactors, and accordingly we shall find it necessary to analyze the characteristics of the particular reactor in which the rates are measured in order to obtain the desired information. Thus it follows that the principles necessary to carry out the first phase include those basic to reactor design.

In this book we shall progress systematically from simple to complex systems. First, we discuss chemical reactions as isolated processes: the determination of a chemical reaction rate from experiments, and the relationship between the functional form of the heterogeneous rate expression and reaction mechanisms. We progress to systems wherein transport phenomena modify the true kinetic behavior. In these sections, we seek criteria whereby the importance of physical phenomena can be assessed from experimental measurements. Later chapters emphasize the analysis of reactors.

Nowhere in this book will there be found a master key for the analysis of chemically reactive systems. Each system has peculiarities of its own. However, with a knowledge of the characteristic behavior of processes which mask the kinetic behavior, it should be possible to plan an experimental program to study the basic process—the kinetics—efficiently. Experience gained by analyzing the behavior of elementary systems is valuable in developing a perspective from which the important processes governing the behavior of complex systems are more quickly identified and isolated.

The Rate Expression

2

2.1 Rate of chemical reaction

Chemical reactions are interactions among molecules to alter the molecular species present. A chemical transformation results in a rearrangement of the atoms in a part of the original species present (reactants) to form other species (products) in such a way as to conserve atoms. The extent to which a particular chemical reaction has occurred is then associated with the number of the original molecular species which have been transformed into specified product molecules.

Chemical reactions may take place in a single phase, or in several phases or at phase interfaces, giving rise to their classification as either homogeneous or heterogeneous. In this chapter, we shall be interested in rate laws for both kinds of kinetics. The most useful quantitative description of a chemical rate process relates the specific reaction rate to the relevant intensive properties of the system. In the case of a homogeneous reaction, the specific reaction rate is a measure of the number of molecules undergoing a particular chemical transformation per unit time per unit volume. The heterogeneous reaction rate is similarly defined except that it is based upon a unit area rather than a unit volume. The desirable form of a specific reaction rate is therefore an

3

intensive property of a system and care must be exercised in its mathematical formulation to preserve this property. Although the discussion immediately following applies in the strictest sense only to homogeneous reactions, we shall later recognize its applicability to heterogeneous systems.

2.2 Simple reactions

In much of the early experimental work in chemical kinetics, investigators were concerned with closed, constant volume, homogeneous, isothermal, batch systems. In such a system consider the general simple reaction below:

$$\sum_{i=1}^{n} a_i A_i = 0, \tag{2.2-1}$$

where $a_i < 0$ and $a_i > 0$ are, respectively, the stoichiometric coefficients of reactants and products. The number of molecules of the ith species which react per unit time per unit volume will not in general be equal to the number of molecules of the jth species. However, these rates will be related by a simple ratio of the stoichiometric coefficients. The conservation equation for this system becomes

$$\frac{1}{a_i}\frac{dC_i}{dt} = \frac{1}{a_j}\frac{dC_j}{dt} = \bar{\mathscr{R}}, * \tag{2.2-2}$$

the specific rate of reaction, where C_i and C_j are the concentrations of A_i and A_j, respectively. Note that the form of Eq. 2.2-2 defines a reaction rate which is the same for all n species in the system. This, of course, is a direct consequence of the fundamental meaning of the stoichiometric equation.

The contention that the specific rate of the reaction $\bar{\mathscr{R}}$ is uniquely determined by a set of intensive properties of the system is supported by an overwhelming preponderance of experimental evidence as well as by complete consistency with kinetic theory. We shall consider the function $\bar{\mathscr{R}}$ to be of the form

$$\bar{\mathscr{R}} = \bar{\mathscr{R}}(T, C_{A_1}, C_{A_2}, C_{A_3}, \ldots, C_{A_n}), \tag{2.2-3}$$

i.e.,

$$\frac{\bar{\mathscr{R}}_i}{a_i} = \frac{\bar{\mathscr{R}}_j}{a_j} = \bar{\mathscr{R}}. \tag{2.2-4}$$

A chemical reactor designed to carry out the reaction of Eq. 2.2-1 on an industrial scale may not meet the restrictions imposed upon the system used to obtain the rate law $\bar{\mathscr{R}}$ from Eqs. 2.2-2 and 2.2-3; however, whether it does or does not is irrelevant, because the function $\bar{\mathscr{R}}$ is an intensive property of the particular system and can be used along with the appropriate equations

---

* The bar notation refers to reaction rate per unit volume or the rate in a reference volume. The absence of a bar refers to a heterogeneous rate expression.

for the conservation of species i and energy to obtain in principle the correct design. The danger in the restricted definition as given in Eq. 2.2-2 is, therefore, that an incorrect formulation of the function $\bar{\mathscr{R}}$ will result if the experimental reactor does not meet the restrictions implicit in the equation used to interpret the experimental results.

In an effort to obtain a more general equation for determining $\bar{\mathscr{R}}$, consider a closed, homogeneous, isothermal, batch system, but not constant volume. Figure 2.2-1(a) shows a cylindrical batch reactor of unit cross-sectional

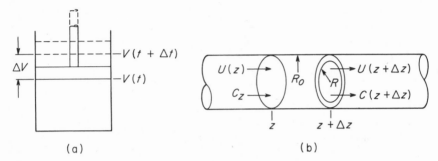

(a)   (b)

Fig. 2.2-1. Schematic diagrams of batch and piston flow reactors.

area fitted with a piston so that the volume of the reactor can be varied arbitrarily during the course of reaction by, say, varying the pressure on the external side of the piston. Suppose that there are $N(t)$ molecules of certain reactant species present at a time t, and at some later time, $t + \Delta t$, there are $N(t + \Delta t)$ molecules of the same species. Then during the time interval Δt, $N(t) - N(t + \Delta t)$ molecules have reacted. Now the conservation equation must be modified because the specific rate $\bar{\mathscr{R}}$ is concerned with the number of molecules undergoing reaction per unit volume per unit time. Under the given set of conditions the value of $\bar{\mathscr{R}}$ is given by Eq. 2.2-5:

$$\text{Limit}_{\Delta t \to 0} \left\{ \frac{1}{V(t)} \frac{N(t + \Delta t) - N(t)}{\Delta t} \right\} = \frac{1}{V(t)} \frac{dN(t)}{dt} \qquad (2.2\text{-}5)$$

Equation 2.2-6 extends this definition to give a rate expression which is the same for all species. This equation is more general than Eq. 2.2-2 and may be used together with Eq. 2.2-1 to predict the rate of reactions in most batch reactors and from which $\bar{\mathscr{R}}$ can be obtained from experimental data.

$$\frac{1}{V(t)a_i} \frac{dN_i(t)}{dt} = \frac{1}{V(t)a_j} \frac{dN_j(t)}{dt} = \bar{\mathscr{R}}(T, C_{A_1}, C_{A_2}, \ldots, C_{A_n}) \qquad (2.2\text{-}6)$$

There seems to be considerable confusion in the literature on the formulation and use of the rate law. The difficulty appears to stem from a conflict in the intended use of kinetic equations. At the risk of being repetitious, attention should again be called to several points which follow directly from the discussion in the introduction to this chapter. The rate function $\bar{\mathscr{R}}$ is a well-defined intensive property of the system. To determine values of $\bar{\mathscr{R}}$, it is necessary to measure how many molecules of a species (for simple reactions of the type in Eq. 2.2-1) react per unit time in a unit volume. Under the conditions of the first system discussed (constant volume), the number of molecules reacted is directly proportional to the concentration and Eq. 2.2-2 correctly describes the system. In the second system, the concentration of a species may vary for two reasons; reaction of the species and a volume change. We must, therefore, account for volume changes in the conservation equation in such a way that only the reacted molecules of the species are measured and equated to $\bar{\mathscr{R}}$. To determine the nature of the $\bar{\mathscr{R}}$ function, it is necessary to compute the corresponding concentrations of all species and temperature for each value of $\bar{\mathscr{R}}$. Since the determination of the rate function is the objective of most kinetic studies, the equation used to interpret kinetic data should be formulated to apply to the particular apparatus used.

As a final illustration consider the open, isothermal flow system shown in Fig. 2.2-1(b). If $U = U(z)$ is uniform across a given cross section at z, then the equipment is generally referred to as a piston or plug-flow reactor. Under steady-state conditions, conversion is a function of position z, rather than time. Then

$$\frac{1}{a_i} \, \text{div} \, (UC_i) = \frac{1}{a_j} \, \text{div} \, (UC_j) = \bar{\mathscr{R}}, \qquad (2.2\text{-}7)$$

where $-\text{div} \, (UC)$ is equal to the net accumulation per unit volume per unit time in the differential volume owing to the flow flux, UC_i.* For this one-dimensional system Eq. 2.2-7 becomes

$$\frac{1}{a_i} \, \frac{d(UC_i)}{dz} = \frac{1}{a_j} \, \frac{d(UC_j)}{dz} = \bar{\mathscr{R}}. \qquad (2.2\text{-}8)$$

Note that $\Delta z/U$ is a measure of residence time in the differential volume.

Equation (2.2-8) is not a particularly useful expression when the number of moles in a reference mass of feed changes with chemical reaction. This latter condition can be expressed mathematically as

$$\sum_{i=1}^{n} a_i \neq 0. \qquad (2.2\text{-}9)$$

When the number of moles changes during the course of reaction, the velocity becomes a function of z, the distance along the reactor. For such systems, an alternate expression will be adopted at this time and used

* Readers not familiar with vector notation should refer to the brief discussion in Appendix I.

throughout the remainder of the book. Take as a basis a mass of feed equal numerically to the average molecular weight of the feed stream, $\bar{M}$. The concentration variable Y_i is then defined as the number of moles of the ith species in a mass of reacting mixture numerically equal to $\bar{M}$. Thus, Y_{i0}, the concentration of i in the initial feed mixture, corresponds to the mole fraction of i therein. Substituting into Eq. 2.2-7,

$$\frac{1}{a_i} \operatorname{div}(UC_i) = \frac{1}{a_i} \operatorname{div}\left\{\frac{\rho_T U}{\bar{M}} \frac{\bar{M}C_i}{\rho_T}\right\} = \frac{G_0}{a_i \bar{M}} \operatorname{div} Y_i, \qquad (2.2\text{-}10)$$

where ρ_T = the density at any point within the flow reactor,

$\qquad G_0 = \rho_T U$ = the mass velocity—a constant throughout the plug-flow reactor.

Eq. 2.2-8 becomes

$$\frac{G_0}{a_i \bar{M}} \frac{dY_i}{dz} = \bar{\mathscr{R}}, \qquad (2.2\text{-}11)$$

which may be used to obtain $\bar{\mathscr{R}}$ in an isothermal flow reactor in which the number of moles of reactants in the stoichiometric equation differs from the number of moles of products.

Looking back through this section, we note that in Eqs. 2.2-2, 2.2-6, and 2.2-11 the specific rate function $\bar{\mathscr{R}}$ has been set equal to three different expressions. Throughout the remainder of this book, many more expressions will appear which contain this function. To argue that any one of these is more correct than all of the others as its defining equation is to confuse a conservation equation with a definition. The function $\bar{\mathscr{R}}$ is a source term in a conservation equation and the remaining terms in the above equations vary with the type of system in question. In this respect, it is instructive to note that every design equation in this book in which $\bar{\mathscr{R}}$ appears may be viewed as a possible means of determining it, but none of them is its defining equation.

We see that the $\bar{\mathscr{R}}$ function is independent of the system in which it was obtained. Its functional dependence upon the relevant intensive properties of the system will be most reliably determined in simple systems wherein the kinetic phenomena are emphasized and transport phenomena minimized. Conversely, it is usually unreliable to infer the kinetics from the over-all performance of equipment encumbered by complex transport mechanisms. Thus the design engineer is faced generally with two problems: finding the $\bar{\mathscr{R}}$ function from an experimental apparatus making use of valid conservation equations for that system, and its subsequent combination with the relevant equations of motion and conservation for a particular reactor to predict the latter's performance.

2.3 Complex reactions

Reactions of industrial importance are frequently not simple and cannot, therefore, be represented by a single stoichiometric equation of the form shown in Eq. 2.2-1. The departure from the simple system may arise for a variety of reasons. As examples, the formation of a given set of products may occur by more than one reaction path, or a given set of reactants may go to several sets of products, or a reaction may take place between the reactants and the intermediate products to form additional products. The analysis of such systems may be undertaken by writing a set of stoichiometric equations each of which corresponds to a reaction which is known to occur in the system. Let us assume that the number of such equations corresponds to m. A careful survey of these equations may show that they are not all linearly independent, i.e., it may be possible to obtain one of the stoichiometric equations by adding or subtracting two or more of the other members of the set. Should this be the case, then it is possible to reduce the m equations to, say, k equations which are now linearly independent. The system can be represented completely by the set of k equations.

A simple example which illustrates this point is the reaction of graphite with oxygen. Three reactions may be presumed to take place:

$$C + \tfrac{1}{2} O_2 = CO \qquad (1)$$

$$C + O_2 = CO_2 \qquad (2)$$

$$CO + \tfrac{1}{2} O_2 = CO_2 \qquad (3)$$

$$(2.3\text{-}1)$$

In this case $m = 3$. By inspection, we can see that these three equations are not linearly independent because adding (1) and (3) of Eq. 2.3-1 gives (2). Thus, we say one of the equations is linearly dependent and $k = 2$. The choice as to which two equations are retained is arbitrary from the standpoint of stoichiometry, although all may be valid paths mechanistically.

If the original set of m equations included all of the reactions which take place to an appreciable extent, it then follows that it is necessary to know the rates of appearance or disappearance with respect to k components in order to determine the rate at which each reaction of the original scheme has occurred at a particular point. The analysis of the system has been reduced to the problem of solving k simultaneous equations in k unknowns. Obviously, if the system is small (k is small), there is no compelling reason to develop a formal system of analysis and the familiar algebraic methods for handling such equations are adequate. However, a formal method of analysis offers some computational advantages when k is large for two reasons: it minimizes the opportunity for computational errors, and it makes use of standard programs available for large digital computers.

Consider the general set of stoichiometric reactions

$$\sum_{i=1}^{n} a_{ij}A_i = 0 \qquad (j = 1, 2, 3 \ldots m), \qquad (2.3\text{-}2)$$

which is a shorthand representation of the following set of equations:

$$\left.\begin{array}{l} a_{11}A_1 + a_{21}A_2 + a_{31}A_3 + \ldots + a_{n1}A_n = 0 \\[4pt] a_{12}A_1 + a_{22}A_2 + \ldots\ldots\ldots + a_{n2}A_n = 0 \\[4pt] a_{1k}A_1 + a_{2k}A_2 + \ldots\ldots\ldots + a_{nk}A_n = 0 \\[4pt] a_{1m}A_1 + a_{2m}A_2 + \ldots\ldots\ldots + a_{nm}A_n = 0 \end{array}\right\} \qquad (2.3\text{-}3)$$

where values of a_{ij} are the stoichiometric coefficients and where $a_{ij} < 0$ refer to reactants and $a_{ij} > 0$ refer to products. As before, assume that the first k of these m equations are linearly independent, where of course $m > k$. Another way of saying this is that we form an n by m matrix of the stoichiometric coefficients and determine the rank of the largest *nonsingular* matrix* which for the above case will be k.

What we generally seek in the analysis is to determine the rate at which each of the k independent equations occurs under a prescribed set of conditions and to compute the compositions of each of the components and the temperature corresponding to these rates. Similar analyses are carried out for a wide variety of conditions in order to establish the rate at which each reaction occurs as a function of concentrations of the various species present, the temperature, and other conditions such as catalyst activity, etc., in order to establish the nature of the $\mathcal{R}$ function for each reaction. The hope is that this information will lead to some kinetic model. It may be pertinent to remark at this point that the mechanistic equations which describe the kinetic path model, if indeed they are obtained, will almost certainly be different from the set of k stoichiometric equations as written. In the absence of a kinetic model, the $\mathcal{R}$ functions may be represented as an empirical function of reaction conditions.

This objective cannot be realized without taking into account the type of reactor in which the rate data are determined. By analogy with our earlier discussion of simple reactions; compositions, temperature, and rates of complex reactions are related by a system of conservation equations. Because these latter equations contain terms corresponding to transport processes which vary with the type of reactor, we cannot give a general analysis of complex reaction systems. However, we shall develop a general relationship among the rates of complex reactions which will serve as the basis for analyzing all types of reactors. Then, as was done for simple reactions, the

---

* The largest nonsingular matrix of the n by m matrix of the stoichiometric coefficients is the k by k matrix of the set of independent reactions. See Appendix II.

analysis will be applied to differential and piston flow reactors as examples. In later sections we shall make further use of the following section when particular types of reactors are considered.

With the above objective in mind the formal analysis will be presented. The analysis is concerned with the independent sub-set k of the m equations shown in Eq. 2.3-2 which may be written as

$$\sum_{i=1}^{n} a_{ij}A_i = 0 \qquad (j = 1, 2, 3, \ldots, k), \qquad (2.3\text{-}4)$$

where k is the order of the largest nonsingular matrix of the original matrix formed from the coefficients of the set of m reactions.

The rate at which the ith component is produced as a result of the jth reaction is

$$\bar{\mathscr{R}}_{ij} = \bar{\mathscr{R}}_{ij}[C_1, C_2, C_3, \ldots, C_n, T]. \qquad (2.3\text{-}5)$$

These rates are related through the stoichiometric equations as shown below:

$$\frac{\bar{\mathscr{R}}_{ij}}{a_{ij}} = \frac{\bar{\mathscr{R}}_{kj}}{a_{kj}} = \bar{\mathscr{R}}_j \qquad (j = 1, 2, 3, \ldots, k). \qquad (2.3\text{-}6)$$

Suppose now that we know the values of $\bar{\mathscr{R}}_j$ for each of the k reactions. To find the production rates of ith species P_i as a result of all the reactions we would simply multiply the stoichiometric coefficient of the ith species in each of the reactions times its corresponding rate and add these products. The mathematical equivalent of this statement is

$$P_i = \sum_{j=1}^{k} a_{ij}\bar{\mathscr{R}}_j. \qquad (2.3\text{-}7)$$

However, we are generally faced with the problem in reverse, i.e., we are given, or we must obtain experimentally, the production rates of the various species and compute values of $\bar{\mathscr{R}}_j$ from the measurements. Since by supposition we have k independent equations, we need the independent determination of the production rates of k components of the mixture. Writing Eq. 2.3-7 in matrix* form to include the production rates of each of the k components:

$$[P_k] = [\bar{\mathscr{R}}_k][a_{kk}], \qquad (2.3\text{-}8)$$

where

$$[P_k] \equiv [P_1 \quad P_2 \quad P_3 \quad \cdots \quad P_k]$$
$$[\bar{\mathscr{R}}_k] \equiv [\bar{\mathscr{R}}_1 \quad \bar{\mathscr{R}}_2 \quad \bar{\mathscr{R}}_3 \quad \cdots \quad \bar{\mathscr{R}}_k]$$
$$[a_{kk}] \equiv \begin{bmatrix} a_{11} & a_{21} & a_{31} & \cdots & a_{k1} \\ a_{12} & a_{22} & & & \\ a_{13} & & & & \\ a_{1k} & \cdots\cdots\cdots & & & a_{kk} \end{bmatrix} \qquad (2.3\text{-}9)$$

---

* Readers not familiar with matrix multiplication should refer to the brief discussion in Appendix II.

Note that it has been assumed that the first k components are the ones which have been determined experimentally. If this does not correspond to the way in which the original equations were written, they can be renumbered to make this true.

If each side of Eq. 2.3-8 is multiplied by the inverse matrix of $[a_{kk}]$, i.e., $[a_{kk}]^{-1}$, and simplified, Eq. 2.3-10 is obtained.

$$[P_k][a_{kk}]^{-1} = [\bar{\mathscr{R}}_k][a_{kk}][a_{kk}]^{-1}.$$

Therefore,

$$[\bar{\mathscr{R}}_k] = [P_k][a_{kk}]^{-1}. \tag{2.3-10}$$

Using Eq. 2.3-10, the rates of each of the reactions may be obtained from known production rates of k species. Of course, having computed values of $\bar{\mathscr{R}}_j$, Eq. 2.3-7 may be used to compute the rates of production of the unmeasured species $k + 1$ to n. Through Eq. 2.3-7 and 2.3-10, we learn that the rates of production of the species $k + 1$ to n may be expressed as a linear combination of the rates of production of the independent set of components 1 to k. The values of the coefficients of the expansion may be easily obtained by the following operations. The production rates of the components $k + 1$ to n become

$$[P_g] = [\bar{\mathscr{R}}_k][a_{gk}], \tag{2.3-11}$$

where

$$[P_g] \equiv [\; P_{k+1} \quad P_{k+2} \quad \cdots \quad P_n \;]$$

$$[a_{gk}] \equiv \begin{bmatrix} a_{k+1,1} & a_{k+2,1} & \cdots & a_{n,1} \\ a_{k+1,2} & a_{k+2,2} & \cdots & \cdots \\ a_{k+1,3} & & & \\ a_{k+1,k} & \cdots & \cdots & a_{n,k} \end{bmatrix} \left.\vphantom{\begin{bmatrix} a \\ a \\ a \\ a \end{bmatrix}}\right\} \quad (2.3\text{-}12)$$

Substituting Eq. 2.3-10 into Eq. 2.3-11, we obtain

$$[P_g] = [P_k][a_{kk}]^{-1}[a_{gk}] \tag{2.3-13}$$

$$= [P_k][\gamma_{gk}], \tag{2.3-14}$$

where $[\gamma_{gk}]$ is defined by comparing Eq. 2.3-13 and Eq. 2.3-14. From its definition $[\gamma_{gk}]$ contains $n - k$ columns each containing k elements. In later sections we shall make use of Eq. 2.3-14 in the summation form shown below.

$$P_g = \sum_{i=1}^{k} \gamma_{gi} P_i \quad (g = k+1, k+2, \ldots, n), \tag{2.3-15}$$

where the coefficients γ_{gi} are the corresponding elements of the matrix $[\gamma_{gk}]$.

The above analysis is general and applies to complex reactions in any system. The results of the analysis may be summarized by two statements:

1. If a system of m reactions involving n components involves k independent reactions (i.e., a matrix formed from the stoichiometric coefficients is of

rank k), then it is necessary to measure the production rates of each of the k components to characterize the rates of each of the k reactions in the system.

2. The rates of production of the remaining components, $k + 1$ to n, may be computed as linear combinations of the rates of production of the components 1 to k.

The first half of our objective has been accomplished; that of relating rates of each reaction from the known production rates of the k species. To complete the analysis, this information must be incorporated into the system of conservation equations in order to compute the corresponding concentrations of each of the species. Two reactor types will be considered: the differential reactor and the piston-flow, integral reactor. At this time

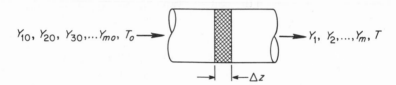

Fig. 2.3-1. Diagram of a differential reactor.

we are purposely avoiding more complex reactors which involve additional transport phenomena and nonisothermal behavior because rate data should be obtained in simple reactors whenever possible and because the method of approach is illustrated without involving more difficult mathematics. Other reactor types will be dealt with later when the objective is to design or predict the performance of a reactor from available rate data.

The concept of a differential reactor is an idealization in that we endeavor to measure rates of reaction under constant conditions of concentration and temperature by making the conversion within the reactor approach zero. Paradoxically, to measure reaction rates, some reaction must take place and to this extent, the conditions are changed. However, the concept is useful and the physical counterpart of this idealized type is a reactor in which the reaction is allowed to proceed only to the point where changes in composition owing to reaction can be accurately detected by analytical equipment. At the same time, because the reaction involves the conversion of only an insignificant fraction of the components present, the compositions and temperature remain essentially uniform throughout the differential reactor. Insofar as these conditions are mutually compatible, the data on conversions in differential reactors are easily transformed into rates.

Consider the differential reactor of length Δz shown in Fig. 2.3-1 being fed a mixture $Y_{10}, Y_{20}, \ldots, Y_{n0}$, at a temperature T_0. Since by definition, differential reactors are of uniform conditions throughout, the production rate of the ith component is given by analogy to Eq. 2.2-11 and from

Eq. 2.3-7 by

$$Y_i - Y_{i0} = \frac{\bar{M} \Delta z}{G_0} P_i, \tag{2.3-16}$$

where we shall again use as the concentration variable Y_i, which was defined as the number of moles of the ith species per mass of reactant numerically equal to the average molecular weight of the feed mixture. Thus, Y_i is the moles of i per mole of feed and it follows that Y_{i0}, the value of Y_i in the initial mixture, is the initial mole fraction of i in the feed.

Without loss in generality, the composition with respect to the first k components may be assumed to be measured at various points in the reactor, i.e., analyses of the A's; Y_1, Y_2, Y_3, ..., Y_k are measured in the differential reactor. The total change in the concentration of, say, A_1, equal to $Y_{10} - Y_1$, is equal to the initial concentration minus the sum of individual amounts consumed in each reaction. In mathematical form:

$$Y_1 - Y_{10} = \frac{\bar{M} \Delta z}{G_0} \sum_{j=1}^{k} a_{1j} \bar{\mathscr{R}}_j, \tag{2.3-17}$$

with a similar equation for each of the k species. These equations can be compactly written in the matrix form below.

$$[Y_k - Y_{k0}] = \frac{\bar{M} \Delta z}{G_0} [\bar{\mathscr{R}}_k][a_{kk}] \tag{2.3-18}$$

where

$$\left.\begin{array}{l} [Y_k] \equiv [Y_1 \quad Y_2 \quad \dots \quad Y_k] \\[4pt] [Y_{k0}] \equiv [Y_{10} \quad Y_{20} \quad \dots \quad Y_{k0}] \\[4pt] [\bar{\mathscr{R}}_k] \equiv [\bar{\mathscr{R}}_1 \quad \bar{\mathscr{R}}_2 \quad \dots \quad \bar{\mathscr{R}}_k] \end{array}\right\} \tag{2.3-19}$$

and $[a_{kk}]$ is defined in Eq. (2.3-9). It follows, therefore, that

$$[\bar{\mathscr{R}}_k] = \frac{G_0}{\bar{M} \Delta z} [Y_k - Y_{k0}][a_{kk}]^{-1}, \tag{2.3-20}$$

where $[a_{kk}]^{-1}$ is the inverse of the matrix $[a_{kk}]$. Thus $\bar{\mathscr{R}}_k$ may be obtained from the measured values of Y_k by routine operations.

The concentrations of the remaining species in the system may be computed from known values of $\bar{\mathscr{R}}_j$ by the relationship

$$Y_l = Y_{l0} + \frac{\bar{M} \Delta z}{G_0} \sum_{j=1}^{k} a_{lj} \bar{\mathscr{R}}_j \qquad (k < l \le n). \tag{2.3-21}$$

For kinetic interpretation mole fractions or related concentrations are generally used. Define a quantity v_j for each reaction such that

$$v_j = \sum_{i=1}^{n} a_{ij} \qquad (j = 1, 2, 3, \dots, k). \tag{2.3-22}$$

The total change in moles due to all of the k reactions, hence the total moles in the reference mass at any point Y_T, is given by

$$Y_T = 1 + \frac{\bar{M}\,\Delta z}{G_0} \sum_{j=1}^{k} \nu_j \bar{\mathscr{R}}_j. \tag{2.3-23}$$

It follows then that the mole fractions are given by Y_i/Y_T. The equation of state for the mixture completes the calculation of the concentrations needed. The second term on the right of Eq. 2.3-23 approaches zero for a differential reaction because the constant multiplier of the summation approaches zero.

The objective of the foregoing analysis was to present a systematic method for interpreting conversion data from a differential reactor wherein several chemical reactions are occurring simultaneously. The method gives us directly the exit concentrations of all species present in terms of the minimum number of experimental analyses necessary to define the system. In order to determine the form of the rate expression, experiments should be carried out over a wide variety of conditions.

As a second example, we shall consider the piston-flow integral reactor discussed earlier. Equation 2.2-11 must be modified to account for the production of the species i from each of the k reactions. In so doing, an equation for each of the species present may be written in the form:

$$\frac{G_0}{\bar{M}} \frac{dY_i}{dz} = \sum_{j=1}^{k} a_{ij} \bar{\mathscr{R}}_j \qquad (i = 1, 2, 3, \ldots, n), \tag{2.3-24}$$

or from Eq. 2.3-7,

$$\frac{G_0}{\bar{M}} \frac{dY_i}{dz} = P_i \qquad (i = 1, 2, 3, \ldots, n). \tag{2.3-25}$$

However, from Eq. 2.3-15,

$$P_g = \sum_{i=1}^{k} \gamma_{gi} P_i \qquad (g = k+1, k+2, \ldots, n), \tag{2.3-26}$$

and it follows that

$$\frac{G_0}{\bar{M}} \frac{dY_g}{dz} = \frac{G_0}{\bar{M}} \sum_{i=1}^{k} \gamma_{gi} \frac{dY_i}{dz}. \tag{2.3-27}$$

Integrating, we obtain

$$Y_g - Y_{g0} = \sum_{i=1}^{k} \gamma_{gi}(Y_i - Y_{i0}). \tag{2.3-28}$$

The set of equations 2.3-24 is thereby reduced to k equations which must be solved simultaneously involving only $Y_1, Y_2, \ldots, Y_k$ because Y_{k+1},

$Y_{k+2}, \ldots, Y_n$ can be computed from the former set using Eq. 2.3-28. This set of equations may be written compactly in the matrix form

$$\frac{d}{dz}[q_k] = [\bar{\mathscr{R}}_k][a_{kk}],$$ (2.3-29)

where

$$\left.\begin{array}{l}[q_k] = \dfrac{G_0}{M}[Y_1 \quad Y_2 \quad Y_3 \quad \ldots \quad Y_k] \\[2mm] [\bar{\mathscr{R}}_k] = [\bar{\mathscr{R}}_1 \quad \bar{\mathscr{R}}_2 \quad \bar{\mathscr{R}}_3 \quad \ldots \quad \bar{\mathscr{R}}_k]\end{array}\right\}$$ (2.3-30)

To solve this set of equations, an extension of the usual procedure would be to assume the forms of the $\bar{\mathscr{R}}_j$ functions and compare the integrated function of Y_i versus z with the experimental. Any conclusions based upon such a procedure should be accepted with caution. These two examples demonstrate the inherent advantage for interpretation of rate data offered by differential reactors. A comprehensive analysis of complex reaction systems has been presented by Prater and Wei.*

2.4 Heterogeneous rate expressed as pseudo-homogeneous rate

Partial differential equations which most accurately describe the process occurring in a heterogeneous reactor do not contain a kinetic rate term in the equations themselves. The rate term appears only in the boundary condition because heterogeneous reactions occur at the fluid-solid interface. Certain types of heterogeneous problems can be handled in this way and several will be considered in Chapter 6. However, when the hydrodynamics within the system become complex, or more accurately when the equations of motion are not solvable, such as in packed or fluidized beds, it is customary practice to replace the system by an "equivalent" or pseudo-homogeneous system. The equations are written as though the system did not contain the solid phase. This approach simplifies the equations describing the system, however, not without a price, for as we shall see, the correspondence of the real and equivalent systems depends upon how completely the effects of the solid phase can be included in the equivalent homogeneous equations.

The purpose of this section is to discuss how the techniques developed later may be used to obtain an equivalent homogeneous rate expression for a heterogeneous reaction. As mentioned earlier, specific rates for heterogeneous reactions are based on a unit area, whereas specific rates for homogeneous reactions are of course based upon a unit volume. Evidently, the pseudo-rate expression should be obtained using the specific surface area of

* C. D. Prater and James Wei, *Advan. Catalysis* **13**, 204 (1962).

the solid phase under conditions corresponding to those found in the operating reactor. In many cases, this information alone is insufficient, because the pseudo-rate expression is based upon the bulk phase properties such as temperature and concentrations. The magnitude of these properties at the reaction site may in general be different from the bulk values because of gradients in these properties owing to finite resistances to the transport of energy and mass. Thus, the pseudo-rate expression used in the design of heterogeneous reactors must include and allow for the effects of finite transport rates between the bulk phase and the reaction site.

In general, temperatures and concentrations may differ between the bulk phase and the external surface of the catalyst and between the external surface and the reaction site within a porous catalyst. We shall deal with these two topics separately in later chapters. In keeping with the main theme of this book, these topics will be developed in the forward direction, i.e., the prediction of the form of the pseudo-rate expression from a detailed knowledge of the intrinsic kinetics, the structure of the solid phase and the hydrodynamic conditions in the immediate vicinity of the catalytic surface. Obviously, the general problem of this type cannot as yet be formulated in detail; nevertheless, there have been a number of rigorous inquiries into various phases of this general problem which serve to define under what conditions careful consideration must be given to certain characteristics of the system which do not appear in a simplified analysis but have a strong influence on the behavior of the system. It is equally important, of course, to define the conditions under which the system is insensitive to the detailed processes and a simplified analysis serves equally well for engineering calculations. Hopefully, detailed analyses will lead to experimental criteria whereby the designer can rationally assess the importance of a behavioral characteristic of a particular reactor as applied to a specific process.

In attempting to apply the above technique to a particular reactor, viz of the packed-bed type, additional difficulties are encountered. For example, what do we mean when we say the bulk concentration? Where? Clearly in the real bed, the concentrations do not vary smoothly throughout the volume of the reactor, but rather there is a detailed concentration structure in the vicinity of, as well as within, a particle with a scale of the order of the particle itself. This structure is superimposed upon a longer range structure which more closely approximates the progress of the reaction as the reacting mixture passes through the bed. It is customary to circumvent these difficulties by the suggestion that we are dealing with a differential volume which contains statistical number particles but which is also small compared to the size of the reactor. The bulk concentration is therefore, some kind of space average within this differential volume. This approach is hardly satisfactory when the appreciable conversions take place after the reacting mixture passes one or two particles, such as found with the catalytic oxidation of SO_2 to

SO_3 described by Hall and Smith.* We are forced to assume that the bulk concentration and other averaged properties are smooth and have significance when they are averaged over a space of the order of the packing size, or when they refer to points of more or less corresponding positions within the bed.

It should be evident at this point that the design of catalytic reactors can be complex even when the pseudo-homogeneous approximation is adopted. However, it may occur to some readers that if the latter approach has any merit, perhaps many, if not all, of the difficulties may be obviated by resorting to experiment wherein all of these interaction effects are integrated. The answer to such a suggestion is that a prototype unit is rarely available and even if such equipment were available it would be expensive and time consuming to obtain experimental data corresponding to a wide range of operating conditions. Moreover, kinetics are more easily interpreted when unencumbered by nonkinetic factors. The proper attitude is to make use of whatever tools of analysis are available to reduce the number of experimental points required and to extend the value and meaning of the experimental information.

NOTATION FOR CHAPTER 2

a_i stoichiometric coefficient in a general simple reaction: $a_i < 0$ corresponds to a reactant; $a_i > 0$ corresponds to a product

a_{ij} stoichiometric coefficient in a general complex reaction

A_i the ith species of a chemical reaction

C_i concentration of the ith species

G_0 $\rho_T U$, the mass velocity

$\bar{M}$ average molecular weight of the feed stream to a reactor

N_i number of molecules of the ith species

P_i the production rate of the ith species in a complex reaction system

q_k a matrix defined by Eq. 2.3-30

$\bar{\mathscr{R}}$ rate of a chemical reaction per unit volume

t time

T temperature

U velocity in the direction of the z coordinate

V volume of batch reactor vessel

* R. E. Hall and J. M. Smith, *Chem. Eng. Progr.* **45,** 459 (1949).

Y_i number of moles of the ith species in a mass of fluid equal numerically to the average molecular weight of the feed stream. Thus Y_i at the reactor entrance corresponds to the mole fraction of i.

z axial coordinate

GREEK LETTERS

γ_{gk} a coefficient defined by Eqs. 2.3-13 and 2.3-14

ρ_T density of a reaction mixture, in general a function of the coordinate z

ν_i defined by Eq. 2.3-22

Heterogeneous Kinetics 3

3.1 Introduction

Although this book is primarily concerned with the subject of chemical reaction engineering, i.e., a compilation and integration of the techniques used to translate kinetic information into reactor performance and optimization, it is a matter of cold, hard fact that the successful application of these techniques to a given problem is vitally dependent upon a knowledge of reliable rate data. The rates at which chemical substances react heterogeneously vary over many orders of magnitude and depend upon the concentrations of the species present, the temperature, the structure of the solid phase, and the character of the interaction between the fluid and solid phases. If every heterogeneous reaction followed classical integral order behavior with respect to reactants and if the intrinsic rate constant varied according to an Arrhenius temperature dependence, it would not be necessary for a designer to understand the kinetic mechanisms of heterogeneous reactions. Unfortunately, heterogeneous reactions in general do not follow classical behavior and the adoption of this naïve kinetic framework, although capable of correlating experimental data over modest conversion ranges, results in collection of apparent "rate constants" which often appear to be strong functions of the operating conditions. This follows because the classical description of heterogeneous reactions does not include some of the firmly established facts concerning the nature of heterogeneous reactions and how they differ from some elementary homogeneous reactions. In the interest of rational interpretation of heterogeneous reaction data, it is essential that the engineer familiarize himself with the subject of applied chemical kinetics.

An adequate theory of heterogeneous reactions should provide two types of information: a kinetic description of the detailed path along which reactants are converted into products in the presence of the solid phase and a conceptual foundation by which at least in principle the fundamental parameters of the kinetic description may be computed from the physico-chemical properties of the system. Unfortunately, such a theory does not exist for catalytic reactions, despite the extensive literature on the subject. Nevertheless, it would be unfair to leave the impression that no progress has been made toward the establishment of an adequate theory, particularly with respect to mechanism because much information of this kind exists for a wide variety of reactions. However, this information was obtained only with great difficulty and at a rather impressive expenditure of time and effort. It would appear that an engineer endeavoring to design a reactor for which no kinetic information is available in the literature will probably find it expedient to represent his kinetic data somewhat empirically, however making use of whatever principles of catalysis that time permits. Judgment as to how much empiricism to use is not a subject that can be discussed with precision. The point here is that in general an engineer cannot afford to wait until a thorough understanding of the mechanism of reaction is known before he designs a reactor for that reaction. Had this attitude been universally adopted in the past, many now successful industrial processes would still not be in operation.

In this chapter, no attempt will be made to review the literature systemati-cally, nor to study reactions classified according to type, such as oxidation, hydrogenation, etc. Treatments of this type already exist.* The purpose of this chapter is rather to examine and review some of the important work which has led to the modern view of heterogeneous reactions and how these concepts may be utilized to represent the kinetic behavior of certain reactions. The emphasis will be on an exposé of techniques keeping in mind the prag-matic needs of the user who may want to apply them to specific problems. Every effort will be made to stress physical meaning and the reader should bear in mind that the underlying simple ideas upon which the analyses are based are more important than the results of the specific examples because in application these techniques must be modified to suit particular situations which may differ in certain details from the examples given. This chapter then serves only as a brief introduction to the subject of catalysis.

* See, for example, P. H. Emmett, editor, *Catalysis*, Vols. I–VI, Reinhold Publishing Co., New York (1954–58); *Advances in Catalysis*, Vols. I–XIII, Academic Press, Inc., New York (1948–62); P. H. Groggins, *Unit Processes in Organic Synthesis*, 4th ed., McGraw-Hill Book Company, New York (1952); A. A. Frost and R. G. Pearson, *Kinetics and Mecha-nism*, John Wiley & Sons, Inc., New York (1953); G. C. Bond, *Catalysis by Metals*, Academic Press, Inc., New York (1962); P. G. Ashmore, *Catalysis and Inhibition of Chemical Reactions*, Butterworth and Co. (Publishers) Ltd., London (1963).

3.2 Historical background

A catalyst is a substance which by virtue of its presence in the reaction mixture influences the rate of chemical reactions, but is not consumed stoichiometrically in the reactions. When certain solids are introduced into a mixture of fluid reactants, the rate of chemical reaction may be observed to increase. It may be inferred that the introduction of the solid has, therefore, offered an alternate and parallel path for the course of the reaction to take place, and the kinetic interpretation of the laws of mass action alone no longer explain the rate of the reaction. Examples of catalytic effects were reviewed by J. J. Berzelius* and considered by M. Faraday.† Faraday concluded that the solid attracted and concentrated reacting molecules near its surface, resulting in an increased velocity. Similar hypotheses were put forward to explain catalysis on solids for many years, but in the light of more modern information it is apparent that such hypotheses completely fail to explain the selectivity of catalysts.

Along somewhat different lines Nernst and Bruner‡ suggested a general theory of heterogeneous reactions based upon some dissolution experiments of Noyes and Whitney.§ The general theory was based upon the supposition that the reacting substances diffused through an adsorbed film at the surface of the solid before coming into contact with the solid and that the interfacial reaction rate is always fast compared to the rate of diffusion. Because this theory failed to explain experimental results, the general theory was further modified by Bodenstein and Fink‖ to consider a variable film thickness. However, allowing the film to vary was tantamount to the addition of an adjustable parameter which could not be independently evaluated. Heymann¶ was among those who correctly recognized the Nernst-Bruner mechanism as a limiting case of mass transfer control of the type discussed in Chapter 6.

Langmuir** in his pioneering work with tungsten and carbon and other solid surfaces clearly demonstrated the existence of strongly bonded adsorbed layers of molecules on certain solid surfaces. These layers of extraordinarily high stability dramatically changed the behavior of the base material in its chemical and electron emission properties. He further showed that in order to obtain bonds of this strength, the distances between adsorbed and base material molecules must be of the order of 2–3 angstrom units. This work forms the basis of the modern theory of heterogeneous reactions, which is,

* J. J. Berzelius, *Jahresber. Chem.* **15**, 237 (1836).

† M. Faraday. Phil. Trans. **114**, 55 (1834). See also S. Berkman, J. C. Morell, and G. Egloff, *Catalysis*, p. 155, Reinhold Publishing Co., New York (1940).

‡ W. Nernst and E. Brunner, *Z. Physik Chem.* **47**, 56 (1904).

§ A. A. Noyes and W. R. Whitney, *Z. Physik Chem.* **23**, 689 (1897).

‖ M. Bodenstein and C. G. Fink, *Z. Physik Chem.* **60**, 46 (1907).

¶ H. Heymann, *Z. Physik Chem.* **81**, 204 (1913).

** I. Langmuir, *J. Am. Chem. Soc.* **38**, 2221 (1916).

in essence, that reacting molecules form bonds with the atoms at the surface of the catalyst to form intermediate chemical compounds or complexes with characteristics of chemical compounds. These complexes or chemisorbed species then rearrange or react with other species to form chemisorbed products which subsequently decompose to regenerate the original base surface and desorbed fluid products.

Thus, we have the model by which most heterogeneous reactions are interpreted. It has been a useful theory in the sense that in addition to being capable of correlating a wide variety of kinetic results, it provided a means of predicting the effects of new conditions imposed on the reacting system. The theory has not been free of conceptual difficulties, however, because as experimental data was amassed, it became evident that the catalytic surfaces were not uniform and that not all adsorbed species were capable of reacting. It was found for example by Pease* that the rate of catalytic hydrogenation of ethylene on copper is reduced to 0.5% of its initial value by poisoning the surface with Hg whereas the adsorption of ethylene and hydrogen is reduced by this treatment to 80% and 5% respectively of their untreated values. Hinshelwood and Prichard† showed that the rate of reaction between carbon dioxide and hydrogen on platinum at $1000°C$ is proportional to P_{H_2}/P_{CO_2} whereas the adsorption of the hydrogen is considerable and the adsorption of carbon dioxide is negligible. These results suggest that only a small fraction of the surface is active and that the centers for adsorption are not the same for all species.

Taylor‡ suggested that the chemical reaction is catalyzed only at "active centers" which he visualized as "unsaturated" atoms in the solid, such as at cracks, edges of crystals, along grain boundaries, etc. This suggestion has qualitative appeal, but fails to give a quantitative insight as to what constitutes a "site," nor does it explain why a particular "site" is active to one species but not another. Along quite different lines, Beeck, Smith, and Wheeler§ found that although the adsorption of hydrogen and ethylene on the 110 planes of nickel are approximately the same as on 100 and 111 planes, the rate of reaction is an order of magnitude higher on the former. This suggests that the distance 3.51 angstrom units between nickel atoms in this plane may be of significance.

More recently the interest of the catalytic chemist has been directed to the adaption of developments in solid-state physics and chemistry, especially the developing theories of semi-conductors, to the problem of catalysis. This approach, while in some respects not new, is still in its scientific infancy and holds great promise for the future.

* R. N. Pease, *J. Am. Chem. Soc.* **45,** 1196, 2235, 2296 (1923).

† C. R. Prichard and C. N. Hinshelwood, *J. Chem. Soc.* **127,** 806 (1925).

‡ H. S. Taylor, *Proc. Roy. Soc.* **108A,** 105 (1925).

§ O. Beeck, A. E. Smith, and A. Wheeler, *Proc. Roy. Soc.* **177A,** 62 (1940).

From the point of view of the reactor designer, the theory of catalysis as it exists today must be regarded as phenomenological from the standpoint of understanding the elementary mechanism of the catalytic act. He must recognize that the task of expressing rate data quantitatively is largely an experimental problem. At the same time he may rightly expect to extend the usefulness and reliability of the experimental results and indeed aid in setting up the experimental program by making use of the elementary concepts of the phenomenological theory.

3.3 The catalyst surface

Adsorption of reactant molecules on a solid surface is universally accepted as the first step in the over-all process of catalysis. Without adsorption there is no catalysis. This is why studies of the adsorption process itself and of the chemistry of the adsorbed state assume a dominant role in all investigations seeking a more fundamental understanding of catalytic phenomena. Yet the evidence accumulated reveals no simple relationship between the adsorption process and the act of catalysis, and an understanding of the chemistry of the adsorbed state has not advanced to a stage where it can be used to predict the kinetics of a catalytic reaction. Accordingly, in this section we shall not attempt to systematically review the rich and voluminous literature on catalysis, but rather to try to justify a simple physical model of a catalyst surface which provides a framework for the interpretation of the kinetics of reactions at the catalyst surface. In so doing, we side step some important questions, such as what chemical factors make a material a catalyst for particular reactions? Or, what is the role of promoters in increasing the activity of a catalyst? With a rather limited objective in mind, we look at some of the properties of catalyst surfaces.

Synthetic catalysts generally display a heterogeneous surface. We can infer this from the observation that a particular catalyst may exhibit activity for more than one reaction. More quantitative physical evidence is the variation in the heat of adsorption with the amount of adsorbate on the surface. Three distinct reasons have been suggested to account for the latter evidence: (i) *a priori* heterogeneity, (ii) induced heterogeneity, and (iii) interaction among the adsorbed molecules.

A priori heterogeneity refers to a truly heterogeneous surface—a surface, owing to roughness, dislocations, and its display of various crystalline planes, offers "sites" on which adsorbate molecules are held with bonds of varying strengths. The observed decrease in heat of adsorption with surface coverage is explained by the supposition that the first adsorbate molecules will adsorb on the most active sites or migrate to them. Subsequent adsorption will take place on successively weaker sites.

Induced heterogeneity results from changes in the work function of the surface as coverage increases. Thus, an initially homogeneous surface is made heterogeneous by the adsorption.

Heterogeneity resulting from depole interaction among adsorbed species is generally too small to account quantitatively for the decrease in heat of adsorption although depole interactions account for a part of the effect.

It is not necessary for our purpose to know which of the above reasons is most important in bringing about surface heterogeneity, for we only use the fact that the catalyst surface can offer a variety of sites whereupon molecules can adsorb with various bond strengths. The changes in the chemical structure of the adsorbed species depend upon the strength of the bond formed with the catalyst, and it is reasonable to expect that, for a particular chemical reaction to occur readily, the strength of the bond with the surface must be within certain prescribed limits. Accordingly, sites at which these bond energy requirements are met are the ones which become the "active centers" for catalyzing the particular reaction.

This then is the model for the description of catalytic kinetics in the following section: A fixed number of "active centers" which account for catalytic activity. The remaining sites are active for adsorption but form bonds with the reactant molecules which are either too weak or too strong to serve as "active centers."

3.4 General catalytic kinetics

Throughout the earlier part of this book, we have been concerned with a general reaction of the form

$$\sum_{i=1}^{n} a_i A_i = 0. \tag{3.4-1}$$

The discussion of the catalytic kinetics of this reaction will begin by the consideration of a simple representative of this general reaction in order to keep the mathematical complexities to a minimum and to emphasize the physical concepts. Let us consider the simple representative reaction to be of the form

$$A_1 + A_2 \rightleftarrows A_3 + A_4. \tag{3.4-2}$$

If this reaction is to be catalyzed by the presence of a solid surface, it is clear that the reactants cannot be converted into products mechanistically as shown by the stoichiometric equation because Eq. 3.4-2 does not include the participation of the catalyst. The function of the catalyst is to supply active centers at which points the reactants form complexes or intermediates of the type first discussed by Langmuir. These intermediates proceed to rearrange or react with other reactants to form products which leave the vicinity of the site and restore the latter for reuse. One possible reaction mechanism therefore becomes

Reaction 1:

$$A_1 + \mathbf{X}_1 \underset{k_{-1}}{\overset{k_1}{\rightleftarrows}} A_3 + \mathbf{X}_2$$

Reaction 2:

$$A_2 + \mathbf{X}_2 \underset{k_{-2}}{\overset{k_2}{\rightleftarrows}} A_4 + \mathbf{X}_1$$

$$\left.\begin{array}{c} \\ \\ \\ \\ \end{array}\right\} \qquad (3.4\text{-}3)$$

where $\mathbf{X}_1$ and $\mathbf{X}_2$ refer to the chemical form of the unoccupied and occupied active centers respectively. The essential idea here is that $\mathbf{X}_1$ which is consumed as a result of Reaction 1, is regenerated by Reaction 2.

To proceed with the analysis it is necessary to postulate *a priori* that the number of active centers X_0 in the system is a constant proportional to the mass of catalyst present. The number of active centers in the system is generally small compared to the number of reactants and it becomes unnecessary to correct the fluid phase concentrations to account for molecules in the adsorbed state on the surface of the catalyst. Because the number of active centers is small, a dynamic steady-state is frequently set up between the adsorbed species and the fluid phase immediately adjacent to the surface provided any one of the intermediate steps is sufficiently reactive. These conditions lead to what is known as the *steady-state approximation*. The implication of this assumption physically is that the time scale of the unsteady-state processes by which the fluid phase and the catalyst surface interact is small compared to the rate at which fluid phase concentrations vary. A quantitative statement of this assumption is developed immediately following the steady-state analysis of Eq. 3.4-3.

When the conditions for the steady-state approximation are encountered, and they very frequently are, the analysis is greatly simplified because the distribution of the active centers between the occupied and unoccupied forms is time invariant. The mathematical equations equivalent to the assumptions of constancy of total number of active centers and their time invariancy are:

$$X_1 + X_2 = X_0 \qquad (3.4\text{-}4)$$

$$\frac{dX_1}{dt} = -\frac{dX_2}{dt} = 0 = -k_1 C_1 X_1 + k_{-1} C_3 X_2 + k_2 C_2 X_2 - k_{-2} C_4 X_1,$$

$$(3.4\text{-}5)$$

where C_i = concentration of the ith species, A_i.

Solving for X_1 from this pair of equations we readily obtain

$$X_1 = \frac{X_0(k_{-1} C_3 + k_2 C_2)}{k_1 C_1 + k_2 C_2 + k_{-1} C_3 + k_{-2} C_4} \qquad (3.4\text{-}6)$$

and a similar expression for X_2. Since all net rates are equal under the steady-state approximation, the over-all rate may be determined from either of the consecutive reactions. Choosing Reaction 1, the net steady state rate $\mathscr{R}_S$, is

$$\mathscr{R}_S = k_1 C_1 X_1 - k_{-1} C_3 X_2. \tag{3.4-7}$$

Substituting for X_1 and X_2 and the rate becomes

$$\mathscr{R}_S = X_0 \left[\frac{k_1 k_2 C_1 C_2 - k_{-1} k_{-2} C_3 C_4}{k_1 C_1 + k_2 C_2 + k_{-1} C_3 + k_{-2} C_4} \right]. \tag{3.4-8}$$

Equation 3.4-8 is of no particular importance except in that it shows the form of the kinetic rate expression for a particular system Eq. 3.4-3 as derived using the concept of the constancy of active centers and the steady-state approximation, Eqs. 3.4-4 and 3.4-5 respectively. It is clear that analogous expressions would follow for an alternate set of reaction steps if the same concepts are utilized. In this way many reaction models may be postulated and the corresponding rate expression developed. However, it is noteworthy to mention that Eq. 3.4-8 may be used to obtain the rate provided that the values of five parameters are known: four kinetic and one regarding the number of active centers. This results in an expression which not only is unwieldy but has a flexibility to correlate most any data. In the absence of independent verification of the values of the parameters, the investigator is left with a great deal of uncertainty as to the applicability of a given model.

The foregoing analysis is based upon the constancy of the number of active centers in the system and the validity of the steady-state approximation. It was stated earlier that if the system is sufficiently reactive, the latter approximation is valid. It is of value to investigate this point in more detail to bring out the essence of this idea. If the steady-state approximation is not made, Eqs. 3.4-4 and 3.4-5 become

$$\frac{dX_1}{dt} = -[k_1 C_1 + k_{-2} C_4 + k_{-1} C_3 + k_2 C_2] X_1 + X_0 [k_{-1} C_3 + k_2 C_2]$$

which may be rewritten as $\tag{3.4-9}$

$$\frac{dX_1}{dt} = -P X_1 + Q, \tag{3.4-10}$$

where, of course, P and Q are defined by comparing Eqs. 3.4-9 and 3.4-10, and where the fluid phase concentrations C_i are assumed to be constant during the time scale for the variation in X_1. Solving Eq. 3.4-10 for the initial condition that at $t = 0$, $X_1 = X_0$:

$$X_1 = \frac{Q}{P} (1 - e^{-Pt}) + X_0 e^{-Pt} \tag{3.4-11}$$

and the unsteady state rate $\mathscr{R}(t)$ is

$$\mathscr{R}(t) = \mathscr{R}_S (1 - e^{-Pt}) + k_1 C_1 X_0 e^{-Pt}. \tag{3.4-12}$$

From the form of Eq. 3.4-12, it is clear that the steady-state approximation is valid when $e^{-Pt} \ll 1$, remembering of course that X_0 is included in $\mathscr{R}_S$. From the definition of P, we readily ascertain that e^{-Pt} is small compared to unity when any one of the elementary rate constants, k's, is large, even though the other k's are small. Physically this means that if we choose a time τ which is small compared to the time scale or duration of the kinetic experiment and if the product Pt is much greater than unity, the steady-state approximation is valid for this reaction for all times greater than τ. Obviously, the numerical value of τ depends upon the particular reaction and we would expect that τ for a hydrogenation experiment would be quite different from that chosen for the combustion of a propellant. Then, whether the steady-state approximation is valid or not depends how small $e^{-P\tau}$ is with respect to unity. We now have quantitatively defined the restrictions which have been imposed upon Eq. 3.4-8.

It should be clear to the reader, that it is possible to determine the form of the rate expression corresponding to a postulated elementary reaction mechanism using the technique described above; however, the form of the resulting expression is invariably cumbersome. Equation 3.4-8 is an example of such an unwieldy expression. It is worthwhile to repeat here that there are five constants to be evaluated and although each has physical significance in terms of the reaction model, when fitting kinetic data, these constants are tantamount to having five adjustable parameters. We thereby gain great flexibility in fitting data at the expense of a loss in sensitivity in testing a given reaction model. Fortunately, it is possible to affect a simplification of the rate expression if the rate constants corresponding to one of the elementary steps in the over-all mechanism can be recognized as being small compared to the others.*

To illustrate this technique reconsider the reactions of Eq. 3.4-3. Let us explore the changes in the rate expression of Eq. 3.4-8 resulting from the hypothesis that Reaction 2 is the slow step in the over-all process. Physically what we are saying is that although the net rates at which each reaction takes place must be identical because of the steady-state assumption, the magnitudes of the rate constants are such that the net rate at which Reaction 1 takes place is sufficiently large even close to equilibrium to maintain the over-all rate, whereas Reaction 2 having much smaller rate constants must shift far from equilibrium to maintain an equal net rate. Thus, in the limiting case, all reaction steps of the over-all mechanism are essentially at equilibrium save the rate determining or slow step. Referring now to Eq. 3.4-8, if k_1 and k_{-1} are much larger than k_2 and k_{-2}, then the terms in which the latter appear in the denominator of this equation may be neglected when compared to the remaining terms. Eq. 3.4-8 reduces thereby to

$$\mathscr{R}_s = X_0 \left[\frac{k_2 C_2 - k_{-2} K_1 (C_4 C_3 / C_1)}{1 + K_1 (C_3 / C_1)} \right], \qquad (3.4\text{-}16)$$

---

* Equivalent to the vernacular phase, *the slow step in the reaction*, a jargon which we shall perpetuate from this point on for convenience.

wherein it is noted that k_1 and k_{-1} no longer appear separately. Only their ratio, $K_1 \equiv k_{-1}/k_1$, appears. This, of course, is to be expected because the equilibrium constant alone is all that is needed to determine the state of a reaction at equilibrium.

In summary, we have discussed three useful ideas in this section:

1. The *a priori* assumption of the constancy of the total number of active centers in the system.

2. The steady-state approximation.

3. The so-called slow step in the reaction mechanism.

In the next section, we shall apply these ideas to systems which are more general and accordingly approximate the behavior of real kinetic systems more closely.

3.5 Simple heterogeneous reactions

Kinetic mechanisms seldom follow a reaction path as simple as the one depicted by Eqs. 3.4-3. Although the latter set is useful as a means of presenting the techniques by which heterogeneous reactions are interpreted, the discussion should be extended now to include mechanisms of broader applicability. At the same time, to keep the analysis within manageable bounds, the simplifications learned earlier will be freely utilized to develop limiting forms of the rate expressions.

Consider a simple case

$$A_R \rightleftharpoons A_P, \tag{3.5-1}$$

where the general mechanism is assumed to be

$$A_R + X_1 \underset{k_{-1}}{\overset{k_1}{\rightleftarrows}} X_2 \underset{k_{-2}}{\overset{k_2}{\rightleftarrows}} X_3 \underset{k_{-3}}{\overset{k_3}{\rightleftarrows}} A_P + X_1. \tag{3.5-2}$$

The three reactions are referred to as the adsorption, reaction and desorption steps. The reactant A_R adsorbs on the site X_1 to form the adsorbed complex X_2, which reacts to produce the adsorbed product X_3, which subsequently desorbs to give the product A_P and regenerates the site X_1 for further use. The steady-state description of the system is given, as before, by

$$\left.\begin{aligned} X_1 + X_2 + X_3 &= X_0 \\ \frac{dX_1}{dt} = 0 &= -[k_1 C_R + k_{-3} C_P] X_1 + k_{-1} X_2 + k_3 X_3 \\ \frac{dX_2}{dt} = 0 &= k_1 C_R X_1 - [k_{-1} + k_2] X_2 + k_{-2} X_3 \end{aligned}\right\} \tag{3.5-3}$$

A limiting case frequently encountered is that of reaction rate controlling. In the reaction scheme of Eq. 3.5-2, the reaction step is the conversion of the complex X_2 to complex X_3. Physically, this limiting case corresponds to the assumption that the adsorption and desorption processes are fast compared to the reaction step; thus the adsorption and desorption steps are essentially at equilibrium whereas the reaction step is far from equilibrium. In terms of the symbols of Eq. 3.5-2, these statements are consistent with the contention that magnitudes of $k_1 C_R X_1$, $k_{-1} X_2$, $k_3 X_3$, $k_{-3} C_P X_1$ are much greater than $k_2 X_2$ which is in turn greater than $k_{-2} X_3$ in such a way that

$$k_1 C_R X_1 - k_{-1} X_2 = k_2 X_2 - k_{-2} X_3$$
$$= k_3 X_3 - k_{-3} C_P X_1$$
$$= \text{overall rate of reaction}$$
$$= \mathscr{R}_S. \qquad (3.5\text{-}4)$$

Moreover since $k_2 X_2 \gg k_{-2} X_3$,

$$\mathscr{R}_S = k_2 X_2 \qquad (3.5\text{-}5)$$

to the approximation that the system is reaction rate controlling. This physical picture readily leads to a mathematical expression for X_2, and hence $\mathscr{R}_S$. The third of Eqs. 3.5-3 reduces to the adsorption equilibrium statement

$$X_2 = \frac{k_1 C_R X_1}{k_{-1}}, \qquad (3.5\text{-}6)$$

which when substituted into the second of these equations reduces it to the desorption equilibrium statement

$$X_3 = \left[\frac{k_{-3} C_P}{k_3}\right] X_1. \qquad (3.5\text{-}7)$$

Substituting Eqs. 3.5-7 and 3.5-6 into the first of Eqs. 3.5-3 leads to an expression for X_2 and finally the rate expression:

$$\mathscr{R}_S = \frac{k_2 X_0 (k_1/k_{-1}) C_R}{1 + (k_1/k_{-1}) C_R + (k_{-3}/k_3) C_P} \qquad (3.5\text{-}8)$$

or

$$\mathscr{R}_S = k_2 X_0 \left[\frac{K_R C_R}{1 + K_R C_R + K_P C_P}\right], \qquad (3.5\text{-}9)$$

which is the familiar Langmuir-Hinshelwood form, where the equilibrium constants K_R and K_P have replaced the ratio of the forward and reverse kinetic constants of the reactants and products.

If another species, a non-reacting impurity for example, is present in the mixture and competes along with the reactants and products for active centers, it is clear that it will add a term of the form $K_I C_I$ in the denominator.*

---

* That is, there are four forms of the active center now:

$$X_1 + X_2 + X_3 + X_I = X_0, \qquad A_I + X_1 \rightleftarrows X_I \quad \text{and} \quad X_I = K_I C_I X_1.$$

Lastly, if the surface reaction occurs between two complexes X_2, then the rate becomes

$$\mathcal{R}_S = k_2 X_2^2 \tag{3.5-10}$$

$$= k_2 X_0^2 \left[\frac{K_R C_R}{1 + K_R C_R + K_P C_P + K_I C_I} \right]^2, \tag{3.5-11}$$

where the impurity term previously discussed has been included.

EXAMPLE 3.5-1 DEHYDROGENATION OF METHYLCYCLOHEXANE TO TOLUENE

This interesting example was reported by Sinfelt, Hurivitz, and Shulman.* Under their experimental conditions, the rate is zero order with respect to the reactant and is not inhibited by additions of benzene or xylene to the reaction mixture. A mechanism kinetically consistent with these observations is that of desorption rate limiting. This limiting case is based upon relationship among the rate constants, the complex concentrations, and the species concentrations given below:

$$k_{-3} C_P X_1 \ll k_3 X_3 \ll k_2 X_2, \qquad k_{-2} X_3, \qquad k_1 C_R X_1, \qquad k_{-1} X_2. \tag{3.5-12}$$

The competition of the impurity for unoccupied active centers is given by the equilibrium relationship

$$A_I + X_1 \underset{k_1}{\overset{k_{-1}}{\rightleftarrows}} X_I. \tag{3.5-13}$$

As before, Eqs. 3.5-3 may be readily solved to give the rate expression corresponding to this kinetic model. However, we shall develop the rate expression from an equivalent method based upon the physical model. The adsorption and reaction steps are essentially at equilibrium

$$\frac{X_2}{X_1} = \frac{k_1 C_R}{k_{-1}} = K_R C_R, \qquad \frac{X_I}{X_1} = K_I C_I, \qquad \frac{X_3}{X_2} = K_2, \tag{3.5-14}$$

and it follows that

$$\frac{X_3}{X_1} = K_2 K_R C_R.$$

The sum of the active centers remains constant, hence

$$X_1 + X_2 + X_3 + X_I = X_0. \tag{3.5-15}$$

Substituting Eqs. 3.5-14 into 3.5-15 we obtain an expression for X_1 of the form

$$X_1 = \frac{X_0}{1 + [K_2 + 1] K_R C_R + K_I C_I}, \tag{3.5-16}$$

which leads to the rate expression shown below:

$$\mathcal{R}_S = k_3 X_3 = k_3 X_0 \left[\frac{K_2 K_R C_R}{1 + [K_2 + 1] K_R C_R + K_I C_I} \right]. \tag{3.5-17}$$

* J. H. Sinfelt, H. Hurivitz, R. A. Shulman, *J. Phys. Chem.* **64**, 1559 (1960).

Equation 3.5-17 is based upon the assumption of a steady-state desorption controlled reaction. When the impurities are chemically similar to the product, a simplification may be realized. The desorption step is far from equilibrium, therefore

$$k_3 X_3 \gg k_{-3} C_P X_1 \quad \text{or} \quad \frac{X_3}{X_1} \gg K_P C_P.$$

For chemically similar species $K_I \approx K_P$, therefore, even when the impurity and product concentrations are of comparable magnitudes, i.e.,

$$K_I C_I \approx K_P C_P,$$

it follows from Eq. 3.5-14 that

$$K_2 K_R C_R \gg K_I C_I.$$

This term can, therefore, be dropped from the denominator of Eq. 3.4-17. Accordingly such impurities cannot appreciably inhibit the rate of reaction.

In the particular example being discussed, it was observed experimentally that the reaction rate was independent of the reactant concentration. Equation 3.5-17 reduces to this form when K_2 and $K_R C_R$ are each much greater than unity whereby the rate expression becomes

$$\mathscr{R}_S = k_3 X_0. \tag{3.5-18}$$

The experimental observations on the mechanism of the dehydrogenation of methylcyclohexane are consistent with slow desorption of the toluene complex from the nickel surface. When the toluene is desorbed from the active center, competition for this unoccupied center greatly favors the methylcyclohexane because its adsorption constant is very much greater than for either a product or impurity molecule. However, because of the large magnitude of the equilibrium constant K_2, $\mathbf{X_2}$ quickly reacts to form $\mathbf{X_3}$.

EXAMPLE 3.5-2 DEHYDROGENATION OF SECONDARY ALCOHOLS

For an example of the use of Eq. 3.5-9, consider the dehydrogenation of secondary alcohols over a nickel catalyst as reported by Claes and Jungers.* In this liquid phase reaction, it is reasonable to assume that the active centers of the catalyst are saturated with reactants and products.† Under these conditions one or more of the terms in the denominator have numerical magnitudes much greater than unity. Thus, Eq. 3.4-9 becomes

$$\mathscr{R}_S = k_2 X_0 \left[\frac{K_R C_R}{K_R C_R + K_P C_P} \right]. \tag{3.5-19}$$

* F. Claes and J. C. Jungers, *Bull. Soc. Chim. France* **8/9**, 1167, (1958).

† Under the conditions of the experiment, hydrogen was removed as fast as it was formed.

Rearranging Eq. 3.5-19 for suitable testing we obtain

$$\frac{1}{\mathscr{R}_S} = \frac{1}{k_2 X_0} + \frac{1}{k_2 X_0}\left[\frac{K_P C_P}{K_R C_R}\right]. \tag{3.5-20}$$

Equation 3.5-20 predicts that the reciprocal of the instantaneous rate is a linear function of the ratio of the product and reactant concentrations. If such linear behavior is observed, then $k_2 X_0$ can be computed from the intercept. Kinetic data corresponding to the hydrogenation of various secondary alcohols was found to be a linear function of $K_P C_P / K_R C_R$. The

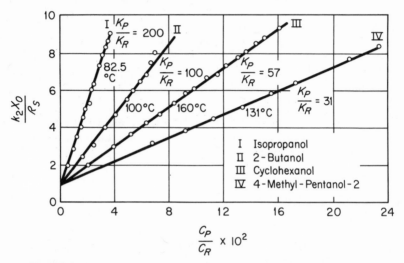

Fig. 3.5-1. Dehydrogenation of secondary alcohols on a nickel catalyst. R—CHOH—R' $\xrightarrow{\text{Ni}}$ R—CO—R' + H$_2$. [Adapted from Claes, F. and J. C. Jungers, *Bull. Soc. Chim. France*, **8/9**, 1167 (1958).]

intercepts were determined and these data may then be replotted as shown in Fig. 3.5-1. According to Eq. 3.5-21 below

$$\frac{k_2 X_0}{\mathscr{R}_S} = 1 + \left(\frac{K_P}{K_R}\right)\left(\frac{C_P}{C_R}\right), \tag{3.5-21}$$

the slopes of these lines represent the ratio adsorption equilibrium coefficients K_P / K_R, and are recorded on the figure. These numerical values show that the ketone products are much more strongly adsorbed than their corresponding alcohols. The limiting form of this rate expression as the reaction goes to completion becomes

$$\mathscr{R}_S = k_2 X_0 \left(\frac{K_R}{K_P}\right)\left(\frac{C_R}{C_P}\right), \tag{3.5-22}$$

where it should be noted that the rate is first order in reactant and inverse first order in the product concentration.

These two examples serve to illustrate how several simple kinetic concepts are applied to gain a better understanding of the detailed mechanism of a particular reaction and to obtain the form of the rate expression. In these examples, we see the final result: a mechanism or model and a rate expression based upon the model which is consistent with the available experimental reaction rate data. The reader probably already realizes the trial and error methods that are frequently necessary in order to arrive at useful models. The attempt to explain a given set of experiments leads to possible mechanisms and their corresponding rate expressions. The forms of these rate expressions suggest crucial experiments which serve to distinguish among the alternatives that single mechanism which best explains all of the experiments. If that mechanism encompasses a sufficiently broad range of conditions, it will be useful for the design of reactors and the more philosophical question of correctness becomes less relevant.

In the last two sections, we have concentrated on the ideas needed to translate a reaction model to its corresponding rate expression. The ideas are few in number but applicable to a wide variety of kinetic situations. We shall now consider some of the unique properties of complex heterogeneous reaction systems.

3.6 Complex heterogeneous reactions

The feed to an industrial scale reactor is almost always a mixture of compounds. It may be a mixture of several compounds which are made more valuable or useful by chemically converting all or part of them into other compounds. Or it may consist essentially of a single chemical species with traces of impurities which do not behave as inerts in the reactor. The decision to separate or purify the feed stream by an operation preceding the reactor is necessarily an economic one hinging on a detailed analysis of the chemical interactions within the reactor. There is more need for an accurate kinetic description for this case than for simple reactions and correspondingly the classical integral order kinetic description is of much less value for design purposes. In fact when only pure component reaction rate information is available, a designer must vigorously resist the temptation to predict the performance of a reactor when it is fed by a mixture of compounds, unless he has a thorough understanding of the kinetic mechanism. An example discussed in this section serves dramatically to illustrate this point.

Actually there is a more important reason for studying complex reactions. The interactions among the many reactant, intermediate and product species at the surface the catalyst manifest themselves in some cases by rather striking changes in the magnitude of the over-all reaction rate. It should not be surprising then that some of the most conclusive and useful information concerning the mechanism of a reaction as well as the relative magnitudes of the parameters in the rate expression come from the comparison of pure component and mixed component rate data. If a kinetic model is based upon both pure reactant and mixed reactant experimental data, it may be used more reliably to predict the magnitude and direction of interaction effects and to learn the conditions under which desired reactions are favored and parasitic reactions are suppressed.

From the earlier discussion of heterogeneous reactions, it should be clear that interactions can result as the reactants compete for active centers. A quantitative discussion of the effect is best deferred until after a mathematical formulation of the problem.

Consider now the following pair of reactions

$$A_1 + A_2 \rightleftarrows A_3 + A_4 \tag{3.6-1}$$

$$A_5 + A_6 \rightleftarrows A_7 + A_8,$$

which are assumed to proceed mechanistically according to the reaction scheme below:

Reaction 1: $\qquad A_1 + \mathbf{X}_1 \underset{k_{-1}}{\overset{k_1}{\rightleftarrows}} A_3 + \mathbf{X}_2$

Reaction 2: $\qquad A_2 + \mathbf{X}_2 \underset{k_{-2}}{\overset{k_2}{\rightleftarrows}} A_4 + \mathbf{X}_1$

$$\tag{3.6-2}$$

Reaction 3: $\qquad A_5 + \mathbf{X}_1 \underset{k_{-3}}{\overset{k_3}{\rightleftarrows}} A_7 + \mathbf{X}_3$

Reaction 4: $\qquad A_6 + \mathbf{X}_3 \underset{k_{-4}}{\overset{k_4}{\rightleftarrows}} A_8 + \mathbf{X}_1$

This proposed mechanism corresponds to the physical situation where two of the reactants A_1 and A_5 compete for the unoccupied active centers $\mathbf{X}_1$ to form complexes $\mathbf{X}_2$ and $\mathbf{X}_3$, respectively. The complexes in turn react with A_2 and A_6 to regenerate the unoccupied active center. No new physical ideas are needed to analyze this system of equations. One form of the rate expression follows directly from the steady-state approximation. In analogy with the earlier analysis, the original active centers $\mathbf{X}_0$ are distributed in some proportion among the possibilities X_1, the unoccupied centers, and X_2 and X_3, the complexes with A_1 and A_5, respectively, and that this distribution is not time dependent. These assumptions lead us to the system of equations shown below:

$$X_1 + X_2 + X_3 = X_0$$

$$\frac{dX_2}{dt} = 0 = k_1 C_1 X_1 - k_{-1} C_3 X_2 - k_2 C_2 X_2 + k_{-2} C_4 X_1 \tag{3.6-3}$$

$$\frac{dX_3}{dt} = 0 = k_3 C_5 X_1 - k_{-3} C_7 X_3 - k_4 C_6 X_3 + k_{-4} C_8 X_1$$

which may be solved* for X_1, X_2, and X_3 in terms of the various k_i, C_i, and X_0. These expressions may then be substituted, as before, into an expression for the rate of one of the reactions, say Reaction 1 as given by Eqs. 3.6-2, and an expression for the rate developed. We have shown how the steady-state approximation may be used to obtain the form rate expression for the case of two parallel reactions. The generalization of this analysis to include m parallel reactions is not difficult; however, we shall not proceed in this direction. In fact, we shall not proceed with general solution to Eqs. 3.6-3 because not only is this solution for a specialized system (Eqs. 3.6-2) but its form is so cumbersome that it has little general utility. We shall rather consider the application of these ideas to a specific case where they have been useful in interpreting kinetic data.

EXAMPLE 3.6-1 LIQUID PHASE HYDROGENATION OF TETRALIN AND p-XYLENE ON RANEY NICKEL CATALYST

The liquid phase hydrogenation of tetralin and p-xylene on a Raney nickel catalyst at 170°C was reported by Wangmier and Jungers.† The order of this reaction is zero with respect to each of the pure aromatic reactants and the products do not exert an inhibiting effect on the reaction. In this case the reaction scheme consists of two reactions of the type shown in Eqs. 3.5-2, each of which appear to be desorption controlled.

$$\left. \begin{array}{l} A_{R1} + X_1 \underset{k_{-11}}{\overset{k_{11}}{\rightleftarrows}} X_2 \underset{k_{-21}}{\overset{k_{21}}{\rightleftarrows}} X_3 \underset{k_{-31}}{\overset{k_{31}}{\rightleftarrows}} A_{P1} + X_1 \\[2ex] A_{R2} + X_1 \underset{k_{-12}}{\overset{k_{12}}{\rightleftarrows}} X_4 \underset{k_{-22}}{\overset{k_{22}}{\rightleftarrows}} X_5 \underset{k_{-32}}{\overset{k_{32}}{\rightleftarrows}} A_{P2} + X_1 \end{array} \right\} \quad (3.6\text{-}4)$$

Following a line of reasoning parallel to that used for the case of dehydrogenation of methylcyclohexane in Example 3.5-1, the following rate expressions are obtained for each component in the mixture

$$\left. \begin{array}{l} \mathscr{R}_{S1} = k_{31}X_0 \left[\dfrac{K_{21}K_{R1}C_{R1}}{K_{21}K_{R1}C_{R1} + K_{22}K_{R2}C_{R2}} \right] \\[3ex] \mathscr{R}_{S2} = k_{32}X_0 \left[\dfrac{K_{22}K_{R2}C_{R2}}{K_{21}K_{R1}C_{R1} + K_{22}K_{R2}C_{R2}} \right] \end{array} \right\} \quad (3.6\text{-}5)$$

where of course the K's are the equilibrium constants for the non-rate limiting steps. The over-all reaction rate $\mathscr{R}_{S0}$ is the sum of $\mathscr{R}_{S1}$ and $\mathscr{R}_{S2}$.

* Note that for a large number of parallel reactions, these equations could easily be formalized to be a matrix representation and analysis reduced to a routine computer problem. This will not be developed here because there is as yet no reliable independent means of determining the values of the k's.

† J. P. Wangmier and J. C. Jungers, *Bull. Soc. Chim.* France **10**, 1280 (1957).

TABLE 3.6-1

KINETICS OF THE LIQUID PHASE HYDROGENATION OF TETRALIN AND p-XYLENE ON RANEY NICKEL

Temperature: 170°C

Concentration		(grams; liter)$^{-1}$	
Tetralin: $\mathscr{R}_{S1}$	p-xylene: $\mathscr{R}_{S2}$		
C_{R1}	C_{R2}		
Pure component rate constant	$k_{31}X_0 = 6.7$	$k_{32}X_0 = 12.9$	(gram moles hydrocarbon) · (min)$^{-1}$· (gram cat)$^{-1}$

Concentration (grams/liter)				Selectivity		$\mathscr{R}_{S0}$
C_{R1}	C_{R2}	$\ln\dfrac{(C_{R1})_0}{(C_{R1})}$	$\ln\dfrac{(C_{R2})_0}{(C_{R2})}$	$\dfrac{k_{31}X_0 K_{21}K_{R1}}{k_{32}X_0 K_{22}K_{R2}}$	$\mathscr{R}$ Calc.	Experiment
280	610	...	...	...	8.5	8.5
235	566	0.069	0.025	2.76	8.9	8.8
139	462	0.280	0.098	2.86	9.4	9.4
57	334	0.650	0.221	2.94	10.4	10.4
10	159	1.390	0.525	2.65	11.4	11.3

To obtain $\mathscr{R}_{S0}$ it is necessary to know $k_{31}X_0$, $k_{32}X_0$, and $K_{21}K_{R1}/R_{22}R_{R2}$. The former two constants are measured directly by observing the rates of each of the pure reactants as given by Eq. 3.5-18. The latter ratio is obtained by a single measurement of the product distribution from a mixture of the reactants.

To show this, we observe that the ratio of the two Eqs. 3.6-5 is

$$\frac{\mathscr{R}_{S1}}{\mathscr{R}_{S2}} = \left(\frac{dC_{R1}}{dC_{R2}}\right) = \frac{k_{31}X_0K_{21}K_{R1}C_{R1}}{k_{32}X_0K_{22}K_{R2}C_{R2}}, \tag{3.6-6}$$

which when integrated gives

$$\frac{\ln[C_{R1}/(C_{R1})_0]}{\ln[C_{R2}/(C_{R2})_0]} = \frac{k_{31}X_0K_{21}K_{R1}}{k_{32}X_0K_{22}K_{R2}}. \tag{3.6-7}$$

Since $k_{31}X_0$ and $k_{32}X_0$ are known, the remaining ratio is obtained. Table 3.6-1 shows the data for the tetralin—p-xylene system as obtained by Wangmier and Jungers.[*] The correspondence between these data and the predictions based upon them beautifully illustrate the utility of the kinetic mechanisms and at the same time point to an unconventional result; unconventional because under these conditions the rate of reaction of the mixture starts at a value close to that for pure tetralin, *the slower reaction,* and then *increases* as the tetralin concentration is reduced to a point where it cannot compete for as many of the active centers. The p-xylene, therefore, occupies more of the active centers and because it can react faster, the over-all rate of reaction, $\mathscr{R}_{S0}$, increases. As shown above, the predicted rates were based upon a knowledge of the mechanism, and the numerical values of three constants.

3.7 The use of tracers in determining the mechanism

An exhaustive discussion of the experimental methods which can be used to establish the mechanism of a catalytic reaction is beyond the scope of this chapter. Indeed, the number of available experimental methods which have been used to study catalytic reactions is very large. Yet certain methods are especially significant because in principle they lead to unequivocal information about the mechanism of a reaction. These powerful methods make use of tracer or "tagged" compounds which by virtue of being distinguishable from otherwise identical molecules can be followed through the course of reaction. What information can be obtained, of course, depends upon the design of the experiment. The number of ways which tracer compounds can be used again precludes exhaustive discussion, but there are in particular two techniques which merit attention here.

The first of these might be referred to as a method for determining the

[*] Wangmiers and Jungers (1957), *op. cit.*

uniqueness of a precursor in a complex network of reactions. To illustrate what is meant by this, let us consider the following case of a series of consecutive reactions:

$$A_1 \xrightarrow{\overline{\mathscr{R}}_{12}} A_2 \xrightarrow{\overline{\mathscr{R}}_{23}} A_3 \xrightarrow{\overline{\mathscr{R}}_{34}} A_4, \tag{3.7-1}$$

where A_1 = reactant species

A_2, A_3, and A_4 = identifiable product species

$\overline{\mathscr{R}}_{12}$, $\overline{\mathscr{R}}_{23}$, and $\overline{\mathscr{R}}_{34}$ = rates in moles/(unit volume)(unit time)

at which the respective reactions take place. The question arises as to whether the mechanism goes according to Eq. 3.7-1 or some alternate scheme such as the one shown below:

$$A_1 \xrightarrow{\overline{\mathscr{R}}_{12}} A_2 \xrightarrow{\overline{\mathscr{R}}_{23}} A_3 \xrightarrow{\overline{\mathscr{R}}_{34}} A_4. \tag{3.7-2}$$

$$\underset{\overline{\mathscr{R}}_{13}}{\underline{}}$$

In comparing the two possibilities it becomes evident that the real question here is: Must A_1 go through the intermediate A_2 to produce A_3 or is there also a path whereby A_1 goes directly to A_3? Does A_3 have a unique precursor, A_2, or more than one precursor, A_1 and A_2? A tracer method may be used to resolve this question.

Consider the reaction as taking place under conditions which maintain the four (or three as the case may be) rates $\overline{\mathscr{R}}_{ij}$ invariant with time.† Note that $\overline{\mathscr{R}}_{ij}$ is a rate, moles/(unit time) (unit volume), and no statement is made about order of reaction or the details of the rate mechanism. At some time, $t = 0$, a known quantity of A_2^*, a tracer compound of A_2, is introduced into the reaction vessel in an amount so small that the concentration of A_2 is not measurably affected. The ratio of the concentrations of A_2^* and A_2 at any time is defined as α, i.e.,

$$\alpha \equiv \frac{C_2^*}{C_2}, \tag{3.7-3}$$

and similarly,

$$\beta \equiv \frac{C_3^*}{C_3}, \tag{3.7-4}$$

where C_3^* is the concentration of the tracer product A_3^*. Because we have postulated steady-state conditions, the conservation equation may be written for A_3 as

$$\overline{\mathscr{R}}_{13} + \overline{\mathscr{R}}_{23} = \overline{\mathscr{R}}_{34}. \tag{3.7-5}$$

† This could be accomplished, for example, in the so-called CFSTR, the continuous-flow stirred-tank reactor.

If now, we assume that the tracer compounds are completely mixed with their respective untagged counterparts, then clearly the probability that a tracer compound will react at any time is equal to the ratio of the number of tracer molecules of that species to the total number of molecules of that species, which for compound A_2 is simply α. Thus, a material balance on A_2^* becomes:

$$C_2 \frac{d\alpha}{dt} = -\bar{\mathscr{R}}_{23}\alpha, \tag{3.7-6}$$

and a material balance on A_3^* is

$$C_3 \frac{d\beta}{dt} = \bar{\mathscr{R}}_{23}\alpha - \bar{\mathscr{R}}_{34}\beta.$$

From Eq. 3.7-5

$$C_3 \frac{d\beta}{dt} = \bar{\mathscr{R}}_{23}\alpha - (\bar{\mathscr{R}}_{13} + \bar{\mathscr{R}}_{23})\beta. \tag{3.7-7}$$

When β goes through a maximum, $(d\beta/dt) = 0$, and from Eq. 3.7-7

$$\frac{\alpha}{\beta} = 1 + \frac{\bar{\mathscr{R}}_{13}}{\bar{\mathscr{R}}_{23}}. \tag{3.7-8}$$

It follows from Eq. 3.7-8 that if A_2 is the sole precursor of A_3, i.e., $\bar{\mathscr{R}}_{13} = 0$, then the maximum in the curve of β vs time should correspond to $\alpha = \beta$. If $\bar{\mathscr{R}}_{13} \neq 0$, the maximum will occur where $\alpha > \beta$. The result shown on Fig. 3.7-1 satisfies the criteria for a unique precursor for the special case of $C_2 = C_3$.

A second example of the use of tracers is in the determination of what is known as the stoichiometric number of the rate limiting step. The stoichiometric number σ is the number of times the limiting step occurs during one occurrence of the main reaction. This idea is developed immediately below. This method can be used to rule out certain elementary steps in the mechanism as possible rate limiting steps. Although it was proposed by Horiuti* as a general technique, its application has been associated primarily with the ammonia synthesis reaction. This latter reaction will therefore be used in the following discussion to illustrate the general method.

Consider the ammonia synthesis reaction

$$N_2 + 3\,H_2 \underset{\longleftarrow}{\overset{\text{catalyst}}{\longrightarrow}} 2\,NH_3 \tag{3.7-9}$$

This reaction has been studied extensively and the experimental data strongly support the contention that the over-all reaction of Eq. 3.7-9 is carried out by the series of elementary steps shown in Table 3.7-1. The meaning of the stoichiometric number can now be made clear by observing how many times

* Enomoto S. Horiuti, *J. Research Inst. Catalysis*, Hokkaido Univ. **2**, 87 (1953).

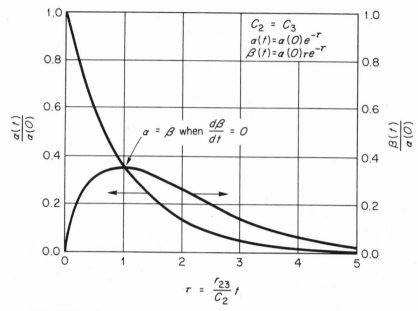

Fig. 3.7-1. A typical plot showing a single precursor in a complex reaction network.

each of the elementary steps in Table 3.7-1 must occur in order to carry out the main reaction of Eq. 3.7-9 once. For example, Step 2 must occur three times and therefore its stoichiometric number is three.

The number of elementary steps in the ammonia synthesis reaction is greater than any considered so far; however, the general pattern is the same. There are two adsorption steps, three reaction steps and a desorption step. To derive a kinetic rate expression for this reaction for the purpose of

TABLE 3.7-1

ELEMENTARY STEPS IN THE AMMONIA SYNTHESIS REACTION

Step	Stoichiometric number σ
(1) $N_2 \rightarrow 2\, N_{ads}$	1
(2) $H_2 \rightarrow 2\, H_{ads}$	3
(3) $N_{ads} + H_{ads} \rightarrow (NH)_{ads}$	2
(4) $(NH)_{ads} + H_{ads} \rightarrow (NH_2)_{ads}$	2
(5) $(NH_2)_{ads} + H_{ads} \rightarrow (NH_3)_{ads}$	2
(6) $(NH_3)_{ads} \rightarrow NH_3$	2

correlating data, it is important to know which of these steps is rate limiting. Having this information, the form of the rate law may be developed by the methods described earlier in Section 3.4.

If indeed there is a rate limiting step, then all remaining steps are essentially in equilibrium and much can be learned about the kinetic behavior of the system by focusing attention on the simple reaction which is rate limiting. Consider the following simple reversible reaction, which is assumed to be the slow step of a complex set of mechanistic equations such as shown in Table 3.7-1.

$$A_1 \underset{k_{-1}}{\overset{k_1}{\rightleftarrows}} A_2 \tag{3.7-10}$$

In general the net rate $\mathscr{R}$ is

$$\mathscr{R} = \mathscr{R}_f - \mathscr{R}_r \tag{3.7-11}$$

where $\mathscr{R}_f =$ rate of the forward reaction
$\mathscr{R}_r =$ rate of the reverse reaction.
For the case of Eq. 3.7-10,

$$\mathscr{R} = k_1 C_1 - k_{-1} C_2. \tag{3.7-12}$$

But at equilibrium when $C_1 = C_{1e}$ and $C_2 = C_{2e}$,

$$\mathscr{R} = 0$$

and

$$\frac{C_2}{C_1} = \frac{k_1}{k_{-1}} = K = \text{equilibrium constant.} \tag{3.7-13}$$

The van't Hoff isotherm for Eq. 3.7-10 is

$$\Delta F_\sigma = -R_g T \ln K + R_g T \ln \left(\frac{C_2}{C_1}\right), \tag{3.7-14}$$

where $\Delta F_\sigma =$ free energy of the rate limiting step
$R_g =$ gas constant.
It follows from Eqs. 3.7-11, 3.7-12, 3.7-13 and 3.7-14 that

$$\mathscr{R} = \mathscr{R}_f(1 - e^{\Delta F_\sigma/R_g T}). \tag{3.7-15}$$

The free energy of the over-all reaction as written is σF_σ, which we shall call simply ΔF. Therefore,

$$\mathscr{R} = \mathscr{R}_f(1 - e^{\Delta F/\sigma R_g T}). \tag{3.7-16}$$

Since the rate of the slow step is identical with the rate of the over-all reaction, the rates in Eq. 3.7-16 may also be thought of as over-all values.

An experimental technique for obtaining the stoichiometric number of the slow step σ from Eq. 3.7-16 in a complex reaction is based upon the simultaneous measurement of $\mathscr{R}$ and $\mathscr{R}_f$. The numerical value of $\mathscr{R}$ is determined by measuring the rate of conversion near equilibrium whereas $\mathscr{R}_f$ is determined by observing the equilibration of tracer reactant (or product).

To show how this is accomplished, we shall first look at a means of evaluating $\mathscr{R}$. Near equilibrium

$$-\Delta F \ll R_g T$$

and Eq. 3.7-16 becomes

$$\mathscr{R} = \mathscr{R}_f \frac{-\Delta F}{\sigma R_g T}. \tag{3.7-17}$$

But if we write an equation for the over-all reaction analogous to Eq. 3.7-14, we obtain

$$\frac{\Delta F}{R_g T} = \sum_i a_i \ln \left[\frac{C_i}{C_{ie}} \right], \tag{3.7-18}$$

where $a_i =$ the stoichiometric coefficient of the ith species in the over-all reaction.

$C_i =$ the concentration of the ith species.

$C_{ie} =$ the concentration of the ith species at equilibrium.

Near equilibrium, $C_i/C_{ie} \approx 1$ and the logarithmic term in Eq. 3.7-18 may be expanded in a power series to obtain

$$\frac{\Delta F}{R_g T} = - \sum_i a_i \left(\frac{C_{ie} - C_i}{C_{ie}} \right). \tag{3.7-19}$$

Substitution of Eq. 3.7-19 into Eq. 3.7-17 results in

$$\mathscr{R} = \frac{\mathscr{R}_f}{\sigma} \sum_i a_i \left(\frac{C_{ie} - C_i}{C_{ie}} \right). \tag{3.7-20}$$

Suppose now that we are going to use a piston-flow isothermal reactor to evaluate σ. We can then use an expression for the rate such as that given by Eq. 2.2-8. However, Eq. 2.2-8 can be simplified because of two considerations characteristic of this special case. First, the operation near equilibrum means that the velocity U is essentially independent of the length coordinate of the reactor z because the conversion is small and the total number of moles per unit mass of reactant thereby also remains almost constant. The velocity is essentially constant even though $\sum_i a_i \neq 0$. Second, the pseudo-homogeneous rate expression $\bar{\mathscr{R}}$ of Eq. 2.2-8 is related to the heterogeneous rate expression $\mathscr{R}$ of Eq. 3.7-20 by

$$\bar{\mathscr{R}} = \rho_p (1 - \epsilon) S \mathscr{R}, \tag{3.7-21}$$

where $\rho_p =$ apparent density of the catalyst.

$\epsilon =$ porosity of the bed of catalyst (excluding porosity of the pellets).

$S =$ specific surface area of the catalyst in area per unit mass of catalyst.

In arriving at Eq. 3.7-21, we preclude specifically the possibility of transport processes influencing the reaction rate.* We postulate explicitly, therefore, that the concentrations within the catalyst are identical with those of the fluid phase immediately adjacent to the catalyst. Bearing these special circumstances in mind, Eq. 3.7-20 becomes

$$\overline{\mathscr{R}} = \frac{U \, dC_i}{a_i \, dz} = \frac{\rho_p(1 - \epsilon)S}{\sigma} \mathscr{R}_f \sum_i a_i \left(\frac{C_{ie} - C_i}{C_{ie}} \right) \tag{3.7-22}$$

The right-hand side of this equation contains a summation of terms, one for each of the species in the over-all reaction. We have already shown a relationship for a single over-all reaction in Eq. 2.2-8, which upon integration yields

$$\frac{(UC_i)_z - (UC_i)_0}{a_i} = \frac{(UC_j)_z - (UC_j)_0}{a_j} \tag{3.7-23}$$

which for constant U simplifies to

$$\frac{C_i - C_{i0}}{a_i} = \frac{C_j - C_{j0}}{a_j}. \tag{3.7-24}$$

We can, therefore, define a conversion X which is independent of any particular species in the reaction mixture as

$$\frac{C_i - C_{i0}}{a_i} \equiv X. \tag{3.7-25}$$

The quantity X is accordingly the number of moles converted per unit volume of fluid.† Equation 3.7-25 when substituted into Eq. 3.7-22 gives

$$\overline{\mathscr{R}} = v \frac{dX}{dV} = \frac{\rho_p(1 - \epsilon)S}{\sigma} \mathscr{R}_f (X_e - X) \sum_i \frac{a_i^2}{C_{ie}}, \tag{3.7-26}$$

where $dV \equiv A_c \, dz$
    $v \equiv A_c U.$

All of the terms on the right-hand side of Eq. 3.7-26 are constant except $(X_e - X)$, and Eq. 3.7-26 yields upon integration

$$\frac{\rho_p(1 - \epsilon)S}{\sigma} \mathscr{R}_f \sum_i \frac{a_i^2}{C_{ie}} = \frac{v}{V} \ln \left(\frac{X_e}{X_e - X} \right). \tag{3.7-27}$$

The rate, as obtained from Eqs. 3.7-26 and 3.7-27, is

$$\overline{\mathscr{R}} = \frac{v}{V} (X_e - X) \ln \left(\frac{X_e}{X_e - X} \right). \tag{3.7-28}$$

* See Section 4.1.
† In accordance with the discussions of Sections 2.2 and 2.3, this is a restricted definition of conversion. The more general definition is based upon a unit mass of fluid and reduces to the one used above for a constant value of the total number of moles per unit mass of fluid.

The right-hand side of Eq. 3.7-27 is thus determined. The left side contains $\mathscr{R}_f$ and σ. Therefore, we can compute σ if $\mathscr{R}_f$ is known.

A tracer technique for determining $\mathscr{R}_f$ is perhaps best developed in terms of the chosen specific example; the ammonia synthesis reaction. The reaction is carried out near equilibrium with a very small amount of tracer added. In this case the tracer is $N^{15}N$, which disappears according to the reaction below to produce $N^{15}H_3$

$$N^{15}N + 3\,H_2 \rightleftarrows NH_3 + N^{15}H^3. \tag{3.7-29}$$

At the same time, the over-all equilibrium is maintained according to

$$N_2 + 3\,H_2 \rightleftarrows 2\,NH_3.$$

Let $C_N^* =$ concentration of tagged nitrogen in the reaction mixture.

     $C_A^* =$ concentration of tagged ammonia in the reaction mixture.

     $C_N =$ concentration of untagged nitrogen in the reaction mixture.

     $C_A =$ concentration of untagged ammonia in the reaction mixture.

Then $C_N^* + C_N \approx C_{Ne}$ is the equilibrium nitrogen concentration in the mixture, and $C_A^* + C_A \approx C_{Ae}$, the equilibrium ammonia concentration in the mixture. The conservation equation for N^{15} is

$$-C_{Ne}U\frac{d\alpha}{dz} = C_{Ae}U\frac{d\beta}{dz} = \rho_p(1-\epsilon)S[\alpha\mathscr{R}_f - \beta\mathscr{R}_r], \tag{3.7-30}$$

where

$$\alpha \equiv \frac{C_N^*}{C_{Ne}}; \qquad \beta \equiv \frac{C_A^*}{C_{Ae}}.$$

The quantity $\alpha\mathscr{R}_f$ represents the rate of disappearance of C_N^* because the probability that a tagged molecule of nitrogen reacts is proportional to the ratio of tagged and untagged nitrogen present. When $C_N^* \ll C_N$, $(C_N^*/C_N) \approx C_N^*/C_{Ne}$ and the ratio approaches α.

Let $\alpha_0 =$ the value of α at $t = 0$,

                       $\alpha_\infty =$ the value of α at $t = \infty$

and

                       $\beta_0 = 0$, the value of β at $t = 0$,

                       $\beta_\infty =$ the value of β at $t = \infty$.

From the first equality of Eq. 3.7-30, we learn that

$$\alpha_0 - \alpha = \frac{C_{Ae}}{C_{Ne}}\beta \tag{3.7-31}$$

and since $\mathscr{R}_f \equiv \mathscr{R}_r$ at equilibrium, at $t \to \infty$, Eq. 3.7-30 tells us that

$$\alpha_\infty = \beta_\infty. \tag{3.7-32}$$

Finally, from Eqs. 3.7-31 and 3.7-32, we get the following relationship between α_∞ and α_0,

$$\alpha_\infty = \frac{\alpha_0}{[1 + C_{Ae}/C_{Ne}]}. \tag{3.7-33}$$

Substitution of Eqs. 3.7-31 and 3.7-33 into Eq. 3.7-30 gives

$$-\frac{d\alpha}{dz} = \frac{\rho_p(1 - \epsilon)S}{U}\left[\frac{C_{Ae} + C_{Ne}}{C_{Ne}C_{Ae}}\right]\mathcal{R}_f[\alpha - \alpha_\infty], \tag{3.7-34}$$

where use is made of the fact that $\mathcal{R}_f = \mathcal{R}_r$ at equilibrium. Integration and substitution of the initial condition leads to

$$\ln\left[\frac{\alpha_0 - \alpha_\infty}{\alpha - \alpha_\infty}\right] = \rho_p(1 - \epsilon)S\mathcal{R}_f\left[\frac{C_{Ae} + C_{Ne}}{C_{Ne}C_{Ae}}\right]\frac{z}{U},$$

which upon rearrangement is

$$\rho_p(1 - \epsilon)S\mathcal{R}_f = \frac{U}{z}\left[\frac{C_{Ne}C_{Ae}}{C_{Ae} + C_{Ne}}\right]\ln\left[\frac{\alpha_0 - \alpha_\infty}{\alpha - \alpha_\infty}\right]. \tag{3.7-35}$$

The stoichiometric number σ is obtained from a combination of Eqs. 3.7-27 and 3.7-35. This relationship is

$$\sigma = \left[\frac{C_{Ne}C_{Ae}}{C_{Ae} + C_{Ne}}\right]\ln\left[\frac{\alpha_0 - \alpha_\infty}{\alpha - \alpha_\infty}\right]\left\{\ln\left[\frac{X_e}{X_e - X}\right]\right\}^{-1}\sum_i\frac{\alpha_i^2}{C_{ie}}, \tag{3.7-36}$$

where for the ammonia synthesis reaction

$$\sum_i\frac{a_i^2}{C_{ie}} = \left[\frac{1}{C_{Ne}} + \frac{9}{C_{He}} + \frac{4}{C_{Ae}}\right].$$

In both parts of this analysis, it has been necessary to work near equilibrium. The integration of Eq. 3.7-26 was carried out without a specific knowledge of the form of $\mathcal{R}_f$ because it was assumed to be essentially constant near equilibrium. Similarly, in the latter part of the analysis, $\mathcal{R}_f$ was assumed constant and equal to $\mathcal{R}_r$ for the same reason. That we must use methods which obviate the need for a specific knowledge of the form of the rate expressions $\mathcal{R}_f$ and $\mathcal{R}_r$ is essential because, after all, the determination of the form of the latter quantities is the objective of the analysis. Being forced to make measurements near equilibrium places a heavy burden upon the accuracy of the analytical equipment, especially in the determination of $\mathcal{R}$.

These measurements have been made for the ammonia synthesis reaction,[*] and although there is still some question as to the value for σ, it appears

* J. Horiuti and N. Takezawa, *J. Res. Inst. Cat.* Hokkaido University **8,** 170–185 (1960); **6,** 34–40 (1957); C. Bolshoven, M. J. Gorgels, and P. Mars, *Trans. Far. Soc.* **55,** 315–323 (1959).

that $\sigma = 1$. If we accept this value, then evidently the adsorption step, number 1 of Table 3.7-1,

$$N_2 \rightarrow 2 N_{ads} \tag{3.7-37}$$

must be the slow step in the reaction. Utilizing the method of Section 3.4, an expression may be derived for the form of the rate expression. Thus, in the nomenclature of Section 3.4, Eq. 3.7-37 becomes

$$N_2 + 2X_1 \underset{k_{-1}}{\overset{k_1}{\rightleftharpoons}} 2X_2, \tag{3.7-38}$$

where $X_2 = N_{ads}$. Steps 2 through 6 are presumed to be in equilibrium which can be represented by

$$3 H_2 + 2X_2 \underset{k_{-e}}{\overset{k_e}{\rightleftharpoons}} 2 NH_3 + 2X_1 \tag{3.7-39}$$

and from Eq. 3.7-39

$$X_2 = K^{1/2}\left[\frac{C_A}{(C_H)^{3/2}}\right]X_1, \tag{3.7-40}$$

where C_A = concentration of ammonia in the reaction mixture.

C_H = concentration of hydrogen in the reaction mixture.

C_N = concentration of nitrogen in the reaction mixture.

$K = k_{-e}/k_e$.

From the relation that $X_0 = X_1 + X_2$ and Eqs. 3.7-38 and 3.7-40, we obtain

$$\mathscr{R} = k_1 C_N X_1^2$$

$$= k_1 C_N \left[\frac{X_0}{1 + K_e^{1/2}\dfrac{C_A}{(C_H)^{3/2}}}\right]^2 \tag{3.7-41}$$

a form for the rate expression which appears to fit the experimental data well.†

NOTATION FOR CHAPTER 3

a_i stoichiometric coefficient of the ith species

A_i ith species

C_i concentration of the ith species

C_i^* tracer concentration of the ith species

ΔF Gibbs free energy

† See A. Ozaki, H. S. Taylor, M. Boudart, *Proc. Royal Soc.* **A258**, 47 (1960).

k rate constants

K equilibrium constant

P_i partial pressure of the ith species

R_g gas constant

S specific surface area based on mass

t time

T absolute temperature

U superficial velocity

$\mathbf{X}$ chemical form of active centers

X concentration of active centers in various forms

z distance coordinate in the direction of flow in a reactor

SCRIPT

$\mathscr{R}$ heterogeneous reaction rate

GREEK LETTERS

α C_2^*/C_2

β C_3^*/C_3

σ stoichiometric number

ρ_p apparent density of a catalyst particle

ϵ porosity of a bed of catalyst particles

Transport of Energy and Mass
Within Reacting Porous
Catalysts

4

4.1 Introduction

The preceding chapter was devoted to the kinetic description of heterogeneous reactions. The detailed study of a reaction at a solid surface ideally results in a heterogeneous rate expression, a mathematical expression which quantitatively relates the reaction rate to the concentrations of the molecular species present and the temperature of the solid surface. The latter is an extensive property of the system, based upon the surface area of the solid phase. Because the activity of a catalyst varies as some direct function of the surface area, it is not surprising that methods of preparation have been sought which make them highly porous, thus making possible, typical ranges of specific surface areas of 100–2000 square meters of surface per gram of catalyst. While it is possible to obtain high specific surface areas by producing finely divided solid particles, such practice leads to difficulties, particularly in the handling of the catalyst in the reactor and its subsequent separation from the reaction mixture. In general, then, heterogeneously catalyzed reactions are carried out in the presence of porous catalysts.

The rate at which a catalyst pellet reacts under certain conditions may be represented by a simple equation which contains two terms: one which accounts for the specific rate of the reaction on a unit surface in terms of the temperature and concentrations, and one which accounts for the magnitude of the surface area. The equation below is written in terms of quantities which are usually known.

$$\bar{\mathscr{R}}_i = \left.\begin{array}{l}\text{rate of reaction} \\ \text{of the } i\text{th species} \\ \text{per unit volume}\end{array}\right\} = \rho_p S(1 - \epsilon)\mathscr{R}_i(C_{10}, C_{20}, C_{30}, \ldots, C_{n0}, T_0), \qquad (4.1\text{-}1)$$

where $\bar{\mathscr{R}}_i^* = $ a pseudo-homogeneous rate of reaction.

$\rho_p = $ apparent density of a single catalyst pellet.

$S = $ surface area per unit mass of catalyst.

$\epsilon = $ porosity of the bed of pellets (interstitial space among pellets).

$\mathscr{R}_i = $ heterogeneous rate of reaction.

This equation is extremely simple to use and is applicable in a surprising number of cases. The temperature and concentrations used are those at the surface where the reaction takes place. In using this equation, one presumes implicitly that these quantities have the same magnitude as found in the fluid phase immediately adjacent to the pellet. But, as so frequently happens in the description of natural phenomena, an equation may adequately describe a process over a range of some variable or parameter, while in another range it breaks down owing to the importance of another phenomenon in this new range. In the particular case in point, we should note the rate of reaction as the specific surface area increases. Physically, an increase in surface area is gained by producing pores of smaller diameters while keeping the pellet porosity essentially constant. Thus, as the specific surface area of the catalyst increases accompanied by an increase in the rate of reaction, the concentration gradients giving rise to the transport of material into the porous structure likewise increase in general for two reasons: they must increase to supply the greater amount of material processed in the interior of the solid; and they must increase to compensate for the decrease in the Knudsen diffusivity with pore size as the pores become very small. When the magnitudes of the concentration gradients result in a significant decrease in the concentration at points in the interior of the solid, we can no longer use this simple formula to predict the rate of reaction. The same argument, of course, holds for temperature.

It will become evident that the performance of a catalyst may be profoundly influenced by its physical structure. The influence of transport phenomena can change the apparent activity of a catalyst. Indeed, two catalysts having different pore sizes, although chemically identical, may exhibit quite different apparent activation energies, selectivities, and behavior toward poisons.

The simplicity of the form of Eq. 4.1-1 is so appealing that it is customary to retain it and account for the influence of appreciable concentration and

---

* A bar over an $\mathscr{R}$ refers to a rate per unit volume or a rate corresponding to a specified volume of catalyst.

temperature gradients by a quantity known as the *effectiveness factor* $\mathscr{E}$. The effectiveness factor is defined as the ratio of the rate at which reaction occurs on a pellet to the rate at which reaction would occur if the temperature and concentrations throughout the pellet were constant at their respective values at the external surface of the pellet. By the very nature of this definition, then, the actual reaction rate is given by multiplying Eq. 4.1-1 by $\mathscr{E}$. The effectiveness factor serves as a convenient and useful means of representing the results of an analysis of the problem of simultaneous heat and mass transfer and chemical reaction in a porous catalyst. It is the purpose of this chapter to develop methods for obtaining the effectiveness factor in terms of various parameters of the system.

It is pertinent to remark here that Eq. 4.1-1 when multiplied by the effectiveness factor does not always represent the actual rate of reaction of a catalytic pellet immersed in a stream of reactants. As defined, the effectiveness factor describes the rate of reaction in terms of the values of the concentrations and temperature at the external surface of the pellet. Under certain conditions these values may differ from those of the bulk fluid stream owing to appreciable transport resistances in the fluid stream near the external surface of the pellet. If we so chose, an analogous factor may be defined to account for this, the external transport factor $\mathscr{T}$. Thus, the pseudo-homogeneous rate expression for a heterogeneous reaction becomes:

$$\bar{\mathscr{R}}_i = \left.\begin{array}{l} \text{rate of actual} \\ \text{reaction per} \\ \text{unit volume} \end{array}\right\} = \rho_p S(1 - \epsilon)\mathscr{R}_i(C_{10}, C_{20}, C_{30}, \ldots, C_{n0}, T_0)(\mathscr{E})(\mathscr{T})$$

$$(4.1\text{-}2)$$

The values of the concentrations and temperature to be used in Eq. 4.1-2 are the bulk values in the fluid stream adjacent to the pellet. A discussion of the external transport factor will be reserved for Chapter 6.

In the present chapter we shall be concerned only with a detailed analysis of heat and mass transport within porous catalysts, and how temperature and concentration gradients within pellets affect their kinetic behavior. The reader should recognize that the factor $\mathscr{T}$ discussed in Chapter 6 may need to be considered simultaneously. In a sense, Chapters 4 and 6 are complementary in that they both deal with the effects of finite transport rates on the kinetic behavior of a system. In a given isothermal kinetic situation it is possible for $\mathscr{T}$ to be unity and $\mathscr{E}$ to differ appreciably from unity, but never the reverse. As a working rule, whenever mass transfer external to a pellet influences the kinetic behavior of a system, internal mass transfer must also influence the kinetic behavior even to a greater extent. For nonisothermal situations, $\mathscr{T}$ may be larger or smaller than unity even when $\mathscr{E}$ is equal to unity. The reason for this is that the greater part of the resistance to heat transfer can be in the film adjacent to the pellet rather than within the pellet itself. Therefore, the pellet temperature can be different from the bulk phase value while remaining essentially constant throughout the pellet.

We shall begin with a discussion of the classic paper of Thiele,* who solved the case of simultaneous diffusion and isothermal simple chemical reaction in a single straight pore of uniform cross section. The solution of this idealized problem is important because the behavior of the system is associated with the numerical value of a single parameter. Furthermore, the quantities which appear in this parameter make evident the type of detailed physical and chemical information which is needed in order to predict the behavior of a given kinetic system. We shall, therefore, set up and solve problems using the single pore model for several functional forms of the rate expression. From these systems it will be seen that the apparent kinetic behavior of a system in the diffusionally influenced region differs from the true kinetic behavior of the surface reaction. The asymptotic behavior of the effectiveness factor in the diffusionally-influenced region can also be obtained. Since the engineer is really only concerned with the asymptotic behavior, a method will be presented which leads directly to the asymptotic solution, circumventing most of the mathematical difficulties associated with the more complete solution of the general nonisothermal simple reaction system. The existence of the powerful asymptotic method of solution leads to a general criterion whereby a designer can determine whether transport processes are influencing the kinetic behavior of a system.

The analogous discussion of the influence of transport phenomena in systems wherein complex reactions occur is much less satisfactory because, in general, the analysis must be accomplished numerically. Fortunately, a general method of analysis does exist, but it is much more difficult to relate the experimental rate data to the framework of the analysis. A more extensive discussion is, therefore, given on experimental methods emphasizing the kinds of experiment which yield the most definite information, and more attention is given to specific cases.

4.2 Single pore model

A sketch of the pore is shown in Fig. 4.2-1. Although it was necessary to use a greatly expanded vertical scale compared to the horizontal, the figure is intended to depict a very long pore, i.e., $r/L \ll 1$. In real systems such a ratio is invariably the case. Under these conditions, a one-dimensional model may be used as a highly accurate approximation.†

---

* E. W. Thiele, *Ind. Eng. Chem.* **31,** 916 (1939). See also the independent and parallel work of Ia. B. Zeldovich, *Zhur. Fiz. Khim.* **13,** 163 (1939).

† Obviously, in Knudsen diffusion where the mean free path of molecules is much greater than the pore diameter, no such assumption is necessary—the problem is inherently one-dimensional.

In the steady state, the amount of reactant diffusing into the pore must be reacted within the pore. Equating the disappearance of reactant by reaction within the elemental volume $\pi r^2\,dx$ to the difference in rate of input and output fluxes, and neglecting mean velocity effects, Eq. 4.2-1 is obtained.

$$-\text{div}\,(-D\,\text{grad}\,C_i) - a\mathcal{R}_i = 0, \qquad (4.2\text{-}1)$$

with the boundary conditions at

$$\left.\begin{array}{ll} x = 0, & C_i = C_{i0} \\[2mm] x = L, & \dfrac{dC_i}{dx} = 0 \end{array}\right\} \qquad (4.2\text{-}2)$$

and where $\mathcal{R}_i$ is the heterogeneous rate expression for the ith component at the catalyst surface and a the surface area per unit volume of the pore. The quantity $a\mathcal{R}_i$ is, therefore, a local, pseudo-homogeneous rate expression.

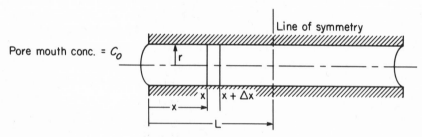

Fig. 4.2-1. Single pore model.

In keeping with our original purpose of obtaining an exact analysis of a simple system, a rate expression of the form $k_n C^n$ will be chosen. For constant D and T, Eq. 4.2-1 becomes

$$\frac{d^2\psi}{d\eta^2} - h_n^2 \psi^n = 0, \qquad (4.2\text{-}3)$$

where

$$\left.\begin{array}{c} a = \dfrac{2\pi r\,dx}{\pi r^2\,dx} = \dfrac{2}{r} \\[4mm] \psi \equiv \dfrac{C}{C_0} \\[4mm] \eta \equiv \dfrac{x}{L} \\[4mm] h_n \equiv L\sqrt{\dfrac{2k_n C_0^{n-1}}{rD}} \end{array}\right\} \qquad (4.2\text{-}4)$$

subject to the boundary conditions

$$\left.\begin{array}{ll} \eta = 0, & \psi = 1 \\[2mm] \eta = 1, & \dfrac{d\psi}{d\eta} = 0 \end{array}\right\} \quad (4.2\text{-}5)$$

The behavior of this system is dependent upon the numerical magnitude of the single parameter h_n, which we shall refer to as the Thiele parameter. The quantities contained in h_n are the length of the pore L, the intrinsic rate constant, k_n, the concentration at the pore mouth C_0, the radius of the pore r, and the diffusivity D. Physically the square of this parameter is the ratio of the kinetic rate to the diffusion rate, i.e., upon rearrangement,

$$h_n^2 = \frac{2\pi r L k_n C_0^n}{\pi r^2 D(C_0/L)} = \frac{\text{surface reaction rate}}{\text{diffusion rate}}.$$

It becomes qualitatively evident that a small value of the Thiele parameter corresponds to a case in which the capacity of the system to diffuse reactants into the pores is large compared to the maximum capacity of the system to react chemically with the catalyst. Thus, the reactant concentration everywhere within the pore approaches that of the pore mouth and the effectiveness factor approaches unity. Large values of the Thiele parameter correspond to the reverse case and the supply of reactant to the interior of the pore can only be maintained by large concentration gradients and the effectiveness factor becomes much less than unity.

The solution to Eq. 4.2-3 gives the concentration profile within the pore. Generally, however, a designer is interested in the rate of reaction rather than the concentration profile. The rate of the reaction is given by the amount of reactants which diffuse into the half pore, which is

$$\bar{\mathscr{R}}_D = -\pi r^2 D \left(\frac{dC}{dx}\right)_{x=0}, \qquad (4.2\text{-}6)$$

where $\bar{\mathscr{R}}_D$ is the actual rate of reaction per half pore in units, say, of moles per unit time. In the absence of a concentration gradient in the pore, the rate $\bar{\mathscr{R}}_0$ is given by

$$\bar{\mathscr{R}}_0 = 2\pi r L k_n C_0^n. \qquad (4.2\text{-}7)$$

Therefore, in accordance with the definition of the effectiveness factor $\mathscr{E}$,

$$\mathscr{E} = \frac{\bar{\mathscr{R}}_D}{\bar{\mathscr{R}}_0} \qquad (4.2\text{-}8)$$

and

$$\bar{\mathscr{R}}_D = 2\pi r L k_n C_0^n \mathscr{E}. \qquad (4.2\text{-}9)$$

Thus, as pointed out previously, the effectiveness factor is merely a convenient way of representing the results of the mathematical model and may be thought of physically as equivalent to the fraction of the total surface of the solid available to the reactants at conditions at the pore mouth.

For this system, then, from Eqs. 4.2-6, 4.2-7 and 4.2-8

$$\mathscr{E} = \frac{-\pi r^2 D \left(\dfrac{dC}{dx}\right)_{x=0}}{2\pi r L k_n C_0^n}, \tag{4.2-10}$$

and in terms of the dimensionless coordinates,

$$\mathscr{E} = -\frac{1}{h_n^2}\left(\frac{d\psi}{d\eta}\right)_{\eta=0}. \tag{4.2-11}$$

Therefore, the quantity sought from Eq. 4.2-3 is $(d\psi/d\eta)_{\eta=0}$, the dimensionless derivative of the concentration at the pore mouth where the coordinate η equals zero.

The solution to Eq. 4.2-3 for the case where $n = 1^*$ is

$$\psi = \frac{\cosh h_1(1 - \eta)}{\cosh h_1}. \tag{4.2-12}$$

An exact expression for $\mathscr{E}$ is obtained from Eq. 4.2-11 and the derivative of Eq. 4.2-12 to give

$$\mathscr{E}_1 = \frac{\tanh h_1}{h_1}. \tag{4.2-13}$$

The asymptotic forms of Eq. 4.2-13 are

$$\text{As } h_1 \to 0, \qquad \mathscr{E}_1 = 1 - \frac{h_1^2}{3}, \tag{4.2-14}$$

$$\text{and as } h_1 \to \infty \qquad \mathscr{E}_1 = \frac{1}{h_1}. \tag{4.2-15}$$

* Consult any standard text on ordinary differential equations or the article of Thiele previously cited. It is perhaps worthwhile to note that Eq. 4.2-3 may be solved for any form of the function $f(\psi)$. Consider

$$\frac{d^2\psi}{d\eta^2} - f(\psi) = 0. \tag{A}$$

Let $p \equiv \dfrac{d\psi}{d\eta}$. Then $\dfrac{d^2\psi}{d\eta^2} = \dfrac{d\psi}{d\eta}\left[\dfrac{d}{d\psi}\left(\dfrac{d\psi}{d\eta}\right)\right] = p\dfrac{dp}{d\psi}$.

Therefore, from Eq. A above.

$$p\,dp = f(\psi)\,d\psi, \qquad \frac{p^2}{2} = \int f(\psi)\,d\psi + \text{const.}$$

Substituting back for p:

$$\eta + \text{const} = \int \frac{d\psi}{\left[2\displaystyle\int f(\psi)\,d\psi + \text{const}\right]^{1/2}}.$$

The problem of solving the general equation is reduced to the evaluation of two quadratures.

A plot of $\mathscr{E}_1$ is shown on Fig. 4.2-2. The asymptotic form given by Eq. 4.2-15 is also shown as a dashed line. Although not developed here,* corresponding values of $\mathscr{E}$ are shown as a function of h_n when n of Eq. 4.2-3 is zero and two. Note the generalized definition of h_n in Eq. 4.2-4. The corresponding asymptotic forms of these are:

$$
\begin{aligned}
\mathscr{E}_0 &= \frac{\sqrt{2}}{h_0} & h_0 &\geq \sqrt{2} \\[2mm]
\mathscr{E}_1 &= \frac{1}{h_1} & h_1 &> 3 \\[2mm]
\mathscr{E}_2 &= \sqrt{\frac{2}{3}} \frac{1}{h_2} & h_2 &> 3
\end{aligned}
\right\} \qquad (4.2\text{-}16)
$$

An important result here is that $\mathscr{E}_n \propto 1/h_n$ for values of $h_n > 3.0$. We shall make considerable use of this relationship in a later section.

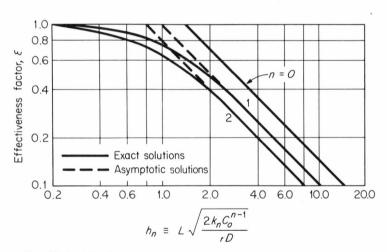

$$
h_n \equiv L \sqrt{\frac{2k_n C_o^{n-1}}{rD}}
$$

Fig. 4.2-2. Effectiveness factor for isothermal integral order reactions in a single pore.

Figure 4.2-2 shows us quantitatively how the rate of reaction in a pore is uniquely related to h_n for given values of n. Thus, statements such as a long pore, a pore of small radius, a fast reaction, etc., have no meaning except as they influence the magnitude of h_n. In this sense, a given pore diameter may be considered large at low temperatures and small at high temperatures.

When the Thiele parameter is large, the kinetic behavior of a pore differs from that at a surface of the same material which is uniformly accessible to

* See A. Wheeler, *Advan. Catalysis* **3**, 250–327 (1950), and Thiele, *op. cit.*, respectively, for the detailed development.

the reactant. When $h_n > 3$, $\mathscr{E} \propto 1/k_n^{1/2}$, and it follows from Eq. 4.2-9 that the rate of reaction is proportional to $k_n^{1/2}$. This leads us to the important result that the apparent activation energy is equal to one-half of the true activation energy of the surface reaction in the diffusion-influenced region (i.e., if $k_n = k_{n0}e^{-\Delta E_{\text{true}}/RT}$, then the rate of reaction is proportional to $e^{-\Delta E_{\text{apparent}}/RT}$, where $\Delta E_{\text{apparent}} = \Delta E_{\text{true}}/2$).

The physical explanation is straightforward. If k_n is increased by elevating the temperature and at the same time all other conditions are held constant, h_n increases and $\mathscr{E}_n$ correspondingly decreases. Effectively, the fraction of the surface available to the reactants decreases and we, therefore, do not get an increase in rate of reaction as large as would be predicted from the intrinsic surface kinetics alone. By increasing the temperature, the reactants in effect withdraw from the pore and have access only to regions closer to the pore mouth. Although we have neglected the effect of temperature and concentration on the diffusivity in this analysis, in nearly all cases this effect is negligible.

A second important result is that the apparent reaction order is changed. When $\mathscr{E} \propto 1/h_n$ the rate of reaction, $\mathscr{R}_D$, is proportional to

$$\frac{C_0^n}{C_0^{(n-1)/2}} = C_0^{(n+1)/2} \qquad (4.2\text{-}17)$$

A first-order reaction remains first order but all other reaction orders are modified. The physical reasoning for the change in order parallels the discussion of the activation energy given above.

The kinetic behavior of the single pore wherein transport is solely by diffusion may be summarized by the following statements:

a. The behavior of the system depends upon the numerical values of the Thiele parameter h_n and the kinetic order of the reaction, n, where

$$h_n \equiv L\sqrt{\frac{2kC_0^{n-1}}{rD}}.$$

b. As the Thiele parameter becomes large, the effectiveness factor varies in inverse proportion to h_n. Asymptotically,[*]

$$\mathscr{E}_n = \left(\frac{2}{n+1}\right)^{1/2}\frac{1}{h_n}. \qquad (4.2\text{-}18)$$

This expression is valid to within

$$0.5\% \quad \text{for} \quad h_n > 3.0,$$
$$1.5\% \quad \text{for} \quad h_n > 2.5,$$
$$3.5\% \quad \text{for} \quad h_n > 2.0.$$

[*] We shall anticipate this result derived later in this chapter. However, it is consistent with Eq. 4.2-16.

As the Thiele parameter becomes small, $h_n \to 0$ and $\mathscr{E} \to 1$ for all values of n. From the behavior of the asymptotes for large and small values of h_n a useful approximation to the behavior of all values of n over the entire h_n space is obtained by defining a new value of n, the Thiele parameter $\hat{h}_n$ defined as

$$\hat{h}_n \equiv \left[\frac{n+1}{2}\right]^{1/2} h_n.$$

Values of $\mathscr{E}_n$ versus this new parameter are shown on Fig. 4.2-3, which illustrates that the exact solutions for all values of n lie in approximately the same position with respect to its asymptotes.

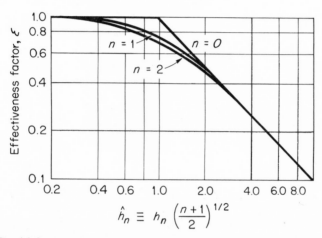

Fig. 4.2-3. Correlation of effectiveness factors for isothermal integral order reactions in a single pore using the generalized Thiele parameter.

c. At values of $h_n > 3.0$ the apparent activation energy is reduced to one-half its intrinsic value and the apparent order of the reaction with respect to concentration is modified to $(n + 1)/2$, where n is the intrinsic order.

4.3 The catalyst pellet

In the foregoing discussion we have been able to interpret the single pore model rigorously and have arrived at several definitive statements about the behavior of such systems. Unfortunately, the physical counterpart, the porous solid, may be thought of as a collection of such ideal single pores only as an approximation. The reason for this is that the "pores" of a porous material more closely approximate the spaces formed among randomly oriented particles than a true solid with holes randomly drilled throughout. Some of the physical quantities in the Thiele parameter, such as the pore radius and the length of the pore, immediately lose their identity. A subtle complication arises regarding the decision as to what is meant by the diffusivity within a porous medium. For example, in Knudsen or molecular flow the diffusivity depends upon the pore size. We shall, therefore, find it necessary to modify and extend the single pore model before the results may be directly applied to a catalytic pellet.

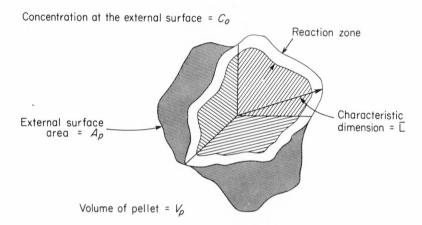

Fig. 4.3-1. Model of an irregular pellet.

Catalyst pellets are generally short cylinders, spherical beads, or crushed particles of roughly spherical shape. The pores contained within are generally not isolated but a system of interconnected channels that is formed among compacted microscopic particles. The geometry of the solid structure is, therefore, quite different from the geometry of the pore system. It is quite possible that the microscopic particles from which the larger pellets are made may themselves be porous and contain pores much smaller than the pore system pores among the particles, leading to a catalyst characterized by a bi-modal distribution of pore sizes. An important characteristic of all pore systems within pellets is the gradual convergence of the system to fewer and fewer pores as one goes from the outside of the pellet toward its interior. This geometric effect has not been accounted for in the single-pore model. The analysis to follow will consider both the spherical particle and an infinitely long cylindrical pellet, and the solutions are obtained in terms of the parameter h with the same rigor as with the single-pore model.

The porous pellet is depicted in Fig. 4.3-1. As before, the concentration at the external surface of the particle is C_0. Equation 4.2-1 is repeated here in slightly different form:

$$-\text{div}\left[-D_e \text{ grad } C_i\right] - a\mathscr{R}_i = 0, \qquad (4.3\text{-}1)$$

where D_e is an effective diffusivity or that value which gives the true flux of C_i in the porous solid through a unit of geometric area when multiplied by the actual concentration gradient in the solid. The effective diffusivity must account for the fact that solid makes the true cross section area for diffusion smaller than the geometric area, as well as other factors. At this time, it may be viewed as a known factor, or the reader may choose to look at the discussion of D_e in the next chapter.

A solution to Eq. 4.3-1 for the concentration profiles within the general pellet of Fig. 4.3-1 would be an involved task. In fact, we could make general arguments about the manner in which the parameters and characteristic dimensions of the system enter the solution similar to those given by Aris.* However, for our purposes, it is more instructive to use a physical argument which in the limit leads to a mathematically exact and equivalent result. From Section 4.2 it is clear that as the Thiele parameter becomes large, reactants effectively withdraw from the pores to utilize only a fraction of the surface area available. This is one physical interpretation of $\mathscr{E}$. Visualize a reaction within an irregular pellet which is confined to the outer regions shown in Fig. 4.3-1 by virtue of a large value of the Thiele parameter. As the thickness of the reaction zone decreases, the effects of curvature of the surface are minimized. The concentration derivative normal to the surface becomes independent of position and independent of the geometry of the pellet. In fact it approaches the value on a flat slab of similar material.

In general the effectiveness factor is proportional to the integral, over the entire particle surface of the component of the concentration derivative normal to the particle surface. The complete expression is

$$\mathscr{E} = \frac{-\displaystyle\iint_{A_p} D_e \text{ grad } C \cdot \vec{n} \, dA_p}{\rho_p S V_p k(T_0) g(C_0)}, \qquad (4.3\text{-}2)$$

where $\vec{n}$ = a vector normal to the surface,
   A_p = external surface area of a particle,
   V_p = volume of a particle,
   ρ_p = particle density (This is the apparent density of a particle rather than the skeletal density.),
   S = surface area per unit mass of catalyst,
and it follows that a of Eq. 4.3-1 is equal to $\rho_p S$.

---

* R. Aris, *Chem. Eng. Sci.* 6, 262 (1957).

Clearly, in the limiting case discussed above in which the normal derivative becomes independent of position on the surface, the integral in the numerator of Eq. 4.3-2 is immediately known, to give

$$\mathscr{E} = \frac{-D_e A_p (dC/d\zeta)_{\zeta=0}}{\rho_p S V_p k(T_0) g(C_0)}, \qquad (4.3-3)$$

where ζ is a coordinate normal to the surface.

If now the characteristic dimension of the pellet is taken as V_p/A_p (i.e., $\overline{L} = V_p/A_p$ since $V_p \propto \overline{L}^3$ and $A_p \propto \overline{L}^2$), then Eq. 4.3-3 can be rearranged to give the dimensionless form

$$\mathscr{E} = -\frac{1}{\hat{h}_p^2}\left(\frac{d\psi}{d\eta}\right)_{\eta=0}, \qquad (4.3-4)$$

where

$$\left.\begin{array}{c} \psi \equiv \dfrac{C}{C_0} \\[2ex] \eta \equiv \dfrac{\zeta A_p}{V_p} \\[2ex] \hat{h}_p \equiv \dfrac{V_p}{A_p}\sqrt{\dfrac{\rho_p S k(T_0) g(C_0)}{D_e C_0}} \end{array}\right\} \qquad (4.3-5)$$

The subscript p has the connotation that $\hat{h}_p$ is the Thiele parameter for the general pellet.

From the way in which Eq. 4.3-4 was developed we can rightly expect that in the limit as $\hat{h}_p \to \infty$, $\mathscr{E}$ is a unique function of $\hat{h}_p$, a result which is generally true for all particle geometries. It remains to show over what range of values of $\hat{h}_p$ this result is useful. Of course, it also follows that as $\hat{h}_p \to 0$, $\mathscr{E}$ approaches unity.

In the following discussion, we shall explore the usefulness of Eq. 4.3-4 by comparing the exact analytical solutions for isothermal, first-order reactions in three geometric shapes: the flat slab, the infinite cylinder, and the sphere. The asymptotic behavior of the exact solutions will then be compared to an asymptotic solution to general pellet in terms of the parameter $\hat{h}_p$ in order to gain a perspective on the range of usefulness of this parameter for particles of arbitrary shape.

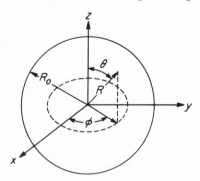

Fig. 4.3-2. Spherical pellet model.

Consider first a spherical pellet. The coordinate system and dimensions are shown in Fig. 4.3-2. We shall assume that the concentration field is symmetric with respect to θ and ϕ, the remaining spherical coordinates, so that C is only a function of R. Thus, for constant D_e, Eq. 4.3-1* becomes

$$\frac{D_e}{R^2}\frac{d}{dR}\left(R^2\frac{dC}{dR}\right) - \rho_p SkC = 0 \tag{4.3-6}$$

for a first-order, isothermal reaction. The first-order reaction is considered here because we have already shown that the results when properly correlated are generally insensitive to the kinetic order. Making the following substitutions,

$$\eta \equiv \frac{R}{R_0}, \qquad \psi \equiv \frac{C}{C_0}, \qquad h_s \equiv R_0\sqrt{\frac{\rho_p Sk_1}{D_e}},$$

Eq. (4.3-1) becomes

$$\frac{1}{\eta^2}\frac{d}{d\eta}\left(\eta^2\frac{d\psi}{d\eta}\right) - h_s^2\psi = 0. \tag{4.3-7}$$

The boundary conditions are:

$$\left.\begin{array}{ll} \text{at } \eta = 1, & \psi = 1 \\[2mm] \eta = 0, & \dfrac{d\psi}{d\eta} = 0 \end{array}\right\} \tag{4.3-8}$$

The solution to this equation is obtained by standard methods.† From this solution and Eq. 4.3-4,

$$\mathscr{E}_s = \frac{3}{h_s}\left[\frac{1}{\tanh h_s} - \frac{1}{h_s}\right]. \tag{4.3-9}$$

The asymptotic form of Eq. 4.3-6 is

$$\mathscr{E}_s = \frac{3}{h_s} \quad \text{for} \quad \frac{h_s}{3} > 3. \tag{4.3-10}$$

Similarly, the basic equation for the infinitely long cylinder (Fig. 4.3-3a) is

$$\frac{1}{\eta}\frac{d}{d\eta}\left(\eta\frac{d\psi}{d\eta}\right) - h_c^2\psi = 0, \tag{4.3-11}$$

where

$$h_c \equiv R_0\sqrt{\frac{\rho_p Sk_1}{D_e}}, \qquad \eta \equiv \frac{R}{R_0}.$$

The solution‡ is

$$\psi = \frac{J_0(ih_c\eta)}{J_0(ih_c)}, \tag{4.3-12}$$

leading to

$$\mathscr{E}_c = \frac{2}{h_c}\frac{iJ_1(ih_c)}{J_0(ih_c)}.$$

* See Appendix 1.

† See cited references by Thiele or Wheeler. If we substitute $v \equiv \psi\eta$, then Eq. 4.3-2 reduces to $d^2v/d\eta^2 - h^2v = 0$, which is the same as Eq. 4.2-3 for $n = 1$.

‡ See for Example, E. E. Petersen, *A.I.Ch.E. Journal* **3**, 443 (1957).

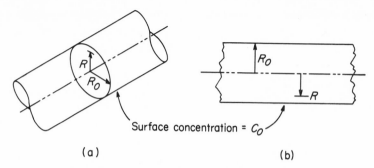

Fig. 4.3-3. (a) The infinite cylindrical pellet model. (b) The infinite slab model.

The asymptotic form of Eq. 4.3-12 is

$$\mathscr{E}_c = \frac{2}{h_c} \quad \text{for} \quad \frac{h_c}{2} > 3. \tag{4.3-13}$$

The effectiveness factor for infinite slab geometry shown on Fig. 4.3-3(b) is identical with the single-pore solution except the Thiele parameter must be modified to read

$$h_f \equiv R_0 \sqrt{\frac{\rho_p S k_1}{D_e}}.$$

The effectiveness factor then becomes

$$\mathscr{E}_f = \frac{\tanh h_f}{h_f}, \tag{4.3-14}$$

which has the asymptotic form

$$\mathscr{E}_f = \frac{1}{h_f} \quad \text{for} \quad h_f > 3. \tag{4.3-15}$$

The solid lines on Fig. 4.3-4 correspond to Eqs. 4.3-9, 4.3-12, and 4.3-14. The dashed lines on the same figure represent the asymptotic forms of these equations. The position of the exact equations with respect to their asymptotes is approximately the same for each geometry, thereby suggesting that a useful correlation may result from modifying the Thiele parameter so that the asymptotes superimpose. The method suggested earlier using $\hat{h}_p$ is the correct way to do this. However, let us show how this can be established for each of the geometries discussed above.

Performing the indicated differentiation, Eq. 4.3-7 becomes

$$\frac{d^2\psi}{d\eta^2} + \frac{2}{\eta}\frac{d\psi}{d\eta} - h_s^2\psi = 0. \tag{4.3-16}$$

Making a substitution in terms of the coordinate ζ in Eq. 4.3-3, we obtain

$$\frac{d^2\psi}{d\zeta^2} - \left(\frac{2}{1-\zeta}\right)\frac{d\psi}{d\zeta} - h_s^2\psi = 0, \tag{4.3-17}$$

where $\zeta \equiv (R_0 - R)/R_0$.

Now note that if a new independent variable is defined:

$$\xi \equiv h_s\zeta, \tag{4.3-18}$$

Eq. 4.3-17 becomes

$$\frac{d^2\psi}{d\xi^2} - \frac{1}{h_s}\frac{2}{(1 - \xi/h_s)}\frac{d\psi}{d\xi} - \psi = 0. \tag{4.3-19}$$

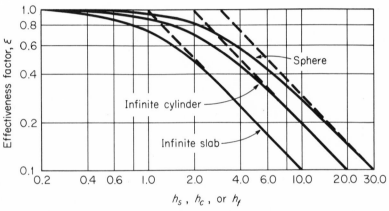

Fig. 4.3-4. Exact solutions for the effectiveness factors for slab, cylindrical and spherical geometries.

and as $h_s \to \infty$, the second term becomes small compared to the remaining terms provided $d\psi/d\xi$ is finite. Thus, the solution to

$$\frac{d^2\psi}{d\xi^2} - \psi = 0 \tag{4.3-20}$$

is useful when h_s is large. Equation 4.3-11 for cylindrical geometry can, by similar reasoning, be reduced to Eq. 4.3-20 and, of course, Eq. 4.3-20 is exact for slab geometry. We therefore conclude that all of the above geometries reduce to the same equation, having identical boundary conditions, viz:

$$\left.\begin{array}{ll} \xi = 0, & \psi = 1 \\[2mm] \xi \to \infty, & \dfrac{d\psi}{d\xi} = 0 \end{array}\right\} \tag{4.3-21}$$

The solution to Eq. 4.3-20 gives a value of $(d\psi/d\xi)_{\xi=0}$ or $(d\psi/d\zeta)_{\zeta=0}$ which may be substituted into Eq. 4.3-3 to give $\mathscr{E}$ for each geometry. Clearly, then, the Thiele parameter should be based upon the characteristic length V_p/A_p.

Figure 4.3-5 shows the effectiveness factor as a function of $\hat{h}_p$ as given by the exact solutions to each geometry. The most important information derived from this figure is that all solutions converge to the asymptote $1/\hat{h}_p$ as $\hat{h}_p$ becomes large. The relation $\mathscr{E} = 1/\hat{h}_p$ is within about 10 per cent for all three geometries for $\hat{h}_p \approx 3$. We shall see later that it is not possible as

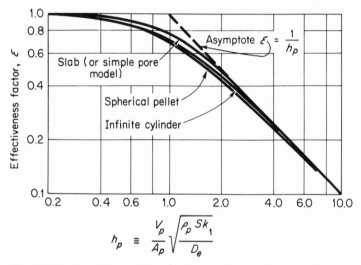

Fig. 4.3-5. Correlation of the effectiveness factors for slab, cylindrical and spherical geometries using the generalized Thiele parameter.

yet to compute $\hat{h}_p$ to this degree of precision for a porous pellet. The close proximity of the spherical pellet and infinite cylindrical pellet solutions indicates that Fig. 4.3-5 would also apply to the pellet of arbitrary shape as a good approximation even in the region where $\hat{h}_p \approx 3$.

In the previous section, we were able to account for the effect of the order of the reaction on the magnitude of the effectiveness factor by using the parameter $\hat{h}_n$, the Thiele parameter for an nth order reaction in a single pore. At large values of $\hat{h}_n$, $\mathscr{E}_n = 1/\hat{h}_n$. In this section, we have accounted for geometric effects on the magnitude of $\mathscr{E}$ by using $\hat{h}_p$. It becomes a relatively simple extension to account for the combined effects of order of reaction and geometry through the use of a parameter $\hat{h}_{pn}$. The general relationship is

$$\mathscr{E}_{pn} = \frac{1}{\hat{h}_{pn}}, \qquad (4.3-22)$$

where

$$\hat{h}_{pn} = \left(\frac{n+1}{2}\right)^{1/2} \hat{h}_p.$$

Equation 4.3-22 becomes asymptotically exact for the nth order reactions in any pellet shape as the numerical magnitude of $\hat{h}_{pn}$ becomes large, and a highly useful approximation for values of $\hat{h}_{pn}$ as low as three. Thus, the asymptotic relationship is valid over most of the range of interest to engineers. The implication of this result is that the behavior of more complex kinetic systems may be analyzed in single pores and the results of the analyses may be used to interpret the behavior of the same system in more complex geometries. The above suggestion is intended as a working rule, however, the reader would be well advised to extend the above procedure to non-isothermal systems with caution.

The simplicity of the asymptotic relationship for $\mathscr{E}_{pn}$ makes it a relatively easy task to decide experimentally whether or not a particular catalyst operates in the diffusion influenced regime. The decision can in principle be based upon two experimental measurements of the over-all reaction rate. The catalyst pellets used in both tests are identical in every respect save its characteristic dimension, V_p/A_p. The catalyst size, for example, can be changed by grinding. From Eqs. 4.1-2 and 4.3-22, the over-all rate per unit volume* of reactor as measured experimentally would be independent of the size of the catalyst if the reaction was kinetically controlled and inversely proportional to the size in the diffusion-influenced region, i.e., $\hat{h}_{pn} > 3$. This time-honored test for diffusion influence is of general validity for simple isothermal reactions of any order on pellets of arbitrary shape as shown by Eq. 4.3-22. We shall show in Section 4.4 that it is also valid for simple nonisothermal reactions if the precaution is taken to use three experimental points. Having established whether the catalyst operates in the kinetic-controlled or diffusion-influenced regimes, other variables such as concentrations and temperatures may be studied and interpreted in accordance with the discussion at the close of Section 4.2.

Another characteristic of Eq. 4.1-2 is not immediately obvious. We stated earlier that in approaching the diffusion-influenced region, the magnitude of the effectiveness factor decreases in inverse proportion to $\hat{h}_{pn}$. An interesting situation develops when $\hat{h}_{pn}$ is increased by virtue of increasing the surface area of the catalyst, holding the porosity constant. This implies physically that the radius of the pores is decreased, and to a first approximation the area increases in inverse proportion to the pore radius. That is, for a simple pellet wherein the total length of the pores in the system is L,

$$\frac{\text{surface area}}{\text{pore volume}} = \frac{2\pi r L}{\pi r^2 L} = \frac{2}{r}.$$

* It is assumed here that the pellets will pack to the same porosity independently of their size. A more accurate test would be based on the over-all rate per unit mass of catalyst.

Accordingly, the quantity S in Eq. 4.1-2 becomes

$$S = \frac{2\epsilon_p}{r\rho_p},$$ (4.3-23)

where ϵ_p is the porosity of the catalyst pellet.

If now the pores are small enough so that Knudsen diffusive flow occurs in the pores, then

$$D_e \propto r.$$ (4.3-24)

In the diffusion-influenced region,

$$\xi_{pn} \propto \frac{1}{\hat{h}_{pn}},$$ (4.3-25)

where

$$\hat{h}_{pn} \equiv \left(\frac{n+1}{2}\right)^{1/2} \frac{V_p}{A_p} \sqrt{\frac{\rho_p S k_n C_0^{n-1}}{D_e}}.$$ (4.3-26)

Simple substitution of Eqs. 4.3-23, 4.3-24, and 4.3-26 into 4.3-25 gives

$$\mathcal{E}_{pn} \propto r.$$ (4.3-27)

Since $S \propto 1/r$, it becomes apparent that the over-all rate of reaction as given by Eq. 4.1-2 is independent of the surface area of the pellet. This interesting result is valid for isothermal diffusion-influenced reactions in porous solids with pores small enough so that under the conditions of operation Knudsen diffusive flow occurs within. Thus, high surface areas gained at the expense of decreasing pore size will not result in a net increase in the over-all rate in the diffusion-influenced region. In a later section, however, we shall show a beneficial effect of high surface areas in connection with surface poisoning.

The analysis of chemical reactions in pores logically proceeds to the general simple nonisothermal reaction and later to complex reactions. At this point the reader may prefer to familiarize himself with the methods for determining the physical and chemical parameters which appear in $\hat{h}_{pn}$ before continuing on to a study of the behavior of more complex systems. This material may be found in Chapter 5.

4.4 General nonisothermal simple reaction in a spherical catalyst pellet

The simple reaction written in general form is

$$\sum_{i=1}^{n} a_i A_i = 0,$$ (4.4-1)

where as before $a_i < 0$ is a reactant and $a_i > 0$ is a product. The rate expression may be written in the form

$$\mathcal{R}_i = \mathcal{R}_i[C_1, C_2, \ldots, C_n, T],$$ (4.4-2)

where $\mathscr{R}_i$ is the rate of production of the ith component and C_i is the concentration of the ith species. From the stoichiometric equation,

$$\mathscr{R} = \frac{\mathscr{R}_i}{a_i} = \frac{\mathscr{R}_j}{a_j}. \qquad (4.4\text{-}3)$$

For a spherical pellet, the conservation of the species i is given by the equation

$$\frac{1}{R^2}\frac{d}{dR}\left(R^2 D_i \frac{dC}{dR}\right) + \rho_p S \mathscr{R}_i(C_1, C_2, C_3, \ldots, C_n, T) = 0$$

$$(i = 1, 2, 3, \ldots, n), \quad (4.4\text{-}4)$$

where D_i = the effective diffusivity of the ith species in the porous solid.

ρ_p = apparent density of the catalyst pellet.

S = surface area per unit mass of catalyst.

The corresponding energy equation is needed to account for the temperature dependence of the function $\mathscr{R}_i$. It is:

$$\frac{1}{R^2}\frac{d}{dR}\left(R^2 \lambda \frac{dT}{dR}\right) - (-\Delta H_i)\rho_p S \mathscr{R}_i = 0, \qquad (4.4\text{-}5)$$

where T = point value of the temperature.

λ = effective* thermal conductivity of the solid.

ΔH_i = the enthalpy of reaction based upon the conventional stoichio-metric equation in which the ith species appears as a reactant. Thus ΔH, is based upon a_i moles of the ith species and, in accordance with convention, it is numerically negative for an exothermic reaction.†

Equations 4.4-4 and 4.4-5 are subject to the boundary conditions:

$$\left.\begin{array}{llll}
\text{At } R = R_0, & T = T_0, & C_i = C_{i0} \\[2mm]
\text{At } R = 0, & \dfrac{dT}{dR} = 0, & \dfrac{dC_i}{dR} = 0
\end{array}\right\} \qquad (4.4\text{-}6)$$

The similarity of the boundary conditions of Eq. 4.4-6 and the relationship of Eq. 4.4-3 suggests that a standard method may be used to eliminate all but a single conservation equation. This is illustrated by dividing Eq. 4.4-4 for the jth species by a_j and for the ith species by a_i and subtracting. Carrying out this operation, we obtain:

$$\frac{1}{a_i}\frac{d}{dR}\left(R^2 D_i \frac{dC_i}{dR}\right) = \frac{1}{a_j}\frac{d}{dR}\left(R^2 D_j \frac{dC_j}{dR}\right). \qquad (4.4\text{-}7)$$

* See Chapter 5.

† Note also that $(-\Delta H_i)\mathscr{R}_i = (-\Delta H_j)\mathscr{R}_j$ and the product, $(-\Delta H_i)\mathscr{R}_i$, is always negative for an exothermic reaction.

When D is not a function of concentration, Eq. 4.4-7 may be integrated twice to give

$$(C_i - C_{i0}) = \frac{a_i}{a_j} \frac{D_j}{D_i} (C_j - C_{j0}). \tag{4.4-8}$$

The subscript 0 refers to the surface values of the concentrations. By a similar method, ignoring the temperature variation of ΔH_i and D_i,* an analogous relationship is obtained between T and C_i of the form

$$T - T_0 = \frac{(-\Delta H_i)D_i}{\lambda} (C_{i0} - C_i). \tag{4.4-9}$$

Although somewhat unrelated to our purpose here in developing Eq. 4.4-9, this equation may be used to calculate the maximum temperature in the pellet. For large values of the Thiele parameter, the value of C_i goes approximately to zero in the interior of the pellet. Setting $C_i = 0$ in Eq. 4.4-9 we obtain:

$$T_{\max} - T_0 = -\frac{\Delta H_i D_i C_{i0}}{\lambda}. \tag{4.4-10}$$

The results of Eqs. 4.4-8 and 4.4-9 are that the temperature and all concentrations may be expressed in terms of a single concentration. Thus

$$\mathscr{R}_i = \mathscr{R}_i(C_1, C_2, C_3, \ldots, C_n, T) = \mathscr{R}'(C_i) \tag{4.4-11}$$

and Eq. 4.4-4 becomes

$$\frac{1}{R^2} \frac{d}{dR}\left(R^2 D_i \frac{dC_i}{dR}\right) + \rho_p S \mathscr{R}'(C_i) = 0, \tag{4.4-12}$$

subject to the following boundary conditions:

$$R = R_0, \qquad C_i = C_{i0}; \qquad R = 0, \qquad \frac{dC_i}{dR} = 0. \quad \left.\right\} \tag{4.4-13}$$

For constant properties,

$$\frac{d^2\psi}{d\zeta^2} - \left(\frac{2}{1 - (\zeta/3)}\right)\frac{d\psi_i}{d\zeta} + \hat{h}_p^2 \mathscr{R}''(\psi_i) = 0, \tag{4.4-14}$$

where

$$\psi \equiv \frac{C_i}{C_{i0}}, \qquad \zeta \equiv \frac{3(R_0 - R)}{R_0}, \qquad \mathscr{R}_i''(\psi_i) \equiv \frac{\mathscr{R}_i'(C_i)}{\mathscr{R}_i'(C_{i0})},$$

and

$$\hat{h}_p \equiv \frac{R_0}{3}\sqrt{\frac{\rho_p S \mathscr{R}_i'(C_{i0})}{D_i C_{i0}}}.$$

* Temperature variations of these quantities may be included in the analysis, but the final result based upon average properties is well within the precision to which other quantities are known.

The solution to Eq. 4.4-14 is not easily obtained. Remember that hidden within the function $\mathscr{R}_i''(\psi_i)$ is an exponential function of the argument ψ_i times some function of ψ_i.

There have been a number of exact methods of approach to find the solution to Eq. 4.4-14. Carberry* and Hawthorne† used digital computers whereas Tinkler and Metzner‡ used an analog computer. Tinkler and Pigford§ suggested a perturbation series in an energy parameter and Schilson and Amundson‖ used an iterative technique.

There have been some approximate methods of solution suggested,¶ but one is not able to estimate *a priori* the errors resulting from the approximations made. Therefore, a method will be described which is very rapid to use and asymptotically exact.**

Define a new coordinate:

$$\xi \equiv \hat{h}_p \zeta, \tag{4.4-15}$$

and substitute it into Eq. 4.4-14. Then

$$\hat{h}_p^2 \frac{d^2 \psi_i}{d\xi^2} - \left(\frac{2}{1 - \dfrac{\xi}{3\hat{h}_p}} \right) \hat{h}_p \frac{d\psi_i}{d\xi} + \hat{h}_p^2 \mathscr{R}_i''(\psi_i) = 0. \tag{4.4-16}$$

Now as $\hat{h}_p$ becomes large, the second term in Eq. 4.4-16 may be neglected because it is small compared to the remaining terms. Equation 4.4-16 becomes

$$\frac{d^2 \psi_i}{d\xi^2} + \mathscr{R}_i''(\psi_i) = 0, \tag{4.4-17}$$

an equation similar to Eq. 4.3-20 encountered earlier. The penetration of reactants within the porous structure is small as $\hat{h}_p$ becomes large, and the concentration drops to a very small value at $R = 0$, i.e., $\xi \to \infty$. Thus, an additional boundary condition is imposed upon Eq. 4.4-17 as $\hat{h}_p \to \infty$:

$$\left. \begin{array}{lll} \text{at } \xi = 0; & \psi_i = 1 \\[2ex] \text{at } \xi \to \infty; & \dfrac{d\psi_i}{d\xi} = 0, & \psi_i = 0 \end{array} \right\} \tag{4.4-18}$$

* J. J. Carberry, *A.I.Ch.E. Journal* **7**, 350 (1961).

† R. D. Hawthorne, *A.I.Ch.E. Annual Meeting*, Preprint No. 136, Dec. 3–7, 1961.

‡ J. D. Tinkler and A. B. Metzner, *Ind. Eng. Chem.* **53**, 663 (1961).

§ J. D. Tinkler and R. L. Pigford, *Chem. Eng. Sci.* **15**, 326 (1961).

‖ R. E. Schilson and N. R. Amundson, *Chem. Eng. Sci.* **13**, 237 (1961).

¶ J. Beek, *A.I.Ch.E. Journal* **7**, 337 (1961); A. Wheeler, *Advan. Catalysis* **3**, pp. 250–327, Academic Press, Inc., New York, 1951.

** E. E. Petersen, *Chem. Eng. Sci.* **17**, 987 (1962).

Eq. 4.4-17 is now immediately integrable by standard methods. Let $p \equiv d\psi_i/d\xi$ then $p\,dp/d\psi_i = d^2\psi_i/d\xi^2$. Hence from Eq. 4.4-17 we obtain

$$\frac{d\psi_i}{d\xi} = -\sqrt{2}\left[\int_0^{\psi_i(\xi)} -\{\mathscr{R}_i''(\psi_i)\}\,d\psi_i\right]^{1/2}. \qquad (4.4\text{-}19)$$

The constant of integration has been evaluated from the last boundary condition of Eq. 4.4-18. The concentration profile may be obtained from an additional integration; however, in general the over-all rate of reaction is sought, and there is little, if any, interest in the concentration profile. Since $\left(\dfrac{d\psi_i}{d\xi}\right)_{\xi=0}$ is proportional to the actual rate of reaction, the effectiveness factor for a spherical pellet, in accordance with Eq. 4.3-4, is

$$\mathscr{E}_p = \frac{-4\pi R_0^2 D_i(dC_i/dR)_{R=R_0}}{\tfrac{4}{3}\pi R_0^3 \rho_p S \mathscr{R}_i'(C_{i0})} = -\frac{1}{\hat{h}_p^2}\left(\frac{d\psi_i}{d\xi}\right)_{\xi=0}. \qquad (4.4\text{-}20)$$

Therefore, Eqs. 4.4-19 and 4.4-20 lead directly to the effectiveness factor to give:

$$\mathscr{E}_p = \frac{\sqrt{2}}{\hat{h}_p}\left[\int_0^1 -\{\mathscr{R}_i''(\psi_i)\}\,d\psi_i\right]^{1/2}. \qquad (4.4\text{-}21)$$

In general it may be necessary to obtain the quadrature of Eq. 4.4-21 by a numerical or mechanical method.

The question remains as to the conditions under which this asymptotically exact method is useful. More directly, the question of importance is: How large must $\hat{h}_p$ be before the effectiveness factor computed from Eq. 4.4-21 can be usefully applied in engineering calculations? To obtain the asymptotic solution we assumed that $\hat{h}_p$ was sufficiently large to make the concentration of reactant drop to zero in the porous structure and to make the second term in Eq. 4.4-16 small compared to the remaining terms. The physical implication of the latter statement is that not only must the concentration drop to zero within the pore, but it must do so sufficiently close to the pellet external surface so that the pellet may be considered a slab, that is, the curvature is not important. We shall answer these questions by comparing the results of the asymptotic method with numerical solutions to the exact equations in Example 4.4-1 below.

EXAMPLE 4.4-1 APPLICATION OF THE ASYMPTOTIC METHOD TO FIRST- AND
    SECOND-ORDER NONISOTHERMAL REACTIONS

Tinkler and Metzner solved the first-order nonisothermal system for both spherical and slab geometries. In order to compare results, Eq. 4.4-17 will be modified in accordance with their assumptions. They modified the

Arrhenius form by a well-known approximation which will be sketched briefly below.

The Arrhenius form of the rate expression is:

$$\mathscr{R}_i = -Ae^{-\Delta E/R_g T}f(C_i), \tag{4.4-22}$$

where A = pre-exponential factor,
ΔE = activation energy,
R_g = gas constant.

For many purposes this may be modified to an acceptable accuracy by the following approximation.* Assume some reference temperature T_f and define a dimensionless temperature of the form

$$\Theta \equiv \frac{T - T_f}{T_f}. \tag{4.4-23}$$

Thus

$$T = T_f(1 + \Theta),$$

and

$$e^{-\Delta E/R_g T} = e^{-[\Delta E/R_g T_f(1+\Theta)]},$$

which for small values of Θ may be approximated by

$$e^{-\Delta E/R_g T} \approx e^{-(\Delta E/R_g T_f)(1-\Theta)}. \tag{4.4-24}$$

If now the reference temperature is chosen as T_0, then from Eqs. 4.4-9, 4.4-11, 4.4-22, and 4.4-24,

$$\mathscr{R}'_i = -k_0\, e^{\delta}\, e^{-\delta\psi_i}f(C_{i0}\psi_i), \tag{4.4-25}$$

where

$$k_0 \equiv A\, e^{-\Delta E/R_g T_0}, \qquad \delta \equiv \frac{(\Delta E)(-\Delta H_i)D_i C_{i0}}{R_g T_0^2 \lambda},$$

and

$$\psi_i \equiv \frac{C_i}{C_{i0}}.$$

Restricting the discussion here to rate expressions wherein the form of the function f is

$$f(C_{i0}\psi_i) = (C_{i0}\psi_i)^n, \tag{4.4-26}$$

Eq. 4.4-17 becomes

$$\frac{d^2\psi_i}{d\xi^2} - e^{\delta}\, e^{-\delta\psi_i}\psi_i^n = 0, \tag{4.4-27}$$

where

$$\xi \equiv \hat{h}_p\zeta = \hat{h}_p\left[\frac{3(R_0 - R)}{R_0}\right] \quad \text{and} \quad \hat{h}_p \equiv \frac{R_0}{3}\sqrt{\frac{\rho_p S k_0 (C_{i0})^{n-1}}{D_i}}.$$

* This approximation is accurate for small values of the activation energy and large heat effects. See for example P. B. Weisz, *Chem. Eng. Sci.* **17**, 265 (1962); E. E. Petersen, *ibid.*, p. 987.

Note that once the order of the reaction has been established there are two parameters which govern the behavior of the system: $\hat{h}_p$ and δ. The parameter $\hat{h}_p$ is the same as that used in connection with isothermal reactions in pellets.

The immediate objective is to find the form of the effectiveness factor for large values of the parameter $\hat{h}_p$. To do this, we again reason that the boundary conditions on Eq. 4.4-27 are:

and when $\xi \to \infty$;

$$\left. \begin{array}{ll} \xi = 0 \quad \text{and} \quad \psi_i = 1 \\[2mm] \psi_i = 0 \quad \text{and} \quad \dfrac{d\psi_i}{d\xi} = 0 \end{array} \right\} \qquad (4.4\text{-}28)$$

From Eqs. 4.4-27 and 4.4-28 one gets for $n = 1$,

$$\frac{d\psi_i}{d\zeta} = \mp \frac{\sqrt{2}\hat{h}_p \, e^{\delta/2}}{\delta}[1 - e^{-\delta\psi i}(1 + \delta\psi_i)]^{1/2} \qquad (4.4\text{-}29)$$

and

$$\left(\frac{d\psi_i}{d\zeta}\right)_{\zeta=0} = \mp \frac{\sqrt{2}\hat{h}_p \, e^{\delta/2}}{\delta}[1 - e^{-\delta}(1 + \delta)]^{1/2}. \qquad (4.4\text{-}30)$$

From Eq. 4.4-30, the effectiveness factor is given asymptotically by the expression

$$\mathscr{E}_p = \frac{\sqrt{2} \, e^{\delta/2}}{\hat{h}_p \, |\delta|} [1 - e^{-\delta}(1 + \delta)]^{1/2} \qquad \text{for all } |\delta| > 0. \qquad (4.4\text{-}31)$$

A similar expression for a second-order reaction is obtained by the same asymptotic procedure. In final form this relationship is

$$\mathscr{E}_p = \frac{\sqrt{2} \, e^{\delta/2}}{\hat{h}_p} \left\{ -\frac{2}{\delta^3}[e^{-\delta}(\delta + 1) - 1] - \frac{e^{-\delta}}{\delta} \right\}^{1/2} \qquad \text{for all } |\delta| > 0. \qquad (4.4\text{-}32)$$

By a similar analysis for $\delta = 0$,

$$\mathscr{E}_p = \frac{1}{\hat{h}_p}\left(\frac{2}{n + 1}\right)^{1/2} \qquad \text{for } n > -1. \qquad (4.4\text{-}33)$$

Eqs. 4.4-31 and 4.4-32 represent the asymptotic solutions to the first- and second-order reactions.

The question may now be discussed as to the conditions under which the asymptotic method can be intelligently used in engineering applications. Keeping in mind that the solution is asymptotically rigorous as $\hat{h}_p \to \infty$, the problem becomes: how large numerically is a large value of $\hat{h}_p$? The problem is logically broken into two parts: first, over what range of values of $\hat{h}_p$ is the asymptotic solution a good representation of the true solution to Eq. 4.4-17, that is, the cartesian system? Does ψ_i go essentially to zero

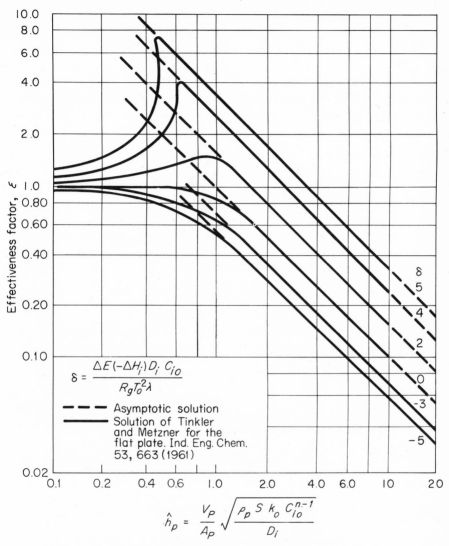

Fig. 4.4-1. Comparison of asymptotic and "exact" solutions for a
nonisothermal first-order reaction in a flat plate of catalyst.

in the porous pellet? Second, over what range of values of $\hat{h}_p$ does the
asymptotic solution accurately represent the exact solution to Eq. 4.4-14?
Can one drop out the middle term of Eq. 4.4-16?

To answer the first question for a first-order nonisothermal system, plots
of the asymptotic solutions are shown in Fig. 4.4-1 along with the "exact"
solutions obtained by Tinkler and Metzner using an analog computer. The

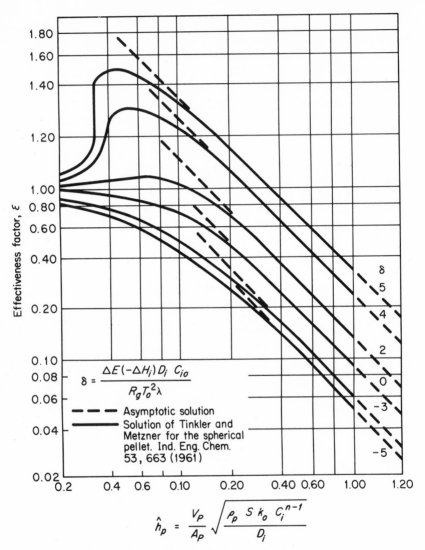

$$\delta = \frac{\Delta E(-\Delta H_i) D_i\, C_{io}}{R_g T_o^2 \lambda}$$

- - - Asymptotic solution
—— Solution of Tinkler and
Metzner for the spherical
pellet. Ind. Eng. Chem.
53, 663 (1961)

$$\hat{h}_p = \frac{V_P}{A_P} \sqrt{\frac{\rho_p\, S\, k_o\, C_i^{n-1}}{D_i}}$$

Fig. 4.4-2. Comparison of asymptotic and "exact" solutions for a
first-order, nonisothermal reaction in a spherical pellet of catalyst.

solid lines represent their solutions and the dashed lines represent the asymptotic solutions given by Eq. 4.4-31. When $\delta = 0$, the solution is more easily
obtained from Eq. 4.4-33. The useful range of the asymptotic solution is for
values of $\hat{h}_p > 1$ and in some cases a little less. The asymptotic solution is,
therefore, an excellent representation of the solution for most engineering
purposes.

The answer to the second question is less definitive. Figure 4.4-2 shows the same asymptotic solutions with the analog computer solutions obtained for spherical coordinate system (Eq. 4.4-16). This comparison is not as good for small values of $\hat{h}_p$. Certainly at values of $\hat{h}_p > 2$, the asymptotic solutions are satisfactory, and the useful region again is probably about $\hat{h}_p > 1$. The important criterion here is how accurately we can determine $\hat{h}_p$ for a given particle. Many of the usual problems of experimental accuracy, and especially the problem of selecting a value for D_i, make the uncertainty of $\hat{h}_p$ substantial.

4.5 A criterion for diffusion-influenced simple chemical reactions in porous solids

In the interpretation of data from an experimental reactor in which a particular heterogeneous reaction occurs on a porous catalyst, one is immediately concerned as to whether transport rates have influenced the measured over-all reaction rates. The experimentally measured reaction rate per unit volume of catalyst $\mathscr{R}_D$ for simple reactions is, in general, from Eqs. 4.1-2 and 4.4-11:

$$\mathscr{R}_D = \rho_p S \mathscr{R}'(C_{i0})\mathscr{E}. \tag{4.5-1}$$

Weisz and Prater† presented a criterion for isothermal reactions on a flat slab based upon the observation that $\mathscr{E}$ is of the order of unity when $\hat{h}_p$ is of the order of unity. (See for example, Fig. 4.2-3.) Substitution of this observation into Eq. 4.5-1 and rearranging, we obtain their criterion for kinetic control:

$$\frac{L^2}{D_e C_{i0}} \mathscr{R}_D < 1. \tag{4.5-2}$$

The corresponding expression for the general pellet is

$$\frac{\left(\dfrac{V_p}{A_p}\right)^2}{D_e C_{i0}} \mathscr{R}_D < 1. \tag{4.5-3}$$

The meaning of Eq. 4.5-2 is that if the left-hand side of the inequality is less than unity, the reaction rate is controlled by the surface reaction and internal transport processes need not be considered in the analysis. Conversely, if the numerical value of the left-hand side of the inequality is greater than unity, internal transport processes must be considered in the analysis.

The forms of Eqs. 4.5-2 and 4.5-3 are particularly useful because the kinetics are brought into the relationship in terms of the measured rate, thereby making these equations easy to use.

† P. B. Weisz and C. D. Prater, *Advan. Catalysis* **6,** 167 (1954).

As a general statement the above criteria are useful guides for most isothermal simple reactions as shown by Figs. 4.2-2 and 4.3-2. However, the criterion lacks generality and can be shown to be greatly in error in certain selected cases. From the analysis of the general simple reaction of the previous section, it is possible to state an analogous criterion which is completely general for the nonisothermal simple reaction.

An asymptotic expression for $\mathscr{E}$ for a spherical pellet is given by Eq. 4.4-21, from which it is evident that $\mathscr{E}$ approaches unity as $\hat{h}_p \to \hat{h}_p^*$ where

$$\hat{h}_p^* \equiv \sqrt{2} \left[\int_0^1 -\{\mathscr{R}_i''(\psi)\} \, d\psi \right]^{1/2}. \tag{4.5-4}$$

The general criterion analogous to the Weisz–Prater criterion therefore becomes

$$\hat{h}_p \le \hat{h}_p^*. \tag{4.5-5}$$

Unfortunately, one cannot rearrange Eqs. 4.5-4 and 4.5-5 so that only the observed reaction rate appears in the expression because the integral depends upon the functional form of $\mathscr{R}_i''(\psi)$. The Weisz–Prater criterion (hereafter referred to as the W–P criterion) corresponds to an assumed value of $\frac{1}{2}$ for this integral. However, for classical isothermal forms of the rate expression: zero, first- and second-order, the criterion for spherical pellets from Eq. 4.5-4 is

$$\hat{h}_p \le \hat{h}_p^* = \sqrt{\frac{2}{n+1}}, \tag{4.5-6}$$

where

$$\hat{h}_p \equiv \frac{V_p}{A_p} \sqrt{\frac{\rho_p S k_n C_0^{n-1}}{D_e}},$$

which is approximately the same as Eq. 4.5-2. If the differences between Eqs. 4.5-2 and 4.5-4 were only as minor as shown immediately above, there would be little point in generalizing the criterion. We shall now consider two examples where the differences in the criteria are larger, one in which the rate expression is of the Langmuir–Hinshelwood type in which the product strongly poisons the catalyst surface and another in which heat effects must be considered.

EXAMPLE 4.5-1 STRONG PRODUCT INHIBITION IN THE RATE LAW

Rate expressions in which one of the products strongly inhibits the rate of reaction are observed for the reduction of carbon dioxide on a carbon surface, or in the ammonia synthesis. The inhibition may be expressed in terms of a Langmuir–Hinshelwood type rate law of the form

$$\mathscr{R} = \frac{k_1 P_A}{1 + k_2 P_B + k_3 P_A}, \tag{4.5-7}$$

where for the carbon-carbon dioxide reaction

$$C + CO_2 \rightarrow 2\,CO, \qquad (4.5\text{-}8)$$

values of the constants at 1000°K are approximately†

$$k_1 = 2.36 \times 10^{-5} \text{ g-moles/cm}^2 \text{ (sec)(atm)},$$
$$k_2 = 5.06 \times 10^4 \text{ atm}^{-1},$$
$$k_3 = 4.12 \text{ atm}^{-1},$$

and where P_A = partial pressure of carbon dioxide in atm,

P_B = partial pressure of carbon monoxide in atm.

In this case, as was pointed out by Austin and Walker, only a slight buildup in the partial pressure of carbon monoxide in the pore structure leads to markedly reduced over-all rate of reaction. Thus, if the above values of the k_i's are accepted, the carbon dioxide partial pressure could remain appreciably constant throughout the porous structure even though the point values of the reaction rates are reduced in the interior of the porous solid owing to the presence of trace quantities of carbon monoxide. Clearly then in this example one cannot correctly conclude that at $h \approx 1$, the effectiveness factor $\mathscr{E}$ is about unity based upon the criterion of a small carbon dioxide concentration gradient at the pore mouth. Indeed, the value of $\mathscr{E}$ is very small at this value. To show this, it is necessary to go back to the basic conservation equations and integrate them for this particular form of the rate law. The asymptotic form of the conservation equation of CO_2 in a spherical particle is

$$\frac{d}{dR}\left[D_A \frac{dP_A}{dR}\right] - \rho_p S\left[\frac{k_1 P_A}{1 + k_2 P_B + k_3 P_A}\right] = 0. \qquad (4.5\text{-}9)$$

For carbon monoxide,

$$\frac{d}{dR}\left[D_B \frac{dP_B}{dR}\right] + 2\rho_p S\left[\frac{k_1 P_A}{1 + k_2 P_B + k_3 P_A}\right] = 0. \qquad (4.5\text{-}10)$$

Multiplying Eq. 4.5-9 by 2 and adding to Eq. 4.5-10.

$$\frac{d}{dR}\left[D_A \frac{dP_A}{dR}\right] = -\frac{1}{2}\frac{d}{dR}\left[D_B \frac{dP_B}{dR}\right]. \qquad (4.5\text{-}11)$$

Integrating Eq. 4.5-11 and satisfying the boundary conditions,

$$P_B = 2\,\frac{D_A}{D_B}(P_{A0} - P_A) + P_{B0}. \qquad (4.5\text{-}12)$$

Consider the case in which the carbon monoxide partial pressure at the external surface of the solid, P_{B0}, is zero. Substituting Eq. 4.5-12 into Eq. 4.5-9 and rearranging,

$$\frac{d^2\psi}{d\zeta^2} - \frac{\hat{h}_p^2}{\alpha}\left[\frac{\psi}{\Delta - \psi}\right] = 0, \qquad (4.5\text{-}13)$$

† L. G. Austin and P. L. Walker, Jr., *A.I.Ch.E. Journal* **9**, 303 (1963).

where

$$\psi \equiv \frac{P_A}{P_{A0}}, \quad \zeta \equiv \frac{3(R_0 - R)}{R_0}, \quad \hat{h}_p \equiv \frac{R_0}{3} \sqrt{\frac{\rho_p S k_1}{D_A(1 + k_3 P_{A0})}}$$
$$\alpha \equiv \frac{2k_2(D_A/D_B)P_{A0} - k_3 P_{A0}}{1 + k_3 P_{A0}}, \quad \Delta \equiv \frac{1 + 2k_2(D_A/D_B)P_{A0}}{2k_2(D_A/D_B)P_{A0} - k_3 P_{A0}} \quad (4.5\text{-}14)$$

The asymptotic solution to Eq. 4.5-13 for large h is obtained using the method of Section 4.4† to give

$$\mathscr{E} = \frac{\sqrt{2}}{\hat{h}_p \alpha^{1/2}} \left\{ -1 + \Delta \ln \left(\frac{\Delta}{\Delta - 1} \right) \right\}^{1/2}. \quad (4.5\text{-}15)$$

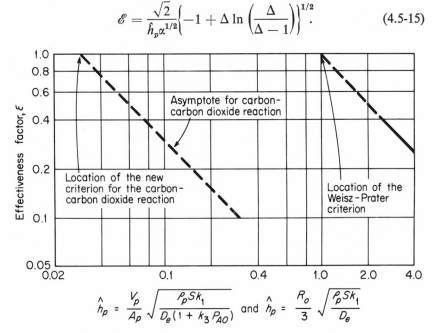

$$\hat{h}_p = \frac{V_p}{A_p} \sqrt{\frac{\rho_p S k_1}{D_e(1 + k_3 P_{A0})}} \quad \text{and} \quad \hat{h}_p = \frac{R_0}{3} \sqrt{\frac{\rho_p S k_1}{D_e}}$$

Fig. 4.5-1. Effectiveness factor for carbon-carbon dioxide reaction in a flat slab of porous solid.

For the example under consideration, substitution of the numerical values of the k's into Eq. 4.5-15 and assuming $D_A/D_B \approx 1$ leads to

$$\mathscr{E} = \frac{3.03 \times 10^{-2}}{\hat{h}_p}, \quad (4.5\text{-}16)$$

where $P_{A0} = 1$ atmosphere. The location of this asymptotic solution is shown on Fig. 4.5-1 along with the solution to the simple first-order reaction. For the carbon-carbon dioxide reaction at $1000°K$, the W–P criterion would correspond to an effectiveness factor of about 0.0303. If the carbon monoxide partial pressure builds up in the gas phase so that P_{B0} in Eq. 4.5-12 is no

† E. E. Petersen, to appear in *Chem. Eng. Sci.*, 1965.

longer zero, then the sensitivity of denominator to changes in P_B within the pores decreases, and the asymptotic solution will shift its position to the right of the solution presented on Fig. 4.5-1. At reasonably high partial pressures of P_{B0}, the W–P criterion will again apply to this system. Clearly, then, the W–P criterion is not useful for the particular case presented above nor for similar cases.

EXAMPLE 4.5-2 NONISOTHERMAL FIRST-ORDER REACTION

For nonisothermal reactions, the governing equations are complicated by an additional parameter δ which contains terms related to the energetics of the reactions. Two different criteria may be usefully developed to answer the following questions about these reactions: (1) For what range of values of δ is the reaction essentially isothermal under all conditions? (2) If δ does not conform to the first criterion, what is $\hat{h}^*$ for the reaction? Although both of these questions can be answered using the criterion of Eq. 4.5-6, it is instructive to illustrate the use of this equation for the general first-order nonisothermal reaction. Equation 4.4-27 in Example 4.4-1 is the conservation equation for this system. It is apparent from this equation that it reduces identically to the isothermal first-order reaction for $\delta = 0$ and $n = 1$. It would be useful to establish the bounds on δ such that the nonisothermal $\mathscr{E}$ does not deviate from the isothermal $\mathscr{E}$ by more than 5 per cent. To find the numerical limits on δ, the exponential term in Eq. 4.4-27 is expanded and the first two terms retained to become

$$\frac{d^2\psi_i}{d\xi^2} - e^{\delta}(1 - \delta\psi_i)\psi_i = 0. \qquad (4.5\text{-}19)$$

The asymptotic solution to Eq. 4.5-19 is

$$\mathscr{E} = \frac{1}{\hat{h}_p} e^{\delta/2}\left(1 - \frac{\delta}{3}\right),$$

which upon expansion becomes

$$\mathscr{E} \cong \frac{1}{\hat{h}_p}\left(1 + \frac{\delta}{6}\right). \qquad (4.5\text{-}20)$$

Therefore, in accordance with the arbitrary tolerance of 5 per cent discussed above, δ must conform to the inequality below.

$$|\delta| \leq 0.3 \qquad (4.5\text{-}21)$$

For this reaction, if $|\delta|$ is less than about 0.3, then nonisothermal effects are unimportant regardless of the value of $\hat{h}_P$ and an analysis of the system can proceed as though the system were isothermal. This is similar to the Anderson criterion.[†]

† J. B. Anderson, *Chem. Eng. Sci.*, **18**, 147 (1963).

When $|\delta| > 0.3$, the system cannot be treated as an isothermal system. To complete the analysis of these systems, a value of $\hat{h}_p^*$ must be computed below which diffusion of heat and mass no longer influence the over-all reaction rate. For endothermic reactions, this is readily found from the asymptotic solution of Eq. 4.4-31, which is

$$\hat{h}_p \leq \hat{h}_p^* = \frac{\sqrt{2}\, e^{\delta/2}}{|\delta|} \{1 - e^{-\delta}(\delta + 1)\}^{1/2}. \tag{4.5-22}$$

For the endothermic first-order reaction, Eq. 4.5-22 serves as a criterion for deciding whether diffusion of heat and mass must be included in the analysis of the system. Equation 4.5-22 also applies to exothermic reactions; however, a word of caution is necessary in interpreting the above criterion for large values of δ. The value of $\hat{h}_p^*$ obtained from Eq. 4.5-22 corresponds to a value of $\mathscr{E}$ equal to unity. However, for a range of values of $\hat{h}_p < \hat{h}_p^*$, the numerical magnitude of $\mathscr{E}$ can increase to values considerably greater than unity. A better means for determining the range of $\hat{h}_p$ values where $\mathscr{E}$ again approaches unity may be obtained from a perturbation solution such as that presented by Tinkler and Pigford.

The time-honored experimental criterion for determining whether a simple reaction is diffusion influenced appears to be valid, with slight modification, even for nonisothermal systems. In brief, this method is based upon change in $\mathscr{E}$ with the parameter $\hat{h}_p$ in the diffusion-influenced range. In fact, we have shown that for large values of h, $\mathscr{E} \propto 1/\hat{h}_p$ for all systems. The easiest method of varying $\hat{h}_p$ is by changing the characteristic dimension V_p/A_p of the catalyst pellet, which is accomplished in practice by crushing. If, under identical reaction conditions, the rate of reaction is the same for *three* particle sizes, one can infer that transport properties are not influencing the over-all rate. Whereas, if the rates differ under the above conditions so that small particles give higher over-all rates, i.e.,

$$\text{over-all rates} \propto \frac{1}{\text{(characteristic dimension)}} \tag{4.5-23}$$

the system is exhibiting transport influence. Note that three different sizes are specified to rule out the possibility of obtaining the same rate on each side of the maximum on the $\mathscr{E}$ versus h curve for exothermic reaction. In principle, the additional run is unnecessary for isothermal and endothermal reactions. Some difficulty would be experienced in interpreting the results of such a test for a reaction such as the one described in Example 4.5-1. However, as explained in the latter example, a situation of this type is not often encountered. The real danger here is to use differential reactors for the study of the kinetics and for analytical reasons, restrict the input composition to pure reactant. Under these conditions the effect of product inhibition on the effectiveness factor is greatest.

4.6 Maxima in effectiveness factors for simple exothermic reactions

There appears to be no simple way to obtain the maximum in the $\mathscr{E}$ versus $\hat{h}_p$ curve. The asymptotic method described earlier in Section 4.4 and the perturbation method about $\hat{h}_p = 0$ are least accurate in the vicinity of $\mathscr{E}_{max}$. The available reliable information on $\mathscr{E}_{max}$ has been obtained either from analog or numerical solutions to the conservation equations. The work of Tinkler and Metzner has already been presented in Figs. 4.4-1 and 4.4-2. Carberry integrated numerically the second-order nonisothermal reaction equations for slab geometry, and recently Weisz* has integrated numerically the first-order nonisothermal equations using the exact Arrhenius form for a range of parameters probably well beyond the range of applicability to real systems. The results from the systems presented above qualitatively demonstrate that the value of $\hat{h}_p$ corresponding to $\mathscr{E}_{max}$ is not particularly sensitive to the order of the reaction, but depends upon the parameters β and γ where

$$\beta \equiv \frac{(-\Delta H) D_i C_{i0}}{\lambda T_0}, \qquad \lambda \equiv \frac{E}{R_g T_0}.$$

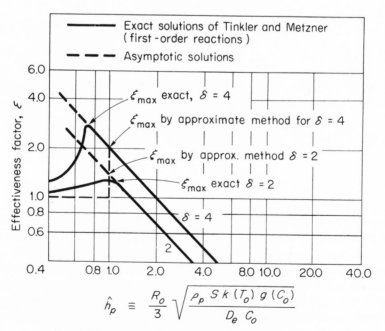

$$\hat{h}_p \equiv \frac{R_o}{3} \sqrt{\frac{\rho_p \, S \, k \, (T_o) \, g \, (C_o)}{D_e \, C_o}}$$

Fig. 4.6-1. Approximate method for determining ε_{max}.

* P. B. Weisz, *Chem. Eng. Sci.* **17**, 265 (1962).

Large values of $\beta\gamma$ product ($\beta\gamma = \delta$) tend to shift the location of the maximum to a value of $\hat{h}_p \approx 1$. Based upon the above observations, the qualitative description of an unknown system for which the functional form of the rate expression is known can be obtained from the asymptotic behavior of the conservation equations for the particular value of δ computed for the particular conditions in question, say δ_1, and for $\delta = 0$ for the same system. These solutions are sketched in Fig. 4.6-1. The method of construction of the curve which approximates the complete solution is simply that $\mathscr{E}$ is unity up to a value of $\hat{h}_p = \hat{h}_p^*$ where $\hat{h}_p^*$ is the value of $\hat{h}_p$ at which the asymptotic solution gives a unity value of $\mathscr{E}$ when $\delta = 0$. At $\hat{h}_p^*$, the solution is said to behave according to the asymptotic solution for $\delta = \delta_1$. The magnitude of $\mathscr{E}_{max}$ obtained in this way is at best a crude approximation, as shown by a comparison of exact and approximate methods on Fig. 4.6-1. The above statements are therefore intended to serve only as a guide to the understanding of the behavior of these systems.

4.7 Effect of poisoning of the catalyst surface on the over-all reaction rate

The feed streams to catalytic reactors often contain impurities which, if not removed, will interact with the catalyst to decrease its over-all activity; and, more important, may change its selectivity characteristics to give a less favorable product distribution. These substances are referred to as *catalyst poisons* and in many cases they have a deleterious effect on the catalyst activity when present even in trace quantities. The effectiveness of poisons in reducing catalyst activity is understandable when we realize that a catalyst contains a vanishingly small number of moles of active centers compared to the moles of reactants processed in prolonged operation. If only a small fraction of the molecules processed adsorb and remain on the catalyst's active centers thereby preventing their further use, we have the necessary ingredients for a serious poisoning problem. The subject of poisoning of catalysts is vast and in the ensuing discussion we shall not attempt to look very deeply at the chemical nature of the poisoning process or seek methods whereby the difficulty may be obviated. The purpose of this section is rather to discover how poisons can effect the over-all reaction rate.

The effects of poisoning in either the experimental or prototype reactor are most easily observed by determining the changes in the apparent activity of a catalyst as a function of time. The shape of this function does not lead directly to an interpretation of the dynamics of the poisoning process because it depends upon many factors, such as the concentration of the poison in the feed stream and how effectively the poison can deactivate the catalyst. The shape of the deactivation function also depends upon whether the unpoisoned catalyst was operating in the diffusion-influenced region.

Whereas the true kinetic picture of deactivation involves the competition for active centers by poisons and reactants, the most serious poisoning problems result from a poison which reacts rapidly and is strongly adsorbed, thereby competing for these active centers to the exclusion of the reactants. Such poisons dominate the behavior of the catalyst and their conservation equations are in the limit independent of the conservation equations of the reactant.

In this section we shall first develop relationships for the limiting behavior of the adsorption of poisons on catalysts to obtain the coverage of poison

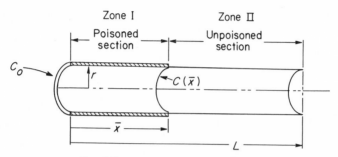

Fig. 4.7-1. Sketch of poisoned pore.

as a function of position within a porous catalyst and time. To do this, we shall look at a more general system to see what kind of restrictions are imposed upon the limiting cases. From this information we can determine the activity of the catalyst as a function of time.

The general equation of conservation of the poison substance in the pore of Fig. 4.7-1 is

$$D \frac{\partial^2 C_I}{\partial x^2} - \frac{2}{r} \frac{\partial \omega}{\partial t} = \frac{\partial C_I}{\partial t}, \tag{4.7-1}$$

where C_I = concentration of poison with respect to a differential volume element in the pore, the first term is the net diffusive influx of poison, the second term is the disappearance of poison owing to its adsorption on the pore wall and the last term is the change in inventory of poison with time. The second term should be examined in more detail.

The quantity ω is the number of moles of poison adsorbed per unit area of catalyst surface and its value at equilibrium depends in part upon the concentration of poison and reactants immediately adjacent to the surface. Although a general expression for ω cannot be written, we can consider how the rate constant for the adsorption process influences the simultaneous solution of Eq. 4.7-1 and the equation describing the adsorption process. If the rate constant is very small, then the middle term of Eq. 4.7-1 is small compared to the remaining terms, and on a time scale suitable for following the adsorption process, the concentration in the pore is essentially constant at C_0. The rate of adsorption at various positions throughout the pore is determined by a dynamic competition between poison and reactants for the active centers. Because the concentration of reactants can vary with position within a pore, a small rate of adsorption does not imply uniform poisoning. When both reactant and poison concentrations are uniform throughout, the competition for active centers can be described in terms of models of the adsorption process—the most widely used being, of course, the model conceived by Langmuir. The rate of adsorption is proportional to the product of the frequency of collisions between the poison molecules and the catalyst surface and the fraction of the surface sites unoccupied. The rate of desorption is similarly proportional to the fraction of the sites occupied. In equation form these statements are, respectively,

$$\text{rate of adsorption} = k_a\left(1 - \frac{\omega}{\omega_0}\right)C_I,$$

$$\text{rate of desorption} = k_d\frac{\omega}{\omega_0}.$$

At equilibrium, these rates are equated to give a relationship between ω and c.

$$\frac{\omega_e}{\omega_0} = \frac{(k_a/k_d)C_{I_e}}{1 + (k_a/k_d)C_{I_e}}, \tag{4.7-2}$$

where ω_0 is the numerical value of ω when adsorption sites are completely occupied. By a slight extension of this reasoning, the nonequilibrium rate of adsorption (or desorption) can be expressed in the form:

$$\text{rate of adsorption per unit area} = k_a\left(1 - \frac{\omega}{\omega_0}\right)C_I - k_d\frac{\omega}{\omega_0}. \tag{4.7-3}$$

Equation 4.7-3 is the expression which should be substituted for $\partial\omega/\partial t$ in Eq. 4.7-1 based upon the Langmuir model. Alternately, Eq. 4.7-3 can be written

$$\text{rate of adsorption per unit area} = \frac{\partial\omega}{\partial t} = k_a\left(1 - \frac{\omega}{\omega_0}\right)[C_I - C_I(\omega)], \tag{4.7-3a}$$

where $C_I(\omega)$ is the concentration which would be in equilibrium with ω. In solving Eq. 4.7-1 there is no advantage in the latter form.

The system of equations 4.7-1 and 4.7-3 can be made easier to examine by letting

$$\psi_I \equiv \frac{C_I}{C_{I0}}, \qquad \Phi \equiv \frac{\omega}{\omega_0}, \qquad \eta \equiv \frac{x}{L}, \qquad \tau \equiv \frac{C_{I0}k_a t}{\omega_0},$$

$$\alpha \equiv \frac{rC_{I0}}{2\omega_0} = \frac{1}{\left(\dfrac{\text{surface area}}{\text{unit volume of pores}}\right)}\frac{C_{I0}}{\omega_0}, \tag{4.7-4}$$

$$h \equiv L\sqrt{\frac{2k_a}{rD}}, \qquad \frac{k_a C_{I0}}{k_d} \equiv K,$$

to obtain upon substitution

$$\frac{\partial^2 \psi_I}{\partial \eta^2} - h^2 \frac{\partial \Phi}{\partial t} = h^2 \alpha \frac{\partial \psi_I}{\partial \tau},$$ (4.7-5)

$$\frac{\partial \Phi}{\partial \tau} = (1 - \Phi)\psi_I - \frac{\Phi}{KC_{I0}}.$$ (4.7-6)

These equations would generally be subject to the following boundary conditions:

$$\psi_I(\tau, 0) = 1, \qquad \left(\frac{\partial \psi_I}{\partial \eta}\right)_{\eta=1} = 0$$

and initial conditions

$$\psi_I(0, \eta) = 0, \qquad \Phi(0, \eta) = 0$$

(4.7-7)

One can show for a reasonably active catalyst that the parameter $\alpha \ll 1$. Although the set of equations are simplified by the recognition of the magnitude of α, the system is still too cumbersome to analyze in any general way.

Fortunately, for the case which is kinetically most interesting, a solution is easily obtained. This corresponds to a poison which absorbs both rapidly and tightly to the surface. We might conclude at first that such a system would immediately lose its activity, but some reflection will reveal a case where the rate at which the activity decline is limited by the rate of diffusion of poison into the pore. Because of the assumptions made above, the pore is at any time divided into two zones as shown in Fig. 4.7-1, the first starting at the pore mouth and extending some distance, say $\bar{x}$, into the pore to form a tube of no catalytic activity, and a second extending from $\bar{x}$ to L having no absorbed poison. Mathematically, then, in

Zone I: $0 < \eta < \bar{\eta},$ $\Phi = 1;$ $\psi_I =$ non-zero

Zone II: $\bar{\eta} < \eta < 1,$ $\Phi = 0;$ $\psi_I = 0$

(4.7-8)

In Zone I,

$$\frac{\partial \Phi}{\partial \tau} = 0 \quad \text{for } K \to \infty$$

$$\frac{\partial \psi_I}{\partial \eta} = \text{const},$$

which from Eq. 4.7-8, yields

$$\frac{\partial \psi_I}{\partial \eta} = \frac{1 - 0}{0 - \bar{\eta}} = -\frac{1}{\bar{\eta}}$$ (4.7-9)

Equation 4.7-5 has no meaning at $\bar{\eta}$ because the functions are discontinuous between Zones I and II. A differential material balance in the volume between $\bar{\eta}$ and $\bar{\eta} + \Delta\bar{\eta}$ becomes:

$$-\Delta\tau\left(\left[\frac{\partial \psi_I}{\partial \eta}\right]_{\tau,\bar{\eta}} - \left(\frac{\partial \psi_I}{\partial \eta}\right)_{\tau,\bar{\eta}+\Delta\bar{\eta}}\right) = h^2 \, \Delta\bar{\eta}[\Phi(\bar{\eta}, \tau + \Delta\tau) - \Phi(\bar{\eta}, \tau)].$$

From the boundary conditions of Eqs. 4.7-8 and 4.7-9, these terms are, respectively,

$$-\Delta\tau\left[-\frac{1}{\eta} - 0\right] = h^2 \Delta\eta[1 - 0],$$

which upon simplification and integration is

$$\frac{\bar{\eta}^2}{2} = \frac{\tau}{h^2},$$ (4.7-10)

or in the original coordinates is

$$\bar{x}^2 = \beta t,$$ (4.7-11)

where

$$\beta \equiv \frac{r D C_{i0}}{\omega_0}.$$ (4.7-12)

Equation 4.7-11 relates the length of the poisoned tube to time. According to this model, when $\bar{x} = L$, the catalyst will exhibit no activity. Although this is obviously a limiting case, it has utility, because in adopting it we have separated the equation describing the poisoning of the catalyst from the equation describing the reaction occurring therein. In fact, when β of Eq. 4.7-11 is small, as is almost always true, the time constant for the poisoning is correspondingly large compared to the time constant for the approach to steady-state reaction within the pores. This is equivalent to saying that the rate at which the reaction rate adjusts to a change in the extent of poisoning is very fast compared to the rate at which the extent of poisoning of the catalyst takes place. We can then calculate a series of steady-state reaction rates at various times along the time scale for the poisoning process.

When the reaction rate within the unpoisoned pore is not diffusion influenced, the rate of reaction falls off in direct proportion to $\bar{x}/L$, i.e., the original catalyst had an active area of L/L or unity and a fraction $\bar{x}/L$ has been completely poisoned resulting in a reaction rate proportional to the remaining unpoisoned fraction of the area $1 - (\bar{x}/L)$. If we define a poisoning factor $\mathscr{P}$, as

$$\mathscr{P} \equiv \frac{\mathscr{R}_D(t)}{\mathscr{R}_u},$$ (4.7-13)

where $\mathscr{R}_D(t)$ = the over-all reaction rate of the poisoned pore as a function of time,

$\mathscr{R}_u$ = the over-all reaction rate of the unpoisoned pore.

Then in accordance with the argument above,

$$\mathscr{P} = 1 - \frac{\bar{x}}{L}.$$ (4.7-14)

This relationship is also shown on Fig. 4.7-2, where $\bar{x}/L$ has been replaced by $(\beta t)^{1/2}/L$ from Eq. 4.7-11.

If the unpoisoned pore operates in the diffusion-influenced region, the activity falls off much faster than $1 - (\bar{x}/L)$.* That this should be so can be explained physically from the meaning of the diffusion-influenced region. In this region, transport of reactants within the pore system results in appreciable concentration gradients. If the pore mouths are poisoned, all of the reactants must diffuse through essentially an inert tube of finite length before encountering active surface, the net result of which is to lower the average

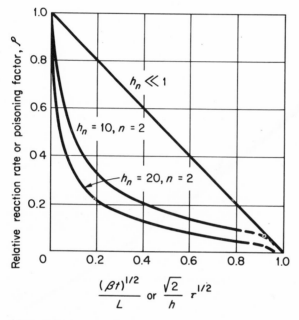

Fig. 4.7-2. Relative reaction rate for poisoned catalysts. Initially kinetic-controlled or diffusion-influenced regions.

concentration of reactants adjacent to the active catalytic surface. In the limit as the $\bar{x}/L$ approaches unity, this argument must become invalid, because no matter how large the Thiele parameter h_n is for the unpoisoned pore, eventually as poisoning approaches completion, the reaction must become kinetic controlled as the over-all rate of reaction for the pore approaches zero.

The quantitative description of this process is easily developed for this model. The rate of transport of reactants in the poisoned section is

$$\text{Diffusion rate} = \iota_1 = \pi r^2 D \left[\frac{C_0 - C(\bar{x})}{\bar{x}} \right]. \tag{4.7-15}$$

* A. Wheeler, *Advan. Catalysis* 3, *op. cit.*

Clearly, the description of the unpoisoned section of the pore is the same as considered in the earlier part of this chapter, Section 4.2, if $C(\bar{x})$ replaces C_0. Therefore, the rate of reaction in the unpoisoned part of the pore for integral order reactions and large values of h_n is, from Eqs. 4.2-9 and 4.2-18,

$$\imath_2 = 2r(1 - \bar{\eta})Lk_nC(\bar{x})^n\left(\frac{2}{n+1}\right)^{1/2}\frac{1}{(1-\bar{\eta})h_n}, \qquad (4.7\text{-}16)$$

where

$$\bar{\eta} \equiv \frac{\bar{x}}{L}$$

and

$$h_n \equiv L\sqrt{\frac{2k_nC_0^{n-1}}{rD}}.$$

The solution to the problem under discussion is $\imath_1(\bar{x}) = \imath_2(\bar{x})$ over the range $0 \leq \bar{x} \leq L$.

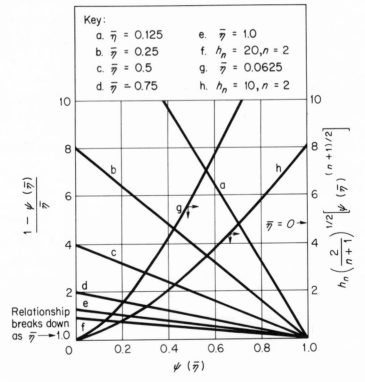

Fig. 4.7-3. Working plot for the solution of Equation 4.7-17 for the over-all reaction rate of a poisoned pore.

Equating $\imath_1$ and $\imath_2$, and rearranging:

$$\frac{1 - \psi(\bar{\eta})}{\bar{\eta}} = h_n \psi^{(n+1/2)}(\bar{\eta}) \left(\frac{2}{n+1}\right)^{1/2}. \qquad (4.7\text{-}17)$$

Equation 4.7-17 is solved by a graphical method shown in Fig. 4.7-3 for two cases of $n = 2$. The results from Fig. 4.7-3 are shown on Fig. 4.7-2 for two values of h_n and demonstrate how the rate falls off with poisoning when the reaction in the unpoisoned pores is in the diffusion-influenced region. This is compared with the decrease in activity with poisoning when there is no diffusion influence in the unpoisoned pore.

If a reacting system contains traces of a poison which cannot be entirely removed and if that poison is rapidly and for practical purposes irreversibly adsorbed, then the above analysis shows that we gain by developing a catalyst with very large surface areas and correspondingly small pores. Although it has been shown earlier that in the absence of poisoning no such net gain results for isothermal systems, effectively an increase in area and a decrease in the pore size decreases the magnitude of β of Eq. 4.7-11 by decreasing the numerator and increasing the denominator thereby increasing the time constant for deactivation.

4.8 General nonisothermal complex reactions

The technique used in Section 4.4 to simplify the general simple reaction to a single ordinary differential equation can be extended to interpret complex reactions without introducing any new concepts. To extend the analysis, the methods discussed in Section 2.3 are applied to the general set of m reactions,

$$\sum_{i=1}^{n} a_{ij}A_i = 0 \qquad (j = 1, 2, 3, \ldots, m) \qquad (4.8\text{-}1)$$

to reduce it to a set of k linearly independent reactions. The analysis is, therefore, concerned with the set

$$\sum_{i=1}^{n} a_{ij}A_i = 0 \qquad (j = 1, 2, 3, \ldots, k) \qquad (4.8\text{-}2)$$

The rate at which the ith component reacts as a result of the jth reaction is

$$\mathscr{R}_{ij} = \mathscr{R}_{ij}[C_1, C_2, C_3, \ldots, C_n, T]$$
$$(i = 1, 2, 3, \ldots, n; j = 1, 2, 3, \ldots, k). \quad (4.8\text{-}3)$$

These rates are related through the stoichiometric equations as shown below.

$$\frac{\mathscr{R}_{ij}}{a_{ij}} = \frac{\mathscr{R}_{kj}}{a_{kj}} = \mathscr{R}_j \qquad (j = 1, 2, 3, \ldots, k). \qquad (4.8\text{-}4)$$

A differential equation can be written for each of the n species present similar to Eq. 4.4-4 except that it must be remembered that each species may be a reactant or a product in each of the k reactions. Accounting for this, it follows that for a single pore*

$$\frac{d}{dx}\left[D_i \frac{dC_i}{dx}\right] + \frac{2}{r}\sum_{j=1}^{k} \mathcal{R}_{ij} = 0 \qquad (i = 1, 2, 3, \ldots, n). \qquad (4.8\text{-}5)$$

From Eq. 4.8-4 we obtain

$$\frac{d}{dx}\left[D_i \frac{dC_i}{dx}\right] + \frac{2}{r}\sum_{j=1}^{k} a_{ij}\mathcal{R}_j = 0 \qquad (i = 1, 2, 3, \ldots, n). \qquad (4.8\text{-}6)$$

It would appear at first from Eq. 4.8-6 that to obtain the solution to this system of equations for an isothermal pore it is necessary to solve n equations simultaneously. However, we found in our earlier analysis of complex reactions that only k of the components are independent. Hence the simultaneous solution of k equations is necessary to determine the point values of the concentrations of k species, and the remaining $k + 1$ through n species are computed from the concentrations of the first k components. In this way, the value of $\mathcal{R}_j$ is a function only of k components. To show this, we go back to Eq. 2.3-15 in which the rates of production of the $k + 1$ to n species are written in terms of the production of the species 1 to k. That is,

$$P_g = \sum_{i=1}^{k} \gamma_{gi} P_i \qquad (g = k + 1, k + 2, \ldots, n), \qquad (4.8\text{-}7)$$

where the reader will recall that

$$P_i = \sum_{j=1}^{k} a_{ij}\mathcal{R}_j \qquad (i = 1, 2, 3, \ldots, n). \qquad (4.8\text{-}8)$$

Making these substitutions into Eq. 4.8-6 results in a relationship between the concentrations of species $k + 1$ to n in terms of concentrations of species 1 to k. This relation is

$$\frac{d}{dx}\left[D_g \frac{dC_g}{dx}\right] = \sum_{i=1}^{k} \gamma_{gi} \frac{d}{dx}\left[D_i \frac{dC_i}{dx}\right] \qquad (g = k + 1, k + 2, \ldots, n), \qquad (4.8\text{-}9)$$

which may be integrated twice for constant diffusivities to give:

$$D_g(C_g - C_{g0}) = \sum_{i=1}^{k} \gamma_{gi} D_i(C_i - C_{i0}) \qquad (g = k + 1, k + 2, \ldots, n). \qquad (4.8\text{-}10)$$

Thus, $n - k$ of the equations are eliminated and k equations of the form of Eq. 4.8-6 must be solved simultaneously.

The discussion so far has been limited to isothermal systems. It is quite possible for the temperature to vary with position within a catalytic particle,

---

* Cartesian coordinates are used here for simplicity; however, no complications are encountered in applying these same methods to spherical coordinates.

especially when heat release or absorption during the course of reaction is large. At first glance, it might seem that the removal of the isothermal restriction would enormously increase the complexity of the system. We shall see below; however, that the nonisothermal analysis introduces another *dependent* equation, i.e., the temperature may be directly obtained from the known values of the composition with respect to k independent components. In this sense, the complexity of the system remains unchanged. However, the $\mathscr{R}_i$ functions are often extremely sensitive to the magnitude of the temperature because of the exponential dependence of the rate of a reaction on temperature. In this latter sense, the solution of the nonisothermal system is more difficult to obtain than that for the isothermal system, because strong nonlinearities are introduced into the equations.

In setting up an energy balance, it will be assumed that enthalpy change resulting from chemical reaction gives rise to a heat source or sink which must be dissipated or supplied by conduction through the solid phase.

The energy equation is based upon a model corresponding to one-dimensional heat conduction in a solid of prescribed geometry containing a distributed, nonuniform heat source. For the case of a single pore, the cross section of the solid surrounding the pore through which heat is conducted is not specified and the pore more closely approaches isothermal operation as the cross section for conduction increases. In the catalytic pellet this cross section for heat flow is determined by the solid structure just as the passages for diffusion are determined by the porous structure. Thus in the analysis of the infinite slab of catalyst given below the effective thermal conductivity λ differs from the true thermal conductivity in that it contains factors which account for the fact that the solid is porous and the length of the conduction path is greater than the geometric distance between points within the solid. It is obtained from a knowledge of the catalyst structure (see Chapter 5). For an infinite slab, the energy equation becomes

$$\frac{d}{dx}\left[\lambda \frac{dT}{dx}\right] - \rho_p S \sum_{i=1}^{n} \tilde{H}_i \mathscr{P}_i = 0, \tag{4.8-11}$$

where λ = effective thermal conductivity in the solid,

$\tilde{H}_i$ = partial molal enthalpy of the ith species in the mixture.

From the set of conservation equations

$$\frac{d}{dx}\left[\lambda \frac{dT}{dx}\right] + \sum_{i=1}^{n} \tilde{H}_i \frac{d}{dx}\left[D_i \frac{dC_i}{dx}\right] = 0. \tag{4.8-12}$$

Using Eq. 4.8-9, the elements $k + 1$ to n may be expressed as a linear combination of the first k. Therefore,

$$\frac{d}{dx}\left(\lambda \frac{dT}{dx}\right) + \sum_{i=1}^{k} \tilde{H}_i \frac{d}{dx}\left(D_i \frac{dC_i}{dx}\right) + \sum_{g=k+1}^{n} \tilde{H}_g \sum_{i=1}^{k} \gamma_{gi} \frac{d}{dx}\left[D_i \frac{dC_i}{dx}\right], \tag{4.8-13}$$

which may be integrated once and put in the form below making use of the symmetry condition at the center of the slab:

$$\lambda \frac{dT}{dx} + \sum_{i=1}^{k} \overline{\Delta H_i} D_i \frac{dC_i}{dx} = 0, \qquad (4.8\text{-}14)$$

where

$$\overline{\Delta H_i} \equiv \tilde{H}_i + \sum_{g=k+1}^{n} \gamma_{gi} \tilde{H}_g. \qquad (4.8\text{-}15)$$

Assuming that $\tilde{H}_i$ ($i = 1, 2, 3, \ldots, n$) are constants, then Eq. 4.8-14 may be integrated again to give

$$\lambda(T - T_0) = -\sum_{i=1}^{k} \overline{\Delta H_i} D_i (C_i - C_{i0}) \qquad (4.8\text{-}16)$$

for constant D_i. It is perhaps well to mention at this point that in Knudsen flow $D_{ki}{}^*$ is not constant, but

$$D_{ki} \propto \frac{2r}{3} \sqrt{\frac{8 R_g T}{\pi M_i}},$$

$$= \mathscr{D}_i T^{1/2}, \qquad (4.8\text{-}17)$$

where r = pore radius,
   R_g = gas constant,
   M_i = molecular weight,
   D_{ki} = effective Knudsen diffusion coefficient,
and $\mathscr{D}_i$ is defined by comparing the two expressions for D_{ki} in Eq. 4.8-17. Under these conditions Eq. 4.8-14 leads to

$$2\lambda[T^{1/2} - T_0^{1/2}] = -\sum_{i=1}^{k} \overline{\Delta H_i} \mathscr{D}_i (C_i - C_{i0}). \qquad (4.8\text{-}18)$$

The general nonisothermal complex reaction is simplified to a set of k simultaneous equations of the form

$$\frac{d}{dx}\left[D_i \frac{dC_i}{dx} \right] - \frac{2}{r} \sum_{j=1}^{k} a_{ij} \mathscr{R}_j' = 0 \qquad (i = 1, 2, \ldots, k), \qquad (4.8\text{-}19)$$

where by analogy to Eq. 4.4-11

$$\mathscr{R}_j' = \mathscr{R}_j'(C_1, C_2, \ldots, C_k). \qquad (4.8\text{-}20)$$

A general solution to this set of equations can of course be obtained numerically. However, the writer prefers the iterative method proposed by Schilson and Amundson.† This method, although laborious, has the advantage that the solution may be obtained to any desired degree of precision and the exact solution approached in the limit.

---

* Effective Knudsen diffusivity. See Chapter 5.
† R. E. Schilson and N. R. Amundson, *Chem. Eng. Sci.* **13**, 236, 237–244 (1961).

4.9 Selectivity as influenced by transport properties

In the early part of this chapter, reference was made to the fact that the selectivity of a catalyst may be influenced by the physical structure of a catalyst. The selectivity $\mathscr{S}$ as used here is an averaged property of the system and is a measure of the ratio of the conversions of the two reactions under a particular set of conditions. The objective of this section is to show to what extent structural features of the catalyst change the ratio of conversions, and to show how under certain conditions the physical structure of the catalyst can be altered to increase its selectivity for a particular reaction.

When several reactions occur within a catalyst pore, the opportunity exists for interactions between the set of differential equations which govern their behavior. The solutions to these sets of equations are obtained only with difficulty, and in most cases it is not feasible to completely map out the spectrum of possible systems as was done for simple reactions. However, it is instructive to consider some representative types of systems for the purpose of illustrating qualitatively the magnitude of the effect which pore diffusion can have on the catalyst's selectivity. Three commonly encountered systems will be selected as examples: (1) independent reactions; (2) parallel reactions; and (3) consecutive reactions. All real systems fall either into one of the above classes, or combinations of the three.

EXAMPLE 4.9-1 INDEPENDENT REACTIONS IN ISOTHERMAL CATALYSTS

As the name implies, a set of independent reactions are ones in which a constituent appears only once as a reactant or a product of a particular reaction. Take as an example a system of two reactions:

Reaction 1: $a_{11}A_1 \xrightarrow{k_1} a_{21}A_2$

Reaction 2: $a_{33}A_3 \xrightarrow{k_2} a_{43}A_4$

$$\left. \right\} \quad (4.9\text{-}1)$$

which will be recognized as a special case of Eq. 4.8-2. According to Eq. 4.8-6, we can write a conservation equation for each of the four components of the mixture; however, as previously discussed, only two of these are independent. One independent set is written below.

$$\frac{d}{dx}\left(D_1\frac{dC_1}{dx}\right) - \frac{2}{r}a_{11}\mathscr{R}_1 = 0$$

$$\frac{d}{dx}\left(D_3\frac{dC_3}{dx}\right) - \frac{2}{r}a_{32}\mathscr{R}_2 = 0$$

$$\left. \right\} \quad (4.9\text{-}2)$$

When $\mathscr{R}_1$ is independent of A_3 and A_4, $\mathscr{R}_2$ is independent of A_1 and A_2, and the diffusivities are either constant or independent of the concentration of the species of the other reaction, the equations of Eq. 4.9-2 are uncoupled. Kinetically this could correspond to a case of low surface coverage on an isothermal catalyst. Under these conditions the independent set of two equations is thereby reduced to solving the Thiele equation for a simple reaction twice.

If Reactions 1 and 2 are each first order, the ratio of their rates in a single pore is, according to Eq. 4.2-9, equal to

$$\mathscr{S} \equiv \frac{\mathscr{R}_{P1}}{\mathscr{R}_{P2}} = \frac{k_1 C_{10} \mathscr{E}_1}{k_2 C_{20} \mathscr{E}_2}, \tag{4.9-3}$$

where the quantity $\mathscr{S}$, the selectivity, has been arbitrarily chosen as the ratio of the rates of production of products from Reactions 1 and 2.

For two limiting cases, Eq. 4.9-3 is simplified. When h_1 and h_2 each approach zero, the corresponding effectiveness factors approach unity, the selectivity approaches $\mathscr{S}_0$, and

$$\mathscr{S}_0 = \frac{k_1 C_{10}}{k_2 C_{20}}. \tag{4.9-4}$$

When both h_1 and h_2 are numerically greater than 3, the corresponding effectiveness factors approach $1/h$ and

$$\mathscr{S}_D = \frac{\mathscr{R}_{P1}}{\mathscr{R}_{P2}} = \frac{k_1 C_{10}}{k_2 C_{30}} \frac{h_2}{h_1}, \tag{4.9-5}$$

where $\mathscr{S}_D$ is the selectivity of the catalyst pore when diffusion rates within the pore influence the reaction rate. The structural features of a catalyst which influence the numerical value of h are the pore length, the pore radius, and a geometric factor. All are identical in the parameters h_1 and h_2. Eq. 4.9-5 therefore becomes

$$\mathscr{S}_D = \frac{k_1 C_{10}}{k_2 C_{30}} \left(\frac{D_1 k_2}{D_3 k_1}\right)^{1/2}, \tag{4.9-6}$$

and the ratio of the selectivities from Eqs. 4.9-6 and 4.9-4 is

$$\frac{\mathscr{S}_D}{\mathscr{S}_0} = \left(\frac{D_1 k_2}{D_3 k_1}\right)^{1/2}. \tag{4.9-7}$$

It is clear then that the selectivity can be either increased or decreased by pore diffusion. If we assume that Reaction 1 is favorable and leads to the desired product and that Reaction 2 is undesired, then, in accordance with Eq. 4.9-7, the selectivity of the catalyst for Reaction 1 can be increased by carrying out the reaction in small pores provided $k_2 > k_1$. Conversely, when $k_2 < k_1$, the selectivity of the catalyst for Reaction 1 is greater in large pores. Note that the diffusivity ratio is neglected because it is rarely large enough to greatly influence selectivity.

The method applied to the specific example in the preceding discussion is easily extended to other reaction-rate laws or to mixed-order systems. The general conclusion is essentially the same, and the corresponding physical interpretation is that when reactions proceed independently within a porous catalyst, $\mathscr{E}$ for the faster reaction is more greatly influenced by pore diffusion and the corresponding value of $\mathscr{E}$ is smaller than for the slower reaction. In small pores, then, the selectivity changes to favor the production of products from the slower reaction. For reactions other than first order, the concentrations at the pore mouth appear in the selectivity ratio, giving additional flexibility in the selection of conditions to favor the desired reaction.

When Eqs. 4.9-2 are coupled because $\mathscr{R}_1$ depends upon the concentrations of A_3 or A_4, or because the reactions are nonisothermal, or for other reasons, their solution is no longer easily obtained. Kinetic examples leading to coupled rate expressions were discussed in Chapter 3. Particular reference was made to the catalytic hydrogenation of a mixture of tetraline and p-xylene in which the active sites of the catalyst are moderately to fully covered by reactants and products. In that example the rate expressions for the production of each product were shown to be interdependent even in an excess of hydrogen. Unfortunately, little quantitative work can be done as yet on the general problem owing to mathematical difficulties. These problems are best handled individually using numerical or analog methods.

EXAMPLE 4.9-2 PARALLEL REACTIONS IN ISOTHERMAL CATALYSTS

Parallel reactions are characterized by one of the reactants going to several products, either by decomposition along different reaction paths to two or more products, or by reaction with other reactants to form several products. Examples of the former are the oxidation of ethylene to ethylene oxide or to CO_2, and the dehydration of ethanol to ethylene or its dehydrogenation to acetaldehyde. On the other hand, examples of the latter would be the oxidation or hydrogenation of a mixture of hydrocarbons.

The selectivity of a catalyst to convert a reactant to several products is not influenced by catalyst structure if the order of the reactions to each of the products is the same and if the rate expressions are uncoupled. Although this can easily be shown mathematically, a physical argument will be used. At each point in the interior of the catalyst structure, the reactions will proceed at rates proportional to their kinetic rate constants, hence the selectivity remains unaltered. However, if the orders of the reactions with respect to the several products are not equal, then small pores ($h > 3$) increase the selectivity of the catalyst to make products formed in the lowest order reactions. As a practical rule with this type of system Wheeler* points

* A. Wheeler, *Advan. Catalysis* 3 (*op. cit.*).

out that if operating a reactor at low partial pressure of reactants gives greater selectivity to the desired reactions, then using small pores should further increase the selectivity to this product. As a corollary, of course, the reverse is true.

The second type of parallel reactions is more involved. An example of this type is the following set of reactions.

Reaction 1: $\qquad a_{11}A_1 + a_{31}A_3 \rightarrow a_{41}A_4$

Reaction 2: $\qquad a_{12}A_1 + a_{22}A_2 \rightarrow a_{52}A_5$

$$\left. \vphantom{\begin{array}{c} a \\ a \end{array}} \right\} \quad (4.9\text{-}8)$$

Although we shall not complete the analysis, it is instructive to apply the general methods developed in Chapters 2 and 4 to illustrate the methods and to show the differential equations which govern the system. For simplicity assume:

$$a_{11} = a_{31} = -1; \qquad a_{41} = 2$$
$$a_{12} = a_{22} = -1; \qquad a_{52} = 2$$
$$\left. \vphantom{\begin{array}{c} a \\ a \end{array}} \right\} \quad (4.9\text{-}9)$$

Further assume the reactions are second order of the form

$$\mathcal{R}_1 = k_1 C_1 C_3$$
$$\mathcal{R}_2 = k_2 C_1 C_2$$
$$\left. \vphantom{\begin{array}{c} a \\ a \end{array}} \right\} \quad (4.9\text{-}10)$$

According to the general development of complex reactions, two independent equations are obtained from Eq. 4.8-6, namely:

$$D_1 \frac{d^2 C_1}{dx^2} - \frac{2}{r}(k_1 C_1 C_3 + k_2 C_1 C_2) = 0, \qquad (4.9\text{-}11)$$

$$D_2 \frac{d^2 C_2}{dx^2} - \frac{2}{r}(k_2 C_1 C_2) = 0. \qquad (4.9\text{-}12)$$

These equations must be solved simultaneously. Equation 4.9-11 contains C_3, which must be eliminated before the solution is attempted. Equation 4.8-9 provides the relationship between the dependent components and the independent. Following the treatment from Chapter 2, γ_{gk} must be evaluated. Equations 2.3-13 and 2.3-14 indicate the required relationship:

$$[\gamma_{gk}] = [a_{kk}]^{-1}[a_{gk}] \qquad (k = 1, 2; g = 3, 4, 5). \qquad (4.9\text{-}13)$$

From Eqs. 4.9-8 and 4.9-9:

$$[a_{kk}] = \begin{bmatrix} -1 & 0 \\ -1 & -1 \end{bmatrix}; \qquad [a_{gk}] = \begin{bmatrix} -1 & +2 & 0 \\ 0 & 0 & +2 \end{bmatrix}. \qquad (4.9\text{-}14)$$

From the inverse of $[a_{kk}]$,

$$[a_{kk}]^{-1} = \begin{bmatrix} -1 & 0 \\ +1 & -1 \end{bmatrix}, \qquad (4.9\text{-}15)$$

it follows that

$$[\gamma_{gk}] = \begin{bmatrix} 1 & -2 & 0 \\ -1 & +2 & -2 \end{bmatrix}. \qquad (4.9\text{-}16)$$

Thus, from the first column of $[\gamma_{gk}]$, $\gamma_{31} = 1$, $\gamma_{32} = -1$; and from Eq. 4.8-10

$$C_3 = C_{30} - \frac{D_1}{D_3} C_{10} + \frac{D_2}{D_3} C_{20} + \frac{D_1}{D_3} C_1 - \frac{D_2}{D_3} C_2. \qquad (4.9\text{-}17)$$

This relationship for $C_3{}^*$ may now be substituted into Eq. 4.9-11. The set of equations 4.9-11 and 4.9-12 are in terms of C_1, C_2 and their derivatives and may be solved simultaneously. It is not easy to determine, by inspection of this set of equations, how the selectivity of the catalyst for these reactions will be affected by pore diffusion. The selectivity will depend upon the numerical values of the ratios D_1/D_3 and D_2/D_3, and the initial composition of the reaction mixture.

It would appear both pointless and laborious to map these solutions here for a wide range of values of each of these parameters; however, it can be shown from certain limiting cases that the selectivity can increase, remain the same, or decrease when the reactions are diffusion influenced. Consider first the case whereby a combination of large values of D_1 and C_{10} allow the concentration of C_1 to be essentially constant throughout the pore. The conditions are analogous to flooding the reaction to render it pseudo first-order and reduce the problem to that already discussed in connection with Eq. 4.9-1. Another limiting case corresponds to the solution obtained when a combination of large values of D_2, D_3, C_{20} and C_{30} make C_2 and C_3 essentially constant throughout the pore structure. These conditions reduce the general equations to the simpler case of parallel reactions discussed earlier and results in no change in selectivity if the order of each reaction is the same.

EXAMPLE 4.9-3 CONSECUTIVE REACTIONS IN ISOTHERMAL CATALYSTS

The name consecutive reactions is given to a system of complex reactions in which the products of one or more of the reactions can react further to form other products. Depending upon the particular system, the intermediate product may or may not be the desired product. The following three examples may serve to amplify this point. An important industrial

---

* An alternate and simpler method of obtaining Eq. 4.9-17 for this particular pair of reactions is to write a third equation in C_3

$$D_3 \frac{d^2 C_3}{dx^2} - \frac{2}{r} k_1 C_1 C_3 = 0.$$

Adding this equation to Eq. 4.9-12 and equating to Eq. 4.9-11 to obtain

$$D_1 \frac{d^2 C_1}{dx^2} = D_2 \frac{d^2 C_2}{dx^2} + D_3 \frac{d^2 C_3}{dx^2},$$

which when integrated gives Eq. 4.9-17. The handling of a more complex set of reactions would be more systematically accomplished by the matrix technique.

reaction is the cracking of large hydrocarbon molecules into lower molecular weight hydrocarbons boiling in the gasoline range. In some instances, it may be desirable to crack some of the initial products, whereas continued cracking to molecules of four or fewer carbon atoms would yield undesirable products for blending into gasoline stocks. Another example is the dehydrogenation of butylene to butadiene. In this case, the catalyst should have a high selectivity to the primary dehydrogenation step relative to the further reaction of butadiene to unwanted by-products such as coke and higher polymers of butadiene. Lastly, in the reforming of certain gasoline stocks a representative reaction is the dehydrocyclization of methylcyclopentane to benzene; the desired product of a multi-step reaction. As was true for other types of complex reactions, the general reaction of this type is not easily analyzed; therefore, a simple representative reaction will be selected which can be carried to an analytical conclusion. Consider the following pair of reactions:

Reaction 1: $\qquad a_{11}A_1 \xrightarrow{k_1} a_{21}A_2$

Reaction 2: $\qquad a_{22}A_2 \xrightarrow{k_2} a_{32}A_3$

$$\left. \begin{array}{} \\ \\ \end{array} \right\} \quad (4.9\text{-}18)$$

Again for simplicity assume $-a_{11} = a_{21} = -a_{22} = a_{32} = 1$, and k_1 and k_2 are uncoupled. The two independent equations which describe this system are shown below.

$$\left. \begin{array}{l} D_1 \dfrac{d^2 C_1}{dx^2} - \dfrac{2}{r} k_1 C_1 \qquad\qquad = 0 \\[3mm] D_2 \dfrac{d^2 C_2}{dx^2} + \dfrac{2}{r} [k_1 C_1 - k_2 C_2] = 0 \end{array} \right\} \quad (4.9\text{-}19)$$

In analogy with Eq. 4.9-17 we obtain from Eqs. 4.9-19

$$D_1 C_1 + D_2 C_2 + D_3 C_3 = D_1 C_{10} + D_2 C_{20} + D_3 C_{30} \qquad (4.9\text{-}20)$$

whereupon a dimensionless concentration ψ can be defined as

$$\psi_i \equiv \frac{D_i C_i}{\displaystyle\sum_{i=1}^{3} D_i C_{i0}}. \qquad (4.9\text{-}21)$$

This definition of ψ_i leads to a normalized concentration variable. A suitable dimensionless set of equations can now be obtained from Eqs. 4.9-19 of the form

$$\left. \begin{array}{l} \dfrac{d^2 \psi_1}{d\eta^2} - h_1^2 \psi_1 \qquad\qquad = 0 \\[3mm] \dfrac{d^2 \psi_2}{d\eta^2} + h_1^2 \psi_1 - h_2^2 \psi_2 = 0 \end{array} \right\} \quad (4.9\text{-}22)$$

where

$$\eta \equiv \frac{x}{L}; \qquad h_1 \equiv L\sqrt{\frac{2}{r}\frac{k_1}{D_1}}; \qquad h_2 \equiv L\sqrt{\frac{2}{r}\frac{k_2}{D_2}}. \qquad (4.9\text{-}23)$$

For this example, Eqs. 4.9-22 are linear and methods are available* for solving this set subject to the following boundary conditions:
When

$$\left. \begin{array}{ll} \eta = 0, & \psi_i = \psi_{i0} \\[2mm] \eta = 1, & \dfrac{d\psi_i}{d\eta} = 0 \end{array} \right\} \qquad (4.9\text{-}24)$$

Rather than solve these equations in general, we shall use the asymptotic method discussed earlier. The asymptotic solution to the first of Eqs. 4.9-21 for large values of h_1 is written down immediately:

$$\psi_1 = \psi_{10}e^{-h_1\eta}. \qquad (4.9\text{-}25)$$

From general methods for linear equations, the solution to the second equation is

$$\psi_2 = \mathscr{A}_1 e^{-h_2\eta} + \mathscr{A}_2 e^{h_2\eta} + \left(\frac{\Delta}{1-\Delta}\right)\psi_{10}e^{-h_1\eta},$$

where $\mathscr{A}_1$ and $\mathscr{A}_2$ are constants to be evaluated by the boundary conditions and where

$$\Delta = \frac{h_1^2}{h_2^2} = \frac{k_1 D_2}{k_2 D_1}. \qquad (4.9\text{-}26)$$

However, if h_2 is also very large then $\mathscr{A}_2 = 0$, and therefore

$$\psi_2 = \psi_{20}e^{-h_2\eta} + \left(\frac{\Delta}{1-\Delta}\right)\psi_{10}(e^{-h_1\eta} - e^{-h_2\eta}). \qquad (4.9\text{-}27)$$

Upon differentiation and some algebraic manipulation Eq. 4.9-27 becomes

$$\left(\frac{d\psi_2}{d\eta}\right)_{\eta=0} = h_1\psi_{10}\left[\frac{\sqrt{\Delta}}{1+\sqrt{\Delta}} - \frac{\psi_{20}}{\sqrt{\Delta}\,\psi_{10}}\right], \qquad (4.9\text{-}28)$$

an equation derived by Wheeler. From Eqs. 4.9-28 and the derivative of 4.9-25, we can calculate the ratio of the rates of production of A_2 and reaction of A_1 for a given gas composition ψ_{20} and ψ_{10} at the pore mouth. This ratio is

$$\frac{\left(\dfrac{d\psi_2}{d\eta}\right)_{\eta=0}}{\left(\dfrac{d\psi_1}{d\eta}\right)_{\eta=0}} = \frac{\left(\begin{array}{c}\text{Rate of production} \\ \text{of } A_2 \text{ per pore}\end{array}\right)}{\left(\begin{array}{c}\text{Rate of reaction} \\ \text{of } A_1 \text{ per pore}\end{array}\right)} = \frac{\sqrt{\Delta}}{1+\sqrt{\Delta}} - \frac{1}{\sqrt{\Delta}}\left(\frac{\psi_{20}}{\psi_{10}}\right). \qquad (4.9\text{-}29)$$

Equation 4.9-29 represents the ratio of the rates of production of A_2 and the rate of reaction of A_1 for specified boundary conditions ψ_{20} and ψ_{10}, the dimensionless concentrations at the pore mouth. This expression is valid when the Thiele parameters h_1 and h_2 are large.

---

* See for example, P. M. Morse and H. Feshbach, *Methods of Theoretical Physics*, Vol. I, pp. 529–530, McGraw-Hill Book Company, New York, 1953.

When h_1 and h_2 are each very small the corresponding ratio of the rates is easily obtained.

$$\left(\begin{array}{c}\text{Rate of production}\\ \text{of } A_2 \text{ per pore}\end{array}\right) \bigg/ \left(\begin{array}{c}\text{Rate of reaction}\\ \text{of } A_1 \text{ per pore}\end{array}\right) = \frac{k_1 C_{10} - k_2 C_{20}}{k_1 C_{10}} \tag{4.9-30}$$

$$= 1 - \frac{1}{\mathscr{A}}\frac{\psi_{20}}{\psi_{10}}. \tag{4.9-31}$$

From a comparison of Eqs. 4.9-29 and 4.9-31, it becomes clear that the selectivity of a catalyst to produce A_2 is less when the reaction is diffusion influenced than when it is kinetic controlled for the same value of the parameter $\mathscr{A}$. The physical explanation of this result is that the ratio of C_2/C_1 within the catalyst pores is always equal to or greater than at the pore mouths because a positive concentration gradient, $(dC_2/dx)_{x=0}$ is necessary for transport of A_2 from the pore. Hence more A_3 and correspondingly less A_2 are produced and the over-all selectivity of catalyst to produce A_2 has decreased owing to diffusion influence.

The designer is generally interested in the fraction of reactants going to a specified product as the mixture passes through an integral reactor. In passing through a piston flow type integral reactor, such as the one described in Chapter 2, the composition of the reaction mixture, and therefore the values of the concentrations at the pore mouths, changes owing to the progress of the reaction. Because the total moles in the system under consideration here does not change with conversion, the conservation equation for A_1, Eq. 2.2-8, or a plug flow reactor becomes

$$\frac{U\, dC_{10}}{dz} + \left(\begin{array}{c}\text{Rate of reaction}\\ \text{of } A_1 \text{ per pore}\end{array}\right)\left(\begin{array}{c}\text{Number of pores}\\ \text{per unit volume}\\ \text{of reactor}\end{array}\right) = 0. \tag{4.9-32}$$

Writing a similar equation for A_2, dividing by Eq. 4.9-32 and using Eq. 4.9-29, we obtain

$$\frac{-dC_{20}}{dC_{10}} = \frac{\sqrt{\mathscr{A}}}{1 + \sqrt{\mathscr{A}}} - \frac{1}{\sqrt{\mathscr{A}}}\left(\frac{\psi_{20}}{\psi_{10}}\right)$$

$$= \frac{\sqrt{\mathscr{A}}}{1 + \sqrt{\mathscr{A}}} - \frac{\beta}{\sqrt{\mathscr{A}}}\frac{C_{20}}{C_{10}}, \tag{4.9-33}$$

where $\beta \equiv \dfrac{D_2}{D_1}$. Integrating* Eq. 4.9-33, we find

$$\phi_{20} = \left(\frac{\mathscr{A}\phi_{10}}{(\mathscr{A} + (1-\beta)\sqrt{\mathscr{A}} - \beta)}\right)(\phi_{10}^{(\beta/\sqrt{\mathscr{A}})-1} - 1), \tag{4.9-34}$$

---

* Equation 4.9-33 is a special case of the general form $dy/dx + f(x)y = g(x)$. Integrate by variation of a parameter or see for example E. Kamke, *Differential-Gleichungen*, 3rd ed., p. 311, Chelsea Publishing Co., New York, 1959.

where the boundary condition is

$$\phi_{10} = 1 \qquad \text{when} \quad \phi_{20} = 0$$

$$\phi_1 = \frac{C_{10}}{\bar{C}_{10}} \qquad \text{and} \quad \phi_{20} \equiv \frac{C_{20}}{\bar{C}_{10}}$$

and

$\bar{C}_{10} =$ the initial concentration of A_1 in the reaction mixture fed to the reactor.

The corresponding differential equation, which describes the point relationships within a piston-flow type integral reactor containing catalyst with large pores, is from Eqs. 4.9-31 and 4.9-32,

$$\frac{-d\phi_{20}}{d\phi_{10}} = 1 - \frac{\beta}{\Delta} \frac{\phi_{20}}{\phi_{10}}, \tag{4.9-35}$$

where the parameter β/Δ is equal to k_1/k_2 and the solution is independent of the diffusivity ratio, which of course it must be. We shall retain the parameter β/Δ for convenience in comparing with Eq. 4.9-34 which does depend upon β as well as $k_1 k_2$.

The solution to Eq. 4.9-35 is

$$\left.\begin{array}{c} \phi_{20} = \left(\frac{(\Delta/\beta)\phi_{10}}{(\Delta/\beta) - 1}\right)(\phi_{10}^{(\beta/\Delta)-1} - 1) \\[2mm] \text{for } \Delta/\beta \neq 1. \end{array}\right\} \tag{4.9-36}$$

Equations 4.9-34 and 4.9-36 are plotted on Fig. 4.9-1 for two sets of values of Δ and β.* The obvious conclusion of these curves is that the over-all yield of intermediate product is decreased by using small pores for the same physical reason discussed earlier in connection with the decrease in the catalyst's selectivity for the intermediate product when it contains small pores.

Another conclusion which may be drawn from the curves on Fig. 4.9-1 is not as readily apparent. This makes use of the fact that when diffusion influenced, the slope $(-d\phi_{20}/d\phi_{10})_{\phi_{10}=1}$ is not unity but rather is $\sqrt{\Delta}/(1 + \sqrt{\Delta})$. This was suggested by Newham and Burwell† as a means of inferring whether a catalyst under a particular set of conditions was operating under a diffusion-influenced limitation. This appears to be a useful idea provided Δ is not too large and if it can be shown that the product A_3 in Eqs. 4.9-18 cannot be

* Note: Eq. 4.9-34 is not valid for $\beta/\sqrt{\Delta} = 1$. In this case

$$\phi_{20} = -\frac{\sqrt{\Delta}}{1 + \sqrt{\Delta}} \phi_{10} \ln \phi_{10}$$

Similarly, Eq. 4.9-36 is $\phi_{20} = -\phi_{10} \ln \phi_{10}$ when $(\Delta/\beta) = 1$.

† John Newham and R. L. Burwell, *J. Phys. Chem.* **66**, 1431 (1962).

directly produced from A_1 as a competing parallel reaction, but must be produced from the intermediate product A_2. In principle, the question can be resolved by the isotopic tracer technique discussed in Section 3.7.

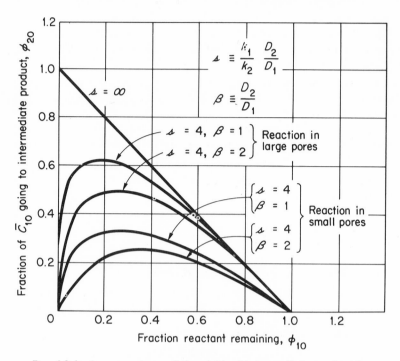

Fig. 4.9-1. A comparison of the yield of intermediate product between piston flow integral reactors packed with catalyst containing large pores and catalyst containing small pores.

4.10 Summary

This chapter has dealt primarily with the general problem of simultaneous heat and mass transfer and chemical reaction within a catalyst pellet.

In terms of a simple isothermal reaction within a single pore of catalyst, we have been able to show that the apparent kinetic order and the apparent activation energy of a chemical reaction change when diffusion rate influences the over-all reaction rate. Since the single-pore model is a highly idealized representation of a real catalyst, the results of the single-pore model treatment have been extended using asymptotic solutions for large numerical values of a generalized Thiele parameter to include nonisothermal simple reactions of any order in pellets of irregular shape. The results of these analyses are presented in terms of an effectiveness factor. Experimental and mathematical criteria are developed which allow an investigator to ascertain whether transport phenomena are concealing the true kinetic behavior.

In simple reaction systems, the important effect of pore geometry is to influence the apparent kinetic behavior, thereby altering the over-all rate of reaction.

The effect of pore geometry on complex reaction systems manifests itself in two ways: (1) the over-all rates of reaction are altered, and (2) the property of selectivity of the catalyst to yield various products is influenced. Because complex reaction systems do not lend themselves to the same asymptotic treatment as do simple reaction systems, a general treatment could not be presented.

The selectivity changes were illustrated by three specific examples. One important result, illustrated by the last example, is the effect of pore geometry on the selectivity of a catalyst for an intermediate product in consecutive reactions. To maximize the selectivity for the intermediate product, catalysts containing large pores should be used.

NOTATION FOR CHAPTER 4

a	surface area per unit volume of pore
A	pre-exponential factor in a kinetic rate expression
A_p	external surface area of a pellet
a_i	stoichiometric coefficient: $a_i < 0$ is a reactant; $a_i > 0$ is a product
A_i	ith species in a stoichiometric equation
$\mathscr{A}_1, \mathscr{A}_2$	integration constants
C_i	concentration of ith species
C_{i0}	concentration of the ith species at the pore mouth (except for Eqs. 4.1-1 and 4.1-2 where they have special meaning)
D	diffusivity
D_e	effective diffusivity
D_i	effective diffusivity of the ith species
D_{Ki}	effective Knudsen diffusivity of the ith species
ΔE	activation energy
$\mathscr{E}$	the effectiveness factor
$\overline{\Delta H_i}$	defined by Eq. 4.8-15
ΔH_i	enthalpy of reaction based upon the ith species
$\tilde{H}_i$	partial molal enthalpy of the ith species in the mixture

h_n $= L\sqrt{\dfrac{2k_n C_0^{n-1}}{rD}}$, the Thiele parameter

$\hat{h}_n$ $= \left(\dfrac{n+1}{2}\right)^{1/2} h_n$, a generalized Thiele parameter

$\hat{h}_p$ $= \dfrac{V_p}{A_p}\sqrt{\dfrac{\rho_p S k(T_0) g(C_0)}{D_e C_0}}$, a generalized Thiele parameter

$\hat{h}_p$ $= \dfrac{V_p}{A_p}\sqrt{\dfrac{\rho_p S R_i'(C_{i0})}{D_i C_{i0}}}$, a generalized Thiele parameter.

$\hat{h}_p^*$ defined by Eq. 4.5-4

k_n nth-order rate constant

L length of a pore

M molecular weight of the ith species

P_i production of the ith species in complex reactions

P_A partial pressure of carbon dioxide

P_B partial pressure of carbon monoxide

$\mathscr{P}$ poisoning factor defined by Eq. 4.7-13

r radius of a pore

$\mathscr{R}_i'$ defined by Eq. 4.4-11

$\mathscr{R}_i''$ defined by Eq. 4.4-14

$\bar{\mathscr{R}}_i$ pseudo-homogeneous rate expression; rate of reaction of the ith species per unit volume

$\mathscr{R}_i$ heterogeneous rate of reaction; rate of reaction of the ith species species per unit area

$\bar{\mathscr{R}}_D$ rate of reaction per half-pore

$\bar{\mathscr{R}}_0$ rate of reaction per half-pore in absence of concentration gradient in the pore

R radial coordinate

S specific surface area per unit mass of catalyst

$\mathscr{S}$ selectivity, defined by Eq. 4.9-2

$\mathscr{A}$ $k_1 D_2 / k_2 D_1$, a parameter defined by Eq. 4.9-26

T temperature

T_0 temperature at pore mouth (except Eqs. 4.1-1 and 4.1-2 where it has special meaning)

$\mathscr{T}$ the transport factor (see Eq. 4.2-2)

t	time
U	average velocity in a packed bed
V_P	volume of a pellet
x	coordinate

GREEK LETTERS

α	dimensionless parameter defined in Eq. 4.5-14
β	dimensionless parameter defined in Eq. 4.7-12
Δ	dimensionless parameter defined in Eq. 4.5-14
α	dimensionless parameter defined in Eq. 4.7-4
δ	$= \dfrac{(\Delta E)(-\Delta H_i) D_i C_{i0}}{R_g T_0^2 \lambda}$, a dimensionless parameter
ϵ	porosity of a bed of pellets (interstitial space among pellets)
ϵ_p	porosity of a catalyst pellet
ρ_p	apparent density of a single catalyst pellet
λ	effective thermal conductivity of the pellet
η	dimensionless distance
$\gamma_{g,k}$	parameter defined by comparing Eq. 2.3-13 and 2.3-14
ψ	dimensionless concentration
Θ	dimensionless temperature
θ	spherical angular coordinate
ϕ	spherical angular coordinate
Φ	ω/ω_0, defined in Eq. 4.7-4
ζ	$\dfrac{R_0 - R}{R_0}$
ξ	$h\zeta$, a stretched coordinate
ω	moles of poison adsorbed per unit area of catalyst
τ	dimensionless time defined by Eq. 4.7-4

Physical Properties of Porous Catalysts

5

The use of traveling is to regulate imagination
by reality, and instead of thinking how things may be,
to see them as they are.

SAMUEL JOHNSON

5.1 Introduction

The results of the mathematical treatment of simultaneous diffusion and reaction in porous materials are expressed in terms of dimensionless parameters such as the effectiveness and the transport factors which in turn are composed of groups of physical and chemical properties of the system. The numerical values of many of these properties may be obtained by well established techniques and require no additional discussion here. Examples of such properties are the enthalpy of reaction and the activation energy, in addition to the intensive thermodynamic properties. The geometric properties by and large also need no further amplification. The intrinsic kinetic properties are always difficult to establish, but these have already been treated in an earlier chapter.

There remain three properties of a porous material which are difficult to formulate or even to estimate. These are the effective diffusivity D_e, the effective thermal conductivity λ, and the specific surface area S of a solid. These properties are seductive in that they are labeled by familiar names and immediately bring forth associations with well-defined concepts. For instance, the latter quantity is ostensibly a purely geometric quantity, but as used it is intimately and inextricably associated with the kinetics of a particular heterogeneous reaction. Its separation from the kinetics is based upon the assumption that two solids can be prepared which have different physical surface areas and at the same time exhibit unit surface areas having identical kinetic properties. To a first approximation, this is perhaps a reasonable assumption and warrants the separation of a purely geometric term from the kinetic expression. The usefulness of this procedure depends in part upon how well the geometric surface area may be measured. A brief discussion of the methods of measurement of surface area forms the topic of the next section.

The effective diffusivities and conductivities as used in the mathematical treatment are phenomenological quantities and completely ignore the presence of the solid phase. They are those quantities which when multiplied by the gradients of concentration and temperature respectively yield the true rate of mass and energy transport within the porous structure of the solid. As such, then, each of these quantities has implicitly contained within it the geometric characteristics of the solid phase in addition to the physical variables which make up their kinetic theory counterparts. Unlike the problem of surface areas, our present inability to predict effective diffusivities and conductivities results from mathematical rather than conceptual difficulties.

The problem of the prediction of conductances in two-phase systems is a very old one which has maintained the interest of researchers to the present day. While much has been learned about such systems and a variety of techniques have been proposed to predict the magnitude of the geometric factors in the effective conductivities, the precise determination of these quantities remains an experimental problem. A discussion of this general problem is presented in subsequent sections.

5.2 Surface area of catalysts

The importance of a reliable method for determining surface areas of catalysts has been widely recognized by investigators, and a number of experimental methods have been developed to make these measurements. This topic will be only briefly discussed here because the information is readily available elsewhere.*

The most frequently used method is based upon the adsorption isotherms at low temperatures. The principle is very simple. The surface area is obtained from the product of two quantities: the number of molecules needed to cover the sample with a monolayer of adsorbate and the cross-sectional area of the adsorbate molecule. The cross section of the adsorbate is the amount of surface occupied by a molecule of a particular adsorbed species. The number of molecules equivalent to monolayer coverage is determined from the theory

* P. H. Emmett, "Measurement of Surface Area," *Catalysis*, Vol. I, Reinhold Publishing Corp., New York, 1954.

of Brunauer, Emmett, and Teller.* Their theory is an extension of the Langmuir kinetic picture of monomolecular adsorption. We recall from the Langmuir model that the equilibrium adsorption occurs when the rate of evaporation from the first layer is equal to the rate of condensation on the uncovered surface. This idea is then generalized by assuming that the molecules adsorbed on each successive layer will evaporate at a rate equal to their condensation rate on the preceding layer. If the range of forces of adsorbent extend only to the first layer of adsorbate whereas additional layers see in effect only an adsorbate having bulk liquid properties, the model leads to the familiar BET expression below.

$$\frac{P}{V(P_s - P)} = \frac{(a-1)}{V_m a}\left(\frac{P}{P_s}\right) + \frac{1}{V_m a}, \qquad (5.2\text{-}1)$$

where P = pressure of adsorbate in the system,

$\quad P_s$ = saturation pressure of the adsorbate gas at the temperature of the system,

$\quad V$ = volume at standard temperature and pressure at the pressure of the system,

$\quad V_m$ = volume corresponding to a monolayer of adsorbate, and

$\quad a$ = constant involving the heats of adsorption on adsorbent and heat of condensation.

If a is a constant, then clearly the adsorption data should yield a linear relationship on a plot of $P/V(P_s - P)$ versus P/P_s. Values of V_m and a can then be evaluated from the slope and intercept of the curve at $P/P_s = 0$. Typical curves are shown on Fig. 5.2-1 from which values of V_m can be calculated.

To obtain the cross-sectional area corresponding to a particular adsorbate molecule, a number of methods have been suggested. The cross sections of various adsorbed molecules may be estimated from the density of the liquefied adsorbate,† or by using the method on samples whose areas have been determined by other means. Suffice it to say here that there are available a number of self-consistent values of the cross sections for molecules which are useful in determining surface areas. Unfortunately, the computed surface area of a given sample varies to some extent depending upon the particular adsorbate used. The reasons for this are not fully understood.

Nevertheless, the BET area is a highly useful tool for the assessment of the extent of catalyst surface area because it is reproducible and easily measured and because it agrees well with independent methods of measurements. With respect to the latter statement some mention of the Harkins

* S. Brunauer, P. H. Emmett, and E. Teller, *J. Am. Chem. Soc.* **60**, 309 (1938); references to this theory in the text will hereafter be abbreviated to BET.

† P. H. Emmett and S. Brunauer, *J. Am. Chem. Soc.*, **59**, 1553 (1937).

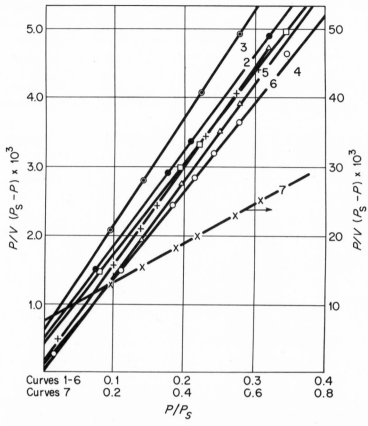

Fig. 5.2-1. BET plots for the adsorption of various gases on 0.606 g of silica gel as follows: curve 1, CO_2 at $-78°C$; curve 2, A at $-183°C$; curve 3, N_2 at $-183°C$; curve 4, O_2 at $-183°C$; curve 5, CO at $-183°C$; curve 6, N_2 at $-195.8°C$; and curve 7, n-butane at $0°C$. [Adapted from Emmett, P. H., *Catalysis*, vol. I, Reinhold Publishing Co., New York (1958) with permission of Reinhold Publishing Co.]

and Jura* method is appropriate. In particular, their results from the heat of wetting measurements are important because no assumption of cross-sectional areas of molecules is needed to obtain the surface areas. The agreement between the BET and Harkins-Jura methods is remarkably good and serves to strengthen the conviction that these methods measure something closely related to the extent of surface within porous media.

Lastly, there are methods of measuring surface area based upon the flow

* W. D. Harkins and G. Jura, *J. Am. Chem. Soc.*, **66**, 919, 1362, 1366 (1944).

of gases through the media.* Steady-flow measurements carried out in the laminar-flow region are probably indicative of the external area of the particles making up a porous medium, whereas transient-flow measurements in the Knudsen region appear to sense blind pores and surface roughness of these particles.

5.3 Effective diffusivity

Both the effective diffusivity and effective conductivity appear in the parameters needed to describe general nonisothermal reactions in porous

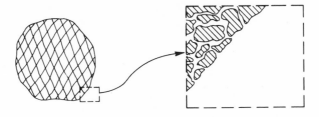

(a) Porous catalyst bead.   (b) Highly magnified section of (a).

Fig. 5.3-1. Schematic diagram of a porous catalyst.

materials. The magnitude of the former quantity determines, in part, the rate at which reactants can be transported in the pore system of the solid. The latter quantity determines, in part, how fast heat can be transported between the interior and the external surface of a catalyst pellet. In general, heat is transported through the solid phase rather than through the fluid phase because the resistance to heat transfer is smaller along this path. However, owing to the analogous forms of the mathematical expressions for the fluxes of mass and energy, the same kind of factors must be considered in their evaluation. The discussion to follow therefore treats the effective diffusivity, and it should be understood that what is said applies equally well to the effective conductivity. Certain differences should be noted, particularly at high temperatures when the radiative mechanism may become important and the effect of total pressure on the effective conductivity.

Figure 5.3-1(b) is a schematic diagram of a highly magnified cross section of the catalyst bead shown in Fig. 5.3-1(a). The cross-hatched part depicts the solid phase whereas the spaces among the particles of solid phase represent the channels—the pore system—for transport of material. Note that the points at which the particles appear to merge do not represent blockages

---

* See for example G. Kraus, J. W. Ross and L. A. Girifalco, *J. Phys. Chem.* **57**, 330, 334 (1953).

because cross sections slightly above or below that shown would likely show openings at these points while other points of contact would appear. Thus, the general picture of a porous material is a three-dimensional system of pores and a three-dimensional system of solid material which have the characteristic property that it is possible to go from any macroscopic "point" (a point large with respect to the pore system but small compared to the pellet) within the pellet to the outer surface by a continuous path either entirely within the solid phase or entirely within the pore phase. We cannot preclude the possibility that each of the particles of Fig. 5.3-1(c) contains microscopic pore systems which offer an alternate path for molecules of fluid in the pore system through the particles. The latter case offers no complication because the effectiveness factor for the small particle is probably very close to unity, because the Thiele parameter is small.

A rigorous mathematical description of a real porous solid appears to be beyond our present hope. A statistical description, which appears to offer more promise, may suffer from the fact that the system may not be completely random owing to the method of manufacture. The extrusion or pelleting processes may indeed render the material anisotropic. From this brief description of the structure of porous materials, it is evident that the transport of material within the porous structure of a solid is a problem beset with complexities if the intention is to handle it with mathematical rigor. Furthermore, if we admit of chemical reaction at the surface of the solid and of heat transfer within the solid structure, the problem is further complicated. However, an insight into the nature of the problem is gained by looking at the rate of diffusive transport through porous materials in the absence of chemical reaction.

For the case of equimolal, countercurrent, molecular diffusion, the Laplace equation is valid for the fluid within the pore system, i.e.,

$$-\text{div}\,(-D_M\,\text{grad}\,C) = 0, \tag{5.3-1}$$

where D_M is the molecular diffusion coefficient for A in B. When D_M is considered to be independent of concentration, then

$$\text{div grad}\,C = 0,$$

or

$$\nabla^2 C = 0. \tag{5.3-2}$$

Equation 5.3-2 is subject to boundary conditions of a type which prescribe the concentration or its derivative at all positions on the external surface enclosing the diffusion space.

As an illustration, consider the two-dimensional diffusion space shown in Fig. 5.3-2. In this illustration, we assume that the volume $\Delta x \Delta y \Delta z$ (the z coordinate is normal to the page) is small compared to the size of the system, but large compared to the channels within the porous structure. Further

assume that the cross-hatched solid particles correspond to general cylinders*
and the cross sections of the system for diffusive flow at every value of z are
identical and that the concentrations are independent of z. Because the
section enclosed by the dashed lines is small compared to the total system,
it becomes meaningful to postulate an average concentration along the
coordinates at x and $x + \Delta x$. These are prescribed as constants, independent
of y. The concentration derivatives normal to the dashed line at y and

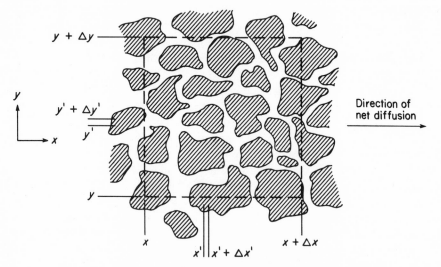

Fig. 5.3-2. Diffusion through a system of nonporous particles.

$y + \Delta y$ between x and $x + \Delta x$ as well as normal to particles are identically
zero. These boundary conditions force the net diffusive flux to flow in the
direction of the x coordinate. Moreover, they uniquely set the mathematical
problem because the Laplace equation applies everywhere within the channels
(the regions not cross-hatched). If, for this example, the area enclosed by
the dashed line is representative in a statistical sense of every other part of
the particulate system, the solution to this particular system is useful in
describing diffusive transport through a macroscopic pellet of this material.

We now solve the detailed Laplace equation through the channels shown
in Fig. 5.3-2 with respect to new coordinates x', y', and z'. These new
coordinates have the property that their differentials $\Delta x'$, $\Delta y'$, and $\Delta z'$ are
small compared to the corresponding Δx, Δy, and Δz. Having the solution

---

* The term general cylinder, as used here, refers to a body of constant cross section,
in size and shape, in all x-y planes, whose surface is generated by extending its x-y projection
in the z-direction. A triangular column, therefore, would be an example of a general
cylinder.

to this equation, i.e., $C(x', y')$, the flux through the volume $\Delta x \Delta y \Delta z$ is

$$N_x = - D_M \Delta z \int_0^{\Delta y} \left[\frac{\partial C(x', y')}{\partial x'} \right]_{y'} dy', \qquad (5.3\text{-}3)$$

where the integration may be carried out at any value of x'. If the concentrations and coordinates are now made dimensionless according to the definitions

$$\psi \equiv \frac{C(x', y') - C(x)}{C(x + \Delta x) - C(x)} \; ; \\[2mm] \eta \equiv \frac{x'}{\Delta x} \quad \text{and} \quad \xi \equiv \frac{y'}{\Delta y}, \qquad \Bigg\} \qquad (5.3\text{-}4)$$

and substituted into Eq. 6.4-3, we obtain

$$N_x = - D_M \Delta z \, \Delta y \frac{C(x + \Delta x) - C(x)}{\Delta x} \int_0^1 \left[\frac{\partial \psi(\eta, \xi)}{\partial \eta} \right]_\xi d\xi. \qquad (5.3\text{-}5)$$

The integral in Eq. 5.3-5 is a function of the geometry of the pores only, because in the new coordinates the differential equation, Eq. 5.3-2, and its

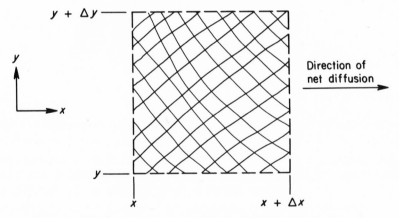

Fig. 5.3-3. Diffusion through an "equivalent" homogeneous medium.

boundary conditions are independent of the substance diffusing and concentrations. The integral is a constant and depends only upon the geometry of the channels within the volume $\Delta x \Delta y \Delta z$. Therefore, Eq. 5.3-5 may be written alternatively as

$$N_x = - D_M \Delta x \, \Delta y \frac{dC(x)}{dx} f_1(\text{geometry}). \qquad (5.3\text{-}6)$$

We do not know the functional form of f_1; however, this solution is useful because in an alternate formulation of the problem as shown in Fig. 5.3-3, the presence of the particles is ignored and the medium is thought of as an "equivalent" homogeneous medium with an effective diffusivity D_e. For the same boundary conditions, we get from the solution to the Laplace equation the following relationship for the flux:

$$N_x = -D_e \, \Delta y \, \Delta z \, \frac{dC(x)}{dx}. \tag{5.3-7}$$

From Eqs. 5.3-6 and 5.3-7 we obtain

$$D_e = D_M f_1 (\text{geometry}). \tag{5.3-8}$$

The illustration used to develop Eq. 5.3-8 is quite elementary. We could pattern a much more general argument along the same lines, but the general result would remain unchanged, viz., that the ratio of the effective and molecular diffusivities is equal to a geometric factor characteristic of the porous medium. The reader should note that this result applies equally well for Knudsen diffusion to give

$$D_e = D_K f_2 (\text{geometry}) \tag{5.3-9}$$

except that the geometric factor relating D_e and D_K is different from that relating D_e and D_M, *even for the same porous medium* although the difference between f_1 and f_2 may not be large. However, for the special case of uniform pore diameters, $f_1 = f_2$.

From the form of Eqs. 5.3-8 and 5.3-9 it is apparent that if a value of D_e for one system of a particular mixture of fluids is known within a given porous material, then it is possible to compute D_e for any other conditions or for any other system of fluids within that same porous material if the corresponding bulk or Knudsen diffusion coefficients can be evaluated. This observation permits the experimental determination of D_e, using any convenient system under conditions easily obtained in the laboratory, to be immediately translated to D_e for other systems at conditions perhaps difficult to attain and control in the laboratory.

Strictly speaking, the validity of this method is limited to nonreacting systems. In the reacting system, it is no longer true that the normal derivative of concentration is zero at the particle surface, because reaction takes place at the surface. As a practical matter; however, very few if any reactions occur so rapidly that appreciable conversion results during the passage of a few particles making up the pellet. It follows that for reacting systems the concentration derivatives normal to the solid surfaces forming the channels, while not zero, are so small that distortion of the profiles is not appreciable. Therefore, Eqs. 5.3-8 and 5.3-9 may also be used as highly accurate approximations for most reacting systems. A logical treatment of effective diffusivities is, therefore, divided into a separate discussion of each of the diffusivities and geometric factors.

5.4 Knudsen diffusivity

We shall not undertake a discussion of the methods for obtaining molecular diffusivities since this topic has been taken up elsewhere* in extensive detail. At the conditions under which many catalytic reactions are carried out, the mean free path of molecules ℓ is greater than the diameter of the catalyst pores, $2r$. When the ratio $2r/\ell \ll 1$, the molecules are transported within the porous structure without intermolecular collisions among them, but collide with the pore walls. This is, of course, the Knudsen flow region, so named in recognition of Knudsen's work† with fine capillaries at low pressures. Knudsen was able to predict the flux of molecules through the capillaries in terms of a model which assumed that molecules, upon collision with the tube wall, were briefly adsorbed whereupon they lost their momentum. Subsequently, they desorbed at random angles according to the cosine law. If the capillary is very long relative to its diameter, an analysis of the problem leads to an expression for the diffusivity which is

$$D_K = \frac{4r}{3}\sqrt{\frac{2R_g T}{\pi M}}, \qquad (5.4\text{-}1)$$

where D_K = Knudsen diffusivity,
r = capillary radius,
R_g = gas constant,
T = absolute temperature, and
M = molecular weight of the transported species.

Equation 5.4-1, while excellent for representing Knudsen's experiments, cannot be directly applied to the conditions found within porous solids because, as we have just shown, pores within catalysts are not well represented by a collection of straight cylindrical capillaries. Nevertheless it is common practice to use Eq. 5.4-1 replacing r by an equivalent radius r_e obtained from experimental values of the surface area and porosity of the porous solid. The equivalent radius is simply the radius of a cylindrical capillary having the same surface-to-volume ratio, i.e.,

$$\frac{\text{volume of a capillary}}{\text{area of a capillary}} = \frac{\pi r^2 L}{2\pi r L}.$$

Therefore, if we let

ϵ = porosity of a catalyst pellet,
ρ_p = apparent density of a catalyst pellet, and
S = surface area per unit mass of catalyst,

---

* See for example: S. Chapman and T. G. Cowling, *Mathematical Theory of Non-Uniform Gases*, Cambridge University Press, New York, 1951; J. O. Hirschfelder, C. F. Curtiss and R. B. Bird, *Molecular Theory of Gases and Liquids*, John Wiley & Sons, Inc., New York, 1954; R. B. Bird, "Theory of Diffusion," *Advan. Chem. Eng.* **1**, 155 (1956).

† M. Knudsen, *Ann. Physik* **28**, 75 (1909).

then

$$r = r_e = \frac{2\epsilon_p}{S\rho_p}.$$ (5.4-2)

On the basis of this model, then, the Knudsen diffusivity is given by

$$D_K = \frac{8\epsilon_p}{3S\rho_p}\sqrt{\frac{2R_gT}{\pi M}}.$$ (5.4-3)

Equation 5.4-3 is a crude adaptation of Knudsen's equation so that it can be used to predict diffusivities in porous solids. To obtain effective diffusivities, the formula must be multiplied by a geometric factor.

In view of the uncertainty in handling the Knudsen diffusivity in a porous medium, we can rightly conclude that the evaluation of diffusivities in the slip region, i.e., where $2r/\ell \approx 1$, would involve even greater uncertainties. While not much can be said about the slip region in a quantitative way, there are currently two formulae which have the correct limiting form and smoothly interpolate the slip region. These are Bosanquet's* additive resistance law,

$$\frac{1}{D_s} = \frac{1}{D_M} + \frac{1}{D_K},$$ (5.4-4)

and Wheeler's† exponential law,

$$D_s = D_M[1 - e^{-(D_K/D_M)}].$$ (5.4-5)

Although neither expression has been verified experimentally, the former agrees closely with a more rigorous expression derived from kinetic theory by Pollard and Present,‡ as does the experimental evidence of Scott and Dullien.§ The reader is referred to an article by Rothfeld‖ for further discussion of this topic as well as the non-equimolar counter-diffusion case.

5.5 Geometric factor

The precise determination of the geometric function in Eq. 5.3-6 remains an experimental problem despite efforts over the past century by many of our great scientists to determine its functional form theoretically or to correlate the results of measurements. However, these theories and correlations serve the important function of providing a means of estimating D_e

---

* C. H. Bosanquet, British TA Report BR-507, September 27, 1944 (discussed by Pollard and Present in work cited below, p. 770).

† A. Wheeler, *Advan. Catalysis* **3**, 266 (1951).

‡ W. C. Pollard and R. D. Present, *Phys. Rev.* **73**, 762 (1948).

§ D. S. Scott and F. A. L. Dullien, *A.I.Ch.E. Journal* **8**, 113 (1962).

‖ L. B. Rothfeld, *A.I.Ch.E. Journal* **9**, 19 (1963).

for preliminary or approximate calculations in the absence of experimental data.

Theoretical approaches to the evaluation of f_1(geometry) are of two types: In the first, the effect of the solid phase is determined at infinite dilution, and the behavior of the system at high porosities is predicted therefrom, whereas in the second type, physical models of the porous structure are assumed and their behavior qualitatively determined. Difficulties are inherent in each approach. In the former, the very manner in which the methods are developed limits their usefulness to rather high porosities and are therefore not reliable when applied to the range of porosities normally encountered within catalysts. On the other hand, methods of the latter type suffer from our inability to define models which retain the properties of real porous materials, yet are sufficiently simple that their quantitative behavior can be analytically predicted.

We shall discuss the geometric factor from two points of view in this section. Theoretical methods for obtaining the effective diffusivity for porous solids of high porosity will be taken up first. A theoretical method for obtaining f_2(geometry) is outlined. Its application also appears to be limited to highly porous materials. Following this, methods of correlating the geometric factor for materials of low porosity are presented. For materials of low porosity, we are led to empirical methods of correlation of effective diffusivities. The correlation of experimental results has, in general, been based upon the recognition of the qualitative factors which make the effective diffusivity smaller in a porous medium than in long cylindrical capillaries. As was brought out earlier, the presence of the solid material forms channels for the transport of materials which differ from capillaries in that they are not in general straight and of uniform size. The presence of the solid phase limits the cross-sectional area for flow of species into the medium and causes the diffusing species to go around the particles thereby increasing the effective distance through which material must be transported.

In 1873 Maxwell* derived an equation for the electrical conductivity of a dilute suspension of sphere in a conducting medium. His method of analysis was both ingenious and simple. He obtained the exact solution for the potential field around a single sphere of finite conductivity immersed in a potential field, having a uniform potential gradient at large distances from the center of the sphere. This solution is also valid for a spherical aggregate of the dilute suspension in terms of the effective conductivity. The relationship sought is obtained from recognizing that the effect on the potential field at large distances from the center of the suspension is simply n times the disturbance of a single particle, where n is the number of particles in the

* J. C. Maxwell, *A Treatise on Electricity and Magnetism*, 2nd ed., Vol. L, Oxford University Press, London, 1881. The equation was also independently formulated by H. A. Lorentz, *Wien. Ann.* **11**, 70 (1880); L. Lorentz, *Wien. Ann.* **9**, 641 (1880).

spherical aggregate of the dilute suspension. The analysis is briefly developed below.

In Fig. 5.5-1(a) a sphere of radius r_0 and conductivity K_D is located at the origin of the coordinate system. The exact solution to this problem is obtained from the solution to the Laplace equation outside and inside the sphere, i.e.,

$$\nabla^2 \psi_0 = 0, \tag{5.5-1}$$

$$\nabla^2 \psi_i = 0, \tag{5.5-2}$$

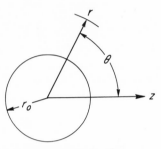

a. Single sphere in a
concentration gradient.

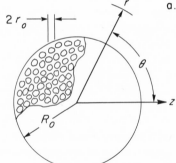

b. Collection of n spheres
of porosity ϵ.

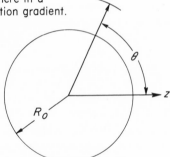

c. Medium of equivalent
conductivity.

Fig. 5.5-1. Maxwell's model for obtaining the effective conductivity
of dilute suspensions.

where ψ_0 and ψ_i are the dimensionless potentials outside and inside the space bounded by the sphere, respectively defined by

$$\left.\begin{aligned}
\psi_0(\xi, \theta) &\equiv 1 - \frac{P_0(\xi, \theta)}{P(\infty, \pi/2)} \equiv 1 - \frac{P_0}{P_\infty}, \\[2mm]
\psi_i(\xi, \theta) &\equiv 1 - \frac{P_i}{P_\infty},
\end{aligned}\right\} \tag{5.5-3}$$

and where

$$\xi \equiv \frac{r}{r_0}.$$

The boundary conditions on this problem are:

at $\xi = \infty$;

$$\psi_0\left(\infty, \frac{\pi}{2}\right) = 0$$

and

$$\left(\frac{d\psi_0}{d\xi}\right)_{\xi=\infty} = -E\cos\theta \quad \text{where} \quad E \equiv \frac{E'r_0}{P_\infty}$$

(5.5-4)

at $\xi = 1$;

$$\psi_i = \psi_0$$

and

$$K_D\left(\frac{\partial\psi_i}{\partial\xi}\right)_{\xi=1} = K_C\left(\frac{\partial\psi_0}{\partial\xi}\right)_{\xi=1}$$

(5.5-5)

where ψ_i is finite inside the sphere and K_C and K_D are the conductivities of the continuous medium surrounding the sphere and the porous sphere respectively.

This is a standard problem and the solution which meets the boundary conditions is of the form:

$$\psi_0 = -E\xi\cos\theta + E\left(\frac{K_D - K_C}{K_D + 2K_C}\right)\frac{\cos\theta}{\xi^2}.$$

(5.5-6)

Applying this solution to the case of a single pellet in a large medium having a uniform potential gradient far from the sphere shown in Fig. 5.5-1(a), we obtain in terms of the physical variables,

$$P_\infty\psi_0 = P_\infty - P_0 = E'\left[-r\cos\theta + r_0^3\left(\frac{K_D - K_C}{K_D - 2K_C}\right)\frac{\cos\theta}{r^2}\right]. \quad (5.5-7)$$

In essence, this equation tells us that the disturbance of the field at a point designated by r and θ is given by the second term on the right-hand side of the equation. Maxwell reasoned that if one had n of such spheres uniformly distributed about the origin in a spherical cluster of radius R_0 as shown in Fig. 5.5-1(b), then, neglecting interactions between spheres, the disturbance at a point far from the n spheres would simply be n times the second term on the right of Eq. 5.5-7, leading to

$$P_\infty - P_0 = E'\left[-r\cos\theta + nr_0^3\left(\frac{K_D - K_C}{K_D - 2K_C}\right)\frac{\cos\theta}{r^2}\right].$$

(5.5-8)

If now we treat the spherical cluster as a single sphere of effective conductivity K_e, then from Eq. 5.6-6 we obtain

$$P_\infty - P_0 = E'\left[-r\cos\theta + R_0^3\left(\frac{K_e - K_C}{K_e - 2K_C}\right)\frac{\cos\theta}{r^2}\right].$$

(5.5-9)

Since both Eqs. 5.5-8 and 5.5-9 are presumably alternate forms of the same potential, they may be equated, yielding

$$\left(\frac{K_e - K_C}{K_e + 2K_C}\right) = \left(\frac{K_D - K_C}{K_D + 2K_C}\right)(1 - \epsilon),$$

(5.5-10)

where $n(r_0/R_0)^3 = (1 - \epsilon)$ and $\epsilon \equiv$ the porosity of the dispersion.

Rearranging Eq. 5.5-10 leads to the desired expression for the effective conductivity in terms of the conductivities of the dispersed and continuous phases:

$$\frac{K_e}{K_C} = \frac{3(K_D/K_C) - 2\epsilon(K_D/K_C - 1)}{3 + \epsilon(K_D/K_C - 1)}. \qquad (5.5\text{-}11)$$

In comparing Eq. 5.5-11 with experimental determinations of K_e, it is found to hold only for very dilute dispersions of solids in conducting media which of course were the conditions specified in its derivation. Bruggeman* recognized that if in the more concentrated suspensions, each particle added to the suspension "saw" the smeared field of those in its immediate vicinity, the range of usefulness of a dilute suspension theory such as Maxwell's could be extended to higher concentrations. The Bruggeman expression is easily derived starting with an expansion of Maxwell's equation in a power series in the volume fraction solid in the suspension, an expression valid for dilute mixtures. Letting $K_D/K_C = 0$ and $\epsilon \equiv 1 - f$ where $f \equiv$ the volume fraction solids, Eq. 5.5-11 becomes

$$\frac{K_e}{K_C} = 1 - \frac{3}{2}f + \ldots, \qquad (5.5\text{-}12)$$

which can be arranged to give

$$\frac{K_e - K_C}{K_C} = -\frac{3}{2}f. \qquad (5.5\text{-}13)$$

This equation, according to Bruggeman, may now be applied to the addition of an incremental volume fraction of solids to a mixture already containing particles by thinking of K_C as the effective conductivity of the mixture prior to the addition. Symbolically,

$$\frac{K_e(f + \Delta f) - K_e(f)}{K_e(f)} = -\frac{3}{2}\left(\frac{\Delta f}{1 - f}\right), \qquad (5.5\text{-}14)$$

where Δf is the incremental volume fraction of particles added and $1 - f$ is the volume fraction of the continuous phase remaining to be replaced by particles. Going to the limit as $\Delta f \to 0$, Eq. 5.5-14 becomes

$$\frac{dK_e}{K_e} = -\frac{3}{2}\left(\frac{df}{1 - f}\right),$$

---

* D. A. G. Bruggeman, *Ann. Physik.* **24**, 636 (1935).

which is easily integrated from $f = 0$ to f to give:

$$\frac{K_e}{K_C} = (1 - f)^{3/2} = \epsilon^{3/2}. \tag{5.5-15}$$

The corresponding form of the Bruggeman equation for finite conductivity of the particles, i.e., $K_D/K_C > 0$, is

$$\frac{(K_e/K_C) - (K_D/K_C)}{(K_e/K_C)^{1/3}(1 - K_D/K_C)} = \epsilon. \tag{5.5-16}$$

Unfortunately, the exact conditions under which the Bruggeman equation is applicable is obscure owing to the restriction that a particle "sees" a smeared field.

Equations 5.5-11 and 5.5-16 have been tested by measuring the effective electrical conductivities of dispersions.* The experimental results lie between Maxwell's and Bruggeman's equations, although generally somewhat closer to the latter. The useful range of the equations is for porosities from 1 to about 0.4, and the equations are most reliable when the conductivity of the dispersed phase is zero. The equations can be applied without modification to estimate effective diffusivities. Because heat is transferred through the solid phase, these equations do not directly apply as a means of estimating thermal conductivities. In the simplest model of the catalyst the solid phase might be considered as the continuous phase, in which case Maxwell's or Bruggeman's equations may be applied directly if ϵ is taken as the fraction of the pores. If the solid-phase structure is such that the particles are more like a dispersed phase, the application of the above treatment is difficult because the range of porosities over which the equations are valid do not include the usual catalyst.

This approach will not be pursued further because the models upon which it is based are inadequate to account for the effective diffusivities found for most catalysts.

A statistical approach to Knudsen diffusion within porous media is attributed to Deryaguin.† It is based upon a model in which the porous medium is considered completely random in nature. Although the model is mathematical and not easily visualized, it allows the precise evaluation of the various statistical quantities making up the diffusivity without being limited by the severe restriction of assuming the geometry of the pores. The derivation of this equation is long and will not be repeated here. The details are given in the original article.

To summarize Deryaguin's analysis, he considers elastic and inelastic collisions between a molecule and the wall—the latter corresponding to

* R. E. Meredith, "Studies on the Conductivities of Dispersions," Ph.D. Thesis, University of California, Berkeley, 1959.

† B. Deryaguin, *Compt. rend. acad. sci.* URSS **53**, 623 (1946).

Knudsen's hypothesis. The interesting results of his analysis may be summarized by the following two equations.

$$D_K = \frac{8\epsilon_p}{3S\rho_p}\sqrt{\frac{2R_gT}{\pi M}} \quad \text{for elastic collisions} \qquad (5.5\text{-}17)*$$

$$D_K = \frac{24}{13}\frac{\epsilon_p}{S\rho_p}\sqrt{\frac{2R_gT}{\pi M}} \quad \text{for inelastic collisions.} \qquad (5.5\text{-}18)$$

Equation 5.5-18, the more realistic model of the diffusion process, differs from Eq. 5.4-3 only by the coefficients $\frac{24}{13}$ and $\frac{8}{3}$, respectively.

In an effort to resolve the question as to which of the expressions is more correct, Kraus, Ross and Girifalco† and Kraus and Ross‡ used Eq. 5.5-18 to compute surface areas of porous materials. The materials used were glass microspheres and $BaSO_4$, $PbCrO_4$, TiO_2 and CuO powders. Two kinds of experiments were conducted, steady state and unsteady state. As brought out earlier, the steady-state measurements should be insensitive to dead-end pores and to surface roughness, whereas the unsteady-state measurements should be able to sense these structural characteristics. This belief was verified by a comparison between unsteady-state surface areas and the BET area which agreed extremely well, whereas the steady-state measurements gave low values of the surface area. The agreement between these results is taken as tentative verification of Eq. 5.5-18 for loosely packed porous media such as those described by Kraus et al. No such evidence is available to test its applicability to diffusive transport in extruded or pelleted materials.

Theoretical methods, while useful in loosely packed and highly porous media, fail to predict effective diffusivities in materials of low porosity. As stated earlier, the accurate determination of D_e remains an experimental problem. We shall present some experimental values of effective diffusivities in terms of three quantities which make up the geometric factor. These quantities are related to D_e in the following expression:

$$\frac{D_e}{D_M} = \frac{\epsilon\sigma}{\tau} = f_1(\text{geometry}), \qquad (5.5\text{-}19)$$

where ϵ = porosity,
σ = constriction factor, and
τ = tortuosity factor.

Similarly in the Knudsen diffusion region,

$$\frac{D_e}{D_K} = \frac{\epsilon\sigma}{\tau} = f_2(\text{geometry}). \qquad (5.5\text{-}20)$$

* The correspondence between Eqs. 5.4-3 and 5.5-17 is simply a curious twist of fate. There is no reason why the constant should be the same in each case.
† G. Kraus, J. W. Ross and L. A. Girifalco, J. Phys. Chem. 57, 330 (1953).
‡ G. Kraus and J. W. Ross, ibid., p. 334.

Qualitatively these factors affect the magnitude of D_e as follows. The porosity factor is included to account for the effective reduction in the area for the diffusion of species at a particular point in the porous medium. The tortuosity factor is a measure of the ratio of the distance which a diffusing species must go on the average and the geometric distance between two points in the solid. This situation arises because a diffusing molecule must follow the channels which in general are at an angle to the line connecting the two points—a tortuous path, as it were. The constriction factor takes into account the fact that channels are not uniform in cross section, but vary with position. Since D_e is generally based upon an equivalent uniform diameter pore network, this factor becomes a part of the geometric factor. The tortuosity and constriction factors are undoubtedly functions of the porosity, as was indicated by the earlier theoretical discussion. For example, the Bruggeman equation predicts $\sigma/\tau = \epsilon^{1/2}$. Equation 5.5-19 represents little more than a method of correlation or presentation of experimental data on D_e.

The constriction factor is not as yet measurable; however, approximate magnitudes of the effect have been discussed theoretically.* Values of σ depend primarily upon a factor β which is equal to the ratio of the maximum and minimum areas in a pore of nonuniform cross section. When β is 1, σ is 1 and when $\beta = 10$, σ is about 0.5. This means that in a porous solid containing pores with a ratio of maximum and minimum effective diameters of about 3, the resistance to diffusion is equivalent to reducing the diffusivity in half.

The tortuosity factor, while a useful qualitative concept, is not easily obtained from first principles. For loosely packed materials we can readily calculate τ, assuming $\sigma = 1$, from the Bruggeman equation, Eq. 5.5-15, i.e. $\tau = \epsilon^{-(1/2)}$. Two porous materials having porosities of 0.5 and 0.4 would yield values of the tortuosity factor of 1.41 and 1.58, respectively. Equations 5.4-3 and 5.5-18 provide a similar comparison from which τ may be computed again for $\sigma = 1$. Equation 5.4-3 gives a value of D_K in terms of an equivalent pore radius, $2\theta/S\rho_p$. To obtain D_e, according to Eq. 5.5-19, D_K must be multiplied by ϵ and divided by τ. Deryaguin's formula, must only be corrected for ϵ. Equating the two expressions gives

$$\frac{8}{3\tau} = \frac{24}{13},$$

from which

$$\tau = \left(\frac{8}{3}\right)\left(\frac{13}{24}\right) = 1.44. \qquad (5.5-21)$$

These results are in good agreement with Wheeler's "deviousness factor," which he was able to evaluate in terms of his colorful "bee" model.† Wheeler

* E. E. Petersen, *A.I.Ch.E. Journal* **4**, 343 (1958).

† A. Wheeler, *op. cit.*

TABLE 5.5-1

DATA OF HOOGSCHAGEN[a] ON DIFFUSION IN POROUS MATERIALS

Material	Composition and preparation	Surface area (in.²/S)	Porosity	D_e/D_M	τ/σ	Remarks
Water gas shift catalyst	Fe_2O_3 + 7% Cr_2O_3 (reduced)	...	0.60	0.054	11.1	Particles making up the pellet were 50–250μ in diameter. Knudsen diffusion range unlikely.
Fused ammonia synthesis catalyst	Fe_3O_4 + 4.3% MgO + 0.55% SiO_2 (reduced at 450°C.)	11.6	0.52	0.040	12.5	Knudsen diffusion range. τ/σ based upon molecular diffusivity.
Glass spheres 1.0–1.25 mm diameter	Packed bed in large tube	...	0.430	0.302	1.42	
Powder particle sizes (100–110μ)	Packed bed in large tube	...	0.416	0.268	1.56	

[a] J. Hoogschagen, *Ind. Eng. Chem.* **47**, 906 (1955).

envisioned a bumble bee located at the center of a pile of rocks. In flying out of this pile, the bee is forced to choose a route which is no longer than the minimum geometric distance to the outside because it is unable to go through rocks. At any time, Wheeler's bee may be traveling at any angle with the geometric route. On the average, according to the model, the bee will be traveling at 45° to the geometric route, which leads to a value of

$$\tau = \frac{1}{\cos 45°} = 1.414 \, .$$

The theoretical prediction, and the intuitive model leading to a value of about $\sqrt{2}$ for τ, corresponds quite well with the experimental values for loosely packed materials. We see this in Tables 5.5-1 and 5.5-2. Some of

TABLE 5.5-2

DATA OF SCOTT AND DULLIEN[a] ON DIFFUSION IN POROUS MATERIALS

Material	Test gases	Porosity	D_e/D_M	τ/σ	Equiv. pore radius[b] in microns
Silas 015 microporous porcelain	O_2—A	0.614	0.36	1.71	1.17
Silas 03–2	H_2—N_2	0.284	0.11	2.54	0.60
Celite catalyst support (diatomaceous earth)	H_2—N_2	0.561	0.124	4.53	0.48
Kaolin—unglazed porcelain	H_2—N_2	0.347	0.07	5.0	0.16

[a] D. S. Scott and F. A. L. Dullien, *A.I.Ch.E. Journal* **8,** 113 (1962).
[b] By mercury penetration.

Hoogschagen's[*] data for pelleted and loosely packed materials are shown in Table 5.5-1. The values of τ/σ are much larger for the former. Note that the porosities of these materials are actually greater than for the loose-packed materials yet D_e/D_M is smaller.

Scott and Dullien[†] investigated the diffusive flow through several porous materials. Their investigation was carried out over a range of pressures such that experiments fell in the region between Knudsen and molecular diffusion. They interpret their data by an equation which reduces to Eq. 5.4-4 for equal molecular weights of the diffusing species. With the aid of this equation, the values of D_e/D_M can be estimated. These values are shown in Table 5.5-2 for several materials.

[*] J. Hoogschagen, *Ind. Eng. Chem.* **47,** 906 (1955).
[†] D. S. Scott and F. A. L. Dullien, *op. cit.*

High values for τ/σ have been reported in the literature by others. Deisler and Wilhelm* found values from 5 to 10 for porous alumina spheres, Wicke and Brötz† measured a value of 6.7 on zinc oxide tablets of 0.5 porosity, Piret et al.‡ measured values of 5, 11.1, and 5.9 at a porosity of 0.24 and Walker, Runisko, and Raats§ measured a value of 5 for graphitic material.

The message in these results seems to be this: With compacted or extruded materials, the value of τ/σ increases either because compacting renders the material anisotropic or causes constricted pores or both. Diffusivities in materials of this type should be estimated from experimental values‖ of the geometric factor using the known effects of temperature, pressure and composition on the diffusivity. Because of anisotropy, care must be taken in the orientation of the porous solid in the experimental apparatus. Values of the geometric factor estimated in the absence of experimental information will probably be quite unreliable. Diffusion in loosely packed solids can be estimated from the porosity if the solids are made of particles of uniform size.

NOTATION FOR CHAPTER 5

a	constant in BET equation
C	concentration
D_e	effective diffusivity
D_K	Knudsen diffusivity
D_M	molecular diffusivity
D_s	diffusivity in the slip region
E	potential gradient
E'	$= \dfrac{EP_\infty}{r_0}$
f	volume fraction solids

* P. F. Deisler and R. H. Wilhelm, *Ind. Eng. Chem.* **45**, 1219 (1953).

† E. Wicke and W. Brötz, *Chem. Ing. Tech.* **21**, 219 (1949).

‡ E. L. Piret, R. A. Ebel, C. T. Kiang, and W. P. Armstrong, *Chem. Eng. Progr.* **47**, 4–5, 628 (1951).

§ P. L. Walker, Jr., F. Runisko, Jr., and E. Raats, *J. Phys. Chem.* **59**, 245 (1955).

‖ For Silica-Alumina Catalysts: R. M. Barrer and T. Gabor, *Proc. Roy. Soc.* **251A**, 353 (1959); M. F. Johnson, W. E. Kreger and H. Erickson, *Ind. Eng. Chem.* **49**, 283 (1957); R. H. Villet and R. H. Wilhelm, *Ind. Eng. Chem.* **53**, 837 (1961); P. B. Weisz and C. D. Prater, *Adv. in Cat.* **6**, 143 (1954); P. B. Weisz and A. B. Schwartz, *J. of Catalysis* **1**, 399 (1962). For Nickel-Alumina Catalysts: N. Wakao, P. W. Selwood, and J. M. Smith, *A.I.Ch.E. J.* **8**, 478 (1962). For Thermal Conductivities: S. Masamune and J. M. Smith, *J. of Chem. and Eng. Data* **8**, 54 (1963); R. A. Mischke and J. M. Smith, *Ind. Eng. Chem. Fundamentals* **1**, 288 (1962); R. A. Sehr, *Chem. Eng. Sci.* **9**, 145 (1958).

f_1 function of geometry (see Eq. 5.3-6)

f_2 function of geometry (see Eq. 5.3-9)

K_C conductivity of continuous phase

K_D conductivity of discontinuous phase

K_e effective conductivity of the dispersion

ℓ mean free path

L length of a pore

M molecular weight

n number of particles in a spherical clump of dispersion

N_x flux of mass in the direction of the x-coordinate

P pressure of adsorbate

P_i potential inside sphere

P_0 potential outside sphere

P_∞ defined by Eq. 5.5-3

P_s saturation pressure of adsorbate at temperature of the system

r radial coordinate

r radius of a pore

r_e equivalent radius of a pore

r_0 radius of a spherical particle

R_g gas constant

R_0 radius of a spherical clump of dispersion

S surface area of a porous solid

T absolute temperature

V volume adsorbed at standard temperature and pressure

V_m volume corresponding to a monolayer of adsorbate

x, y, z
x', y', z' Cartesian coordinates

GREEK LETTERS

β ratio of maximum to minimum cross section in a pore of varying cross section

ϵ_p porosity of a catalyst pellet

θ angular coordinate

λ effective thermal conductivity

ξ $= r/r_0$, a dimensionless radial coordinate

ρ_p apparent density of a catalyst pellet

σ constriction factor

τ tortuosity factor

ψ_i dimensionless potential inside sphere

ψ_0 dimensionless potential outside sphere

Transport of Mass and Energy Between a Fluid Phase and The External Surface of a Reacting Solid

6

Truth, like milk, arrives in the dark
But even so, wise dogs don't bark.
Only mongrels make it hard
For the milkman to come up the yard.

CHRISTOPHER MORLEY

6.1 Introduction

In an earlier chapter our main concern was to account for the influence on its over-all kinetic behavior of transport resistances to energy and mass within a porous catalyst pellet. We found that under certain conditions, which could be characterized by parameters of the system, the concentrations and temperature in the interior of a catalyst differed appreciably from those at the exterior of the catalyst, leading to a variation in the point value of the reaction rate at various positions therein. Thus, unit areas at various positions in the interior of a porous catalyst may contribute unequally to the over-all reaction rate.

In this chapter we shall consider a somewhat similar analysis in which transport resistances external to the catalyst pellet may give rise to appreciable differences between the bulk and external surface values of the temperatures and concentrations. These latter values, it will be recalled, are the boundary conditions to the equations describing processes occurring within porous catalysts. Under certain circumstances it may be necessary to account for the influence of transport resistances external to the catalyst pellet in order to determine the over-all kinetic behavior of a system. As was pointed out in Chapter 4, when external transport resistances are indeed important, an analysis of the system must include the equations describing the processes occurring external to the pellet and as well as those occurring within the pellet. These equations are coupled through the boundary conditions and a solution results from matching the local fluxes of energy and mass and the local temperature and concentrations at the surface of a pellet. Although no completely general solution to this problem exists, there are no conceptual difficulties in writing the equations governing the behavior of the system provided transport equations can be written for each of the regions in the absence of chemical reaction. The general problem is exceedingly complex and will not be considered further. Fortunately, however, certain assumptions lead to greatly simplified methods of analysis of these systems and the remainder of this chapter will be devoted to the description of these methods, their application to kinetic systems and their usefulness as engineering approximations.

The simplest system may be classified as one in which the external surface catalyst is uniformly accessible to the reactants. By this is meant that the thickness of the concentration and thermal boundary layers have constant values over the entire catalyst surface. Therefore the conditions in the fluid phase giving rise to the transport of mass and energy from the bulk fluid phase to each element of external surface are identical over the entire surface. If such conditions are satisfied, the equations describing the behavior of a reacting system are inherently one-dimensional, even though the hydro-dynamic equations may not necessarily be one-dimensional. There are several systems which satisfy these conditions exactly and certain examples will be discussed in detail in the following section. As we shall see, the important characteristic of such a system is that transport behavior determined in the absence of chemical reaction may be immediately and exactly utilized to predict the performance of similar systems in which catalytic reactions are taking place. Unfortunately, the chemical engineering literature has been saturated with analyses based mathematically upon the concept of a uniformly accessible surface, but the analyses have been applied to situations in which the external surface of the catalyst is not uniformly accessible. In principle these methods have no fundamental basis. Yet predictions of the over-all reaction rates based upon these methods are frequently well within the accuracy of the kinetic information. Moreover, in many complex systems, methods based upon the assumption of the uniformly accessible surface offers the only practical approach to the solution of these systems.

A second method of analysis which we shall consider is limited to systems in which the flow fields satisfy the conditions of laminar boundary layer theory. Although the methods are, of course, not universally applicable, the results of these analyses are asymptotically exact and serve as a basis for determining the order of magnitude of the errors made in using less fundamental methods. Strictly speaking, the method applies only to nonporous catalysts. However, it is apparent intuitively that if the conditions under which external transport properties appreciably affect the over-all reaction rate are those which also give rise to a large value of the Thiele parameter h, then the penetration of reactants within the porous catalyst is small and the transport of energy and mass within the porous solid in a direction *parallel* to the surface of the pellet becomes negligible. Under these conditions the true kinetic description of the porous material may be reflected to and replaced by an external surface kinetic expression in terms of the local surface temperature and concentrations and the known functional form for the one-dimensional effectiveness factor discussed in Chapter 4. In this way the porous catalyst surface becomes equivalent to a nonporous catalyst surface.

Another interesting characteristic of systems which exhibit transport resistances and chemical reaction is that of multiple steady-state solutions. This characteristic of exothermic reactions occurs over a range of properties and although known and applied for a number of years in fields of combustion and ignition,* has received some attention in recent years in reactor design.† Some of the features of simple examples of such systems will be examined in detail. Application of the multiple steady-state solutions will be considered more fully in the chapters on reactor design and performance.

6.2 Reaction on a uniformly accessible surface

When the conditions of a uniformly accessible surface are fulfilled, many of the difficulties mentioned earlier disappear. Because each element of external surface behaves kinetically as all others of the pellet, the steady-state analysis of such a system is inherently one-dimensional and it follows that transport phenomena are not influenced by the complexity or the nonlinear character of the rate expression. Therefore, the engineer is at liberty to determine the transport characteristics in the simplest system, presumably in the absence of a heterogeneous chemical reaction. The latter system is, of course, mathematically equivalent to one having a very rapid heterogeneous chemical reaction occurring at the surface. The influence of transport phenomena on the chemical reaction rate may then be computed in a straightforward fashion. The methods which may be used have been

---

* See for example D. A. Frank-Kamenetskii, "Diffusion and Heat Exchange in Chemical Kinetics." Translated by N. Thon, Chapter IX, Princeton Press (1955).

† See Section 8.7.

developed extensively in the literature by many investigators including Hougen and Watson* and Frank-Kamenetskii.†

To illustrate that the coefficient of mass transfer is independent of the nature of the surface kinetics for such systems, consider the very simple system consisting of a single, nonporous spherical catalyst pellet immersed within and in steady state with a large medium of stagnant reactant. The reactant diffuses up to the surface, reacts catalytically, and the product diffuses away. Assume a simple reaction according to the stoichiometric equation

$$A_1 \rightarrow A_2. \tag{6.2-1}$$

The concentration must obey the Laplace equation and is a function only of R. Therefore,

$$D \frac{d}{dR}\left[R^2 \frac{dC}{dR}\right] = 0, \tag{6.2-2}$$

where D = diffusivity,
$\quad C$ = concentration of reactant,
$\quad R$ = radial coordinate.

Defining new dimensionless variables, Eq. 6.2-2 transforms to

$$\frac{d}{d\eta}\left[\eta^2 \frac{d\psi}{d\eta}\right] = 0, \tag{6.2-3}$$

where $\psi \equiv \dfrac{C - C_\infty}{C_\infty}$,

$\quad \eta \equiv \dfrac{R}{R_0}$,

$\quad C_\infty$ = concentration of reactant as $R \rightarrow \infty$,

$\quad R_0$ = radius of the spherical pellet.

The solution to Eq. 6.2-3 is

$$\psi = \frac{-A'_n}{\eta} + B'.$$

Since $\psi_\infty = 0$ as $\eta \rightarrow \infty$, $B' = 0$, and

$$\psi = \frac{-A'_n}{\eta}. \tag{6.2-4}$$

Equation 6.2-4 is the solution to the transport equation which indicates that the rate at which material is transported to the surface depends upon the

* O. A. Hougen and K. M. Watson, *Chemical Process Principles*, Part III, John Wiley & Sons, Inc., New York, 1947.

† D. A. Frank-Kamenetskii, *Diffusion and Heat Exchange in Chemical Kinetics* translated by N. Thon, Princeton University Press, Princeton, 1955.

surface concentration $-A'$, i.e.,

$$D\left(\frac{dC}{dR}\right)_{R=R_0} = \frac{DC_\infty}{R_0}\left(\frac{d\psi}{d\eta}\right)_{\eta=1} = \frac{DC_\infty}{R_0}A_n'. \tag{6.2-5}$$

To evaluate A_n', a surface boundary condition is used of the form

$$D\left(\frac{dC}{dr}\right)_{R=R_0} = \mathcal{R}_1, \tag{6.2-6}$$

where $\mathcal{R}_1 =$ heterogeneous rate of reaction per unit external surface area.

When the function $\mathcal{R}_1$ is taken as $k_f'[C(R_0)]^n$, Eq. 6.2-6 may be rewritten in dimensionless form.

$$\frac{d\psi(1)}{d\eta} = \gamma_n[1 + \psi(1)]^n, \tag{6.2-7}$$

where

$$\gamma_n \equiv \frac{k_n'R_0C_\infty^{n-1}}{D}, \tag{6.2-8}$$

$k_n' =$ heterogeneous rate constant based upon external surface area, and n takes the values 0, 1, and 2 corresponding to zero-, first-, and second-order reactions, respectively.

The exact solutions for the concentration at the surface of the catalyst pellet for zero, first, and second orders are, respectively,

$$\left.\begin{aligned} -\psi_0(1) &= \gamma_0 = A_0' \\[2mm] -\psi_1(1) &= \frac{\gamma_1}{1 + \gamma_1} = A_1' \\[2mm] -\psi_2(1) &= \frac{(1 + 2\gamma_2) - \sqrt{4\gamma_2 + 1}}{2\gamma_2} = A_2' \end{aligned}\right\} \tag{6.2-9}$$

The rate of reaction per pellet $\mathcal{R}_n$ is

$$\mathcal{R}_n = 4\pi R_0 DC_\infty A_n'. \tag{6.2-10}$$

Consider now an alternate approach to the solution of this problem, which makes use of a known local coefficient of mass transfer which is constant over the entire surface of the pellet. Following Frank-Kamenetskii,* a coefficient of mass transfer β_m is defined

$$\beta_m \equiv \frac{k_n'[C(R_0)]^n}{[C_\infty - C(R_0)]}, \tag{6.2-11}$$

* Op. cit., pp. 47–49.

which may be rewritten in dimensionless form

$$-\beta_m = \frac{k'_n C_\infty^{n-1}[1 + \psi(1)]^n}{\psi(1)}. \tag{6.2-12}$$

Equation 6.2-12 is really the boundary condition similar to Eq. 6.2-7. Now if we define

$$\hat{\gamma}_n \equiv \frac{k'C_\infty^{n-1}}{\beta_m},$$

then

$$\hat{\gamma}_n = \frac{\gamma_n}{\mathrm{Nu}}, \tag{6.2-13}$$

where $\mathrm{Nu} \equiv \beta_m R_0/D$.

The solution to Eq. 6.2-12 is the same as given by Eq. 6.2-9 if $\hat{\gamma}_n$ is substituted in place of γ_n. Note that for the case of no flow $\hat{\gamma}_n$ is equal to γ_n because as defined above the limiting value of $\mathrm{Nu} = 1$. We are therefore led to useful conclusions about the nature of uniformly accessible surfaces which may be summarized by the following statements. (1) The rigorous solution of the system yields mass transfer properties identical in form to those obtained using a lumped parameter, i.e., β_m. (2) The mass transfer properties are unaltered by the form of the rate expression describing the

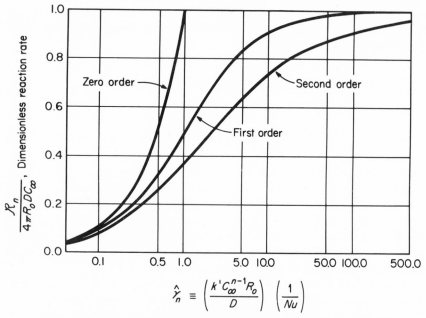

Fig. 6.2-1. Rate of reaction at the surface of a nonporous spherical catalyst pellet when the surface is uniformly accessible.

chemical reaction at the surface. This means that mass transfer, and of course heat transfer, properties obtained in absence of chemical reaction may be used without modification in systems in which surface chemical reactions occur, provided the surfaces are uniformly accessible. (At the same time we must remember that there are very few practical situations in which the surfaces are truly uniformly accessible.)

We frequently encounter the terms "kinetic controlled" and "diffusion controlled" in the literature. The meanings of these terms are easily shown from the form of the solution to Eq. 6.2-12. Figure 6.2-1 shows the dimensionless reaction rate versus the parameter $\hat{\gamma}_n$. At very low values of $\hat{\gamma}_n$, the concentration at the catalyst surface approaches the value in the bulk stream and the over-all rate of the reaction of the system is governed predominantly by the rate of the chemical reaction at the surface. Thus, at low values of $\hat{\gamma}_n$, the over-all rate is proportional to $\hat{\gamma}_n$ and this region of the figure is known as a "kinetically controlled" regime. As the numerical value of $\hat{\gamma}_n$ becomes large, the concentration at the catalyst surface becomes vanishingly small and the rate of reaction is limited by how fast reactants can be transported to the catalyst surface. Accordingly, the over-all rate is independent of $\hat{\gamma}_n$ as $\hat{\gamma}_n$ becomes large and this region of the figure is referred to as a "diffusion controlled" regime. Intermediate values of $\hat{\gamma}_n$ are in what may be called a "mixed controlled" regime and depend upon the kinetic and the transport characteristic of the system. Note that the rate of a zero-order reaction rises rapidly to a value of unity at $\hat{\gamma}_n = 1$ and remains at that value for all $\hat{\gamma}_n > 1$. Therefore, it is a degenerate S-curve.

6.3 Relative magnitudes of the effectiveness and transport factors

We are now in a position to justify a statement which was made at the beginning of Chapter 4. It was said, in effect, that the resistance to mass transfer within a porous catalyst is greater than the resistance between the external surface and the bulk fluid phase. This means that if diffusion to the external surface limits the over-all reaction rate, then internal diffusion must also limit the reaction rate and the designer is obliged to make an analysis which includes both external and internal diffusion. One can therefore dismiss the practical possibility of a system in which external diffusion is controlling in coexistence with an effectiveness factor of unity.

Consider a first-order catalytic reaction on the surface of a spherical pellet in which transport of reactants to the surface is by molecular diffusion. This example represents a limiting case where β_m is a minimum. Any other mode of transport would be faster and would result in a smaller external concentration gradient.

The rate of chemical reaction on a single catalytic porous sphere of radius R_0 is

$$\text{rate per pellet} = \tfrac{4}{3}\pi R_0^3 \rho_p S k_1 C_0 \mathscr{E}. \tag{6.3-1}$$

The rate per unit external surface area of the pellet is

$$\begin{array}{ll}\text{rate per unit external} \\ \text{surface area}\end{array} = \dfrac{R_0 \rho_p S k_1}{3} C_0 \mathscr{E} \tag{6.3-2}$$

$$= k_1' C_0, \tag{6.3-3}$$

where k_1' is defined by comparing Eqs. 6.3-2 and 6.3-3. The parameter γ_n defined by Eq. 6.2-8 is, for a first-order reaction,

$$\gamma_1 = \frac{R_0^2 \rho_p S k_1 (\mathscr{E})}{3D} = 3\left(\frac{D_e}{D}\right) \hat{h}_p \mathscr{E}. \tag{6.3-4}$$

When $\hat{h}_p \gg 1$,

$$\mathscr{E} = \frac{1}{\hat{h}_p} = \frac{3}{R_0}\sqrt{\frac{D_e}{\rho_p S k_1}} \tag{6.3-5}$$

and we get

$$\gamma_1 = 3\hat{h}_p \frac{D_e}{D}. \tag{6.3-6}$$

By analogy with Eq. 4.1-2

$$\text{rate per pellet} = \tfrac{4}{3}\pi R_0^3 \rho_p S k_1 C_\infty \mathscr{T} \mathscr{E}, \tag{6.3-7}$$

where by comparison with Eqs. 6.3-1 and 6.2-9

$$C_0 = (\mathscr{T}) C_\infty$$

and

$$\mathscr{T} = 1 + \psi(1) = \frac{1}{1 + \gamma_1}. \tag{6.3-8}$$

Figure 6.3-1 shows the relative values of $\mathscr{T}$ and $\mathscr{E}$ for values of D_e/D equal to 0.1 and 0.05 which are realistic from the discussion in Chapter 5. This figure shows that even when a pure diffusive transport mechanism operates to supply reactants to the outer surface, $\mathscr{T}$ is greater than $\mathscr{E}$ in the range of values where either must be considered. The analysis can be generalized to include the mass transfer coefficient. Let

$$\hat{\gamma}_1 \equiv \frac{k'}{\beta_m}. \tag{6.3-9}$$

Then from Eqs. 6.3-2 and 6.3-3 we obtain:

$$\left.\begin{array}{l}\hat{\gamma}_1 = 3\left(\dfrac{D_e}{D}\right)\left(\dfrac{D}{R_0 \beta_m}\right)\mathscr{E}\hat{h}_p^2 \\[2em] \hat{\gamma}_1 = 3\left(\dfrac{D_e}{D}\right)\left(\dfrac{1}{\mathrm{Nu}_m}\right)\mathscr{E}\hat{h}_p^2\end{array}\right\} \tag{6.3-10}$$

The quantity $R_0 \beta_m / D$ is a Nusselt number which, of course, increases with Reynolds number associated with the flow past the pellet. As β_m increases, $\hat{\gamma}_1$ decreases for a given value of $\hat{h}_p$ and the importance of the transport factor $\mathcal{T}$ decreases.

Clearly this type of analysis can be extended to any other order of reaction to obtain similar results. The important practical result is that concentration

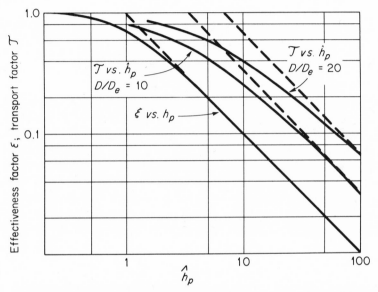

Fig. 6.3-1. Effectiveness factors and transport factors for a first-order reaction on a porous catalyst pellet.

differences between the bulk fluid phase and the external surface of a catalytic pellet owing to external diffusion limitation is never observed in the absence of correspondingly larger internal concentration gradients within the pellet.

6.4 One-dimensional heat and mass transfer
to catalytic surfaces

A more general analysis of the heterogeneous kinetic system should provide for finite transport resistances to both heat and mass transfer between the bulk fluid phase and the external solid surface. When the heat of reaction is not zero, the surface temperature of a catalyst is lower than the bulk fluid value for an endothermic reaction and is higher for an exothermic reaction. The method of analysis for thermal effects parallels that already developed for diffusion effects, and the material immediately to follow extends the treatment of the earlier part of this chapter to the more general problem.

Equations 6.2-9 and 6.2-10 provide the necessary description of a one-dimensional treatment of external mass transfer. By slight modification this equation can be generalized to accommodate the general simple heterogeneous rate expression and to apply to both heat and mass transfer. Consider again the simple reaction

$$\sum_{i=1}^{n} a_i A_i = 0. \tag{6.4-1}$$

The actual rate of a heterogeneous reaction per unit area of external surface is obtained from a modification of Eq. 4.1-1 shown below.

$$\mathscr{R}_x = \begin{array}{c} \text{Rate of reaction} \\ \text{per unit of external} \\ \text{surface} \end{array} = \left[\frac{\rho_p S \mathscr{E}}{a}\right] \mathscr{R}(C_{10}, C_{20}, C_{30}, \ldots, C_{n0}, T_0), \tag{6.4-2}$$

where all symbols have their previous meanings and a is the external surface area per unit volume within the motor bed. Note that the definition of $\mathscr{R}_x$ in Eq. 6.4-2 includes the one-dimensional effectiveness factor. The subscripted intensive properties C_{10}, etc., refer to the values at the external surface of the pellet. The corresponding values of these properties in the bulk phase have the subscript ∞ as $C_{1\infty}$, etc. At steady state, the rates of mass and heat transfer to the external surface in terms of the mass transfer coefficient β_m and the heat transfer coefficient β_h must equal the production of heat and mass dictated by the external surface reaction leading to

$$(C_{i\infty} - C_{i0})\beta_{mi} = -a_i \mathscr{R}_x, \tag{6.4-3}$$

$$(T_\infty - T_0)\beta_h = (+\Delta H_i)\mathscr{R}_x. \tag{6.4-4}$$

For the simple reaction, a single equation again describes the system because the temperature and all concentrations can be described in terms of a single concentration. Therefore, the system is of the form

$$(C_{i\infty} - C_{i0})\beta_{mi} = -a_i \mathscr{R}'_x(C_{i0}), \tag{6.4-5}$$

and

$$C_{j0} = C_{j\infty} - \frac{\beta_{mi}}{\beta_{mj}} \frac{a_j}{a_i} (C_{i\infty} - C_{i0}) \tag{6.4-6}$$

$$T_0 = T_\infty + \frac{\beta_{mi}(-\Delta H)}{\beta_h} (C_{i\infty} - C_{i0}), \tag{6.4-7}$$

where through Eqs. 6.4-6 and 6.4-7

$$\mathscr{R}'_x(C_{i0}) = \mathscr{R}_x(C_{10}, C_{20}, C_{30}, \ldots, C_{n0}, T_0). \tag{6.4-8}$$

Thus, if values of β_{mi} and β_h are known,[*] the solution of Eq. 6.4-5 leads to the unknown values of C_{i0} and T_0. Unfortunately, values of β_{mi} and β_h

---

[*] For packed beds see: C. R. Wilke and O. A. Hougen, *Trans. A.I.Ch.E.*, **41**, 445 (1945); B. W. Gramson, G. Thodos and O. A. Hougen, *Trans. A.I.Ch.E.*, **39**, 1 (1943); or O. A. Hougen and K. W. Watson, *Chemical Process Principles*, Part III, p. 986 (John Wiley & Sons, Inc., New York, 1947).

depend upon both the rate and the quantity $\sum_{i=1}^{n} a_i$. However, this is a standard chemical engineering problem which has been discussed at length elsewhere.* Yoshida *et al*.† have prepared graphs of solutions to Eqs. 6.4-3 and 6.4-4 based upon an experimentally determined functional form of β_{mi} and β_h in packed beds.

A particularly interesting and important case is that of simultaneous heat and mass transfer to catalysts in which both internal and external transport phenomena are considered. This is analogous to the case discussed in Section 6.3 wherein the reader will recall that external mass transfer was always less important than internal mass transfer. When the problem is generalized to include heat transfer, this conclusion is invalid because the effective thermal conductivity within the pellet is generally much larger than the thermal conductivity in the fluid phase in the environment of the pellet. At high Reynolds numbers, based upon the pellet characteristic dimension, the heat and mass transfer coefficients are large and the corresponding temperature and concentration differences between the external surface of the pellet and the bulk fluid stream, $T_\infty - T_0$ and $C_\infty - C_0$, respectively, are small. At low Reynolds numbers, we shall show that $T_\infty - T_0$ can still be appreciable even when the $C_\infty - C_0$ is small and the temperature and concentration gradients within the particle are so small that the effectiveness factor $\mathscr{E}$ is essentially unity.

To do this, we use the result of Eq. 4.5-21, which is

$$-0.3 < \delta < 0.3, \tag{6.4-9}$$

where

$$\delta \equiv \frac{\Delta E(-\Delta H) D_i C_{i0}}{R_g T_0^2 \lambda}, \tag{6.4-10}$$

and ΔE = activation energy,
    $-\Delta H$ = enthalpy of reaction,
    D_i = effective diffusivity of the ith species,
    C_{i0} = concentration of the ith species at the external surface of the catalyst pellet,
    R_g = gas constant,
    T_0 = temperature at the external surface of the catalyst pellet,
    λ = effective thermal conductivity in the catalyst pellet.

According to the interpretation given in Eq. 6.4-9 in Section 4.5, if $|\delta| < 0.3$, the effect of temperature gradients within a pellet may be ignored and the results based upon an isothermal treatment will be within 5 per cent

---

* See for example: T. K. Sherwood and R. L. Pigford, "Absorption and extraction," 2nd Ed. (McGraw-Hill Book Company, New York, 1952) and R. B. Bird, W. E. Stewart and E. N. Lightfoot, "Transport Phenomena" (John Wiley & Sons, Inc., New York, 1960).

† F. Yoshida, D. Rasnaswami and O. A. Hougen, *A.I.Ch.E. Journal*, **8**, 5 (1962).

of the more rigorous nonisothermal result.* Moreover, we have also shown in Section 4.5 that for most systems, internal transport effects are small when the Thiele parameter $\hat{h}_p < 1$, i.e., for a spherical particle

$$\hat{h}_p = \frac{R_0}{3} \sqrt{\frac{\rho_p S \mathscr{R}'(C_{i0})}{D_i C_{i0}}} \leq 1, \tag{6.4-11}$$

where from Eq. 4.4-11 $\mathscr{R}'(C_{i0})$ is

$$\mathscr{R}'(C_{i0}) = \mathscr{R}(C_{10}, C_{20}, \ldots, C_{n0}, T_0). \tag{6.4-12}$$

All other symbols have their previous meanings.

Substitution of Eqs. 6.4-2, 6.4-9, 6.4-11, and 6.4-12 into Eq. 6.4-4 yields

$$\frac{T_\infty - T_0}{T_0} \approx \pm \left(\frac{R_g T_0}{\Delta E}\right)\left(\frac{\lambda}{\lambda_g}\right)\left(\frac{1}{\mathrm{Nu}_h}\right), \tag{6.4-13}$$

where $\mathrm{Nu}_h \equiv \beta_h R_0/\lambda_g$, the Nusselt number, and

λ_g = thermal conductivity of the fluid mixture surrounding the pellet.

Typical values of the three groups on the right-hand side of Eq. 6.4-13 might be 0.05, 10, and a limiting value of 1, respectively. Clearly then the possibility of appreciable temperature differences is demonstrated. As the Reynolds number increases, the Nusselt number likewise increases and the absolute magnitude of $T_\infty - T_0$ decreases.

6.5 Multiple steady-state solutions on surfaces with exothermic reactions

A new phenomenon appears when finite resistances to both heat and mass transfer are present on surfaces—that of multiple steady-state solutions.† And it is characteristic of this type of system that the particular steady-state physically realized in operation depends upon the conditions under which the reaction is started. The characteristics of these systems and reasons for their existence is perhaps best learned by considering a simple example in detail. Let us again look at the system composed of a single nonporous catalytic sphere immersed in an infinite medium of reactant. Reactants are transported by diffusion to the surface and heat is transported away from the surface by conduction. The mathematical formulation of the one-dimensional problem is given below.

$$\frac{d}{dR}\left[R^2 \frac{dC}{dR}\right] = 0, \qquad \frac{d}{dR}\left[R^2 \frac{dT_f}{dR}\right] = 0, \tag{6.5-1}$$

---

* Strictly speaking, this relation for δ was based upon a first-order reaction. However in Chapter 4 we have shown that the result is also useful for second-order kinetics.

† See for example: C. Wagner, *Chemische Technik* **18**, 28 (1945): D. A. Frank-Kamenetskii, *op. cit.*, p. 289.

where C is the concentration of the reactant; T_f is the temperature of the fluid; and where the boundary conditions are

$$\text{at } r = r_\infty, \qquad C = C_\infty, \qquad T_f = T_\infty. \tag{6.5-2}$$

Clearly, the temperature inside the spherical pellet is constant. If the kinetic function is written in the form

$$k[T_f(R_0), C(R_0)] = A_n e^{-\Delta E/RT(R_0)} C^n(R_0) \tag{6.5-3}$$

the following definitions make the above equations dimensionless:

$$\left.\begin{array}{ccc} \Theta_f \equiv \dfrac{T_f - T_\infty}{T_\infty}, & \psi \equiv \dfrac{C - C_\infty}{C_\infty} & \eta \equiv \dfrac{R}{R_0}, \\[2ex] \epsilon \equiv \dfrac{\Delta E}{RT_\infty}, & \beta_n \equiv \dfrac{A_n(-\Delta H)C_\infty^n R_0 e^{-\epsilon}}{\lambda_g T_\infty} & \alpha_n \equiv \dfrac{A_n C_\infty^{n-1} R_0 e^{-\epsilon}}{D} \end{array}\right\} \tag{6.5-4}$$

The problem in dimensionless form becomes

$$\frac{d}{d\eta}\left[\eta^2 \frac{d\psi}{d\eta}\right] = 0, \qquad \frac{d}{d\eta}\left[\eta^2 \frac{d\Theta_f}{d\eta}\right] = 0. \tag{6.5-5}$$

and the boundary conditions at infinity are

$$\Theta_f(\infty) = 0, \qquad \psi(\infty) = 0. \tag{6.5-6}$$

The solution to Eqs. 6.5-5 is

$$\psi = -\frac{\mathscr{A}_1}{\eta} \qquad \Theta = -\frac{\mathscr{A}_2}{\eta}. \tag{6.5-7}$$

The boundary conditions at the catalytic surface are

$$\left.\begin{array}{l} \left(\dfrac{d\psi}{d\eta}\right)_{\eta=1} = \alpha_n e^{\epsilon \Theta_f(1)/1+\Theta_f(1)}[1 + \psi(1)]^n \\[3ex] \left(\dfrac{d\Theta_f}{d\eta}\right)_{\eta=1} = -\beta_n e^{\epsilon \Theta_f(1)/1+\Theta_f(1)}[1 + \psi(1)]^n \end{array}\right\} \tag{6.5-8}$$

The relationships between the coefficients $\mathscr{A}_1$ and $\mathscr{A}_2$ found from Eqs. 6.5-7 and 6.5-8 are

$$\mathscr{A}_1 = -\left(\frac{\alpha_n}{\beta_n}\right)\mathscr{A}_2 \quad \text{and} \quad \mathscr{A}_2 = -\beta_n e^{(\epsilon \mathscr{A}_2/1 - \mathscr{A}_2)}\left[1 + \left(\frac{\alpha_n}{\beta_n}\right)\mathscr{A}_2\right]^n, \tag{6.5-9}$$

and the one-dimensional rate of reaction $\mathscr{R}_1$ of the sphere, therefore, is

$$\mathscr{R}_1 = 4\pi R_0 DC_\infty \frac{d\psi(1)}{d\xi} = 4\pi R_0 DC_\infty \mathscr{A}_1. \tag{6.5-10}$$

The simultaneous solution of Eq. 6.5-9 gives us, of course, the values of the surface temperature which satisfy the above equations. However, it is instructive to look at this system in another way. The rate of surface reaction is Eq. 6.5-10. Thus

$$\frac{\mathscr{R}_1}{4\pi R_0 DC_\infty} = \left(\frac{\alpha_n}{\beta_n}\right)\mathscr{A}_2 \tag{6.5-11}$$

and the surface temperature $\Theta(1) = -\mathscr{A}_2$. Therefore

$$\frac{\mathscr{R}_1}{4\pi R_0 DC_\infty} = \left(\frac{\alpha_n}{\beta_n}\right)\Theta_f(1). \tag{6.5-12}$$

Equation 6.5-12 gives us the rate of heat transported away from the surface as a function of the surface temperature.

The mass transfer equation may now be considered separately. The boundary condition is, in analogy with Eq. 6.2-6,

$$\left(\frac{d\psi}{d\eta}\right)_{\eta=1} = \frac{A_n e^{-\epsilon}R_0 C_\infty^{n-1} e^{\epsilon\Theta_s/1+\Theta_s}}{D}[1+\psi(1)]^n \tag{6.5-13}$$

where $\Theta_s \equiv \Theta_f(1)$. Equation 6.5-13 may be written alternatively as

$$\left(\frac{d\psi}{d\eta}\right)_{\eta=1} = \gamma_n[1+\psi(1)]^n \tag{6.5-14}$$

where γ_n has its previous meaning in Eq. 6.2-8 when it is recognized

$$k_n' = A_n e^{-\epsilon}e^{\epsilon\Theta_s/1+\Theta_s} \tag{6.5-15}$$

Thus the rate of reaction is, for $n = 1$,

$$\mathscr{R}_{11} = 4\pi R_0 DC_\infty\left(\frac{\gamma_1}{1+\gamma_1}\right),$$

and

$$\frac{\mathscr{R}_{11}}{4\pi R_0 DC_\infty} = \left(\frac{\gamma_1}{1+\gamma_1}\right). \tag{6.5-16}$$

Figure 6.5-1 shows plots of Eqs. 6.5-12 and 6.5-16. The curve of Eq. 6.5-16 is identical with that shown on Fig. 6.2-1 and is a representation of the mass transfer and chemical reaction characteristics of the system. The mass transfer curve is in general a function of γ_n which in turn depends upon the numerical values of α_n, ϵ, Θ_s, Nu_m, and the order of the reaction. For this case $n = 1$, $\mathrm{Nu}_m = 1$, $\alpha = 0.00398$, and $\epsilon = 20$. Equation 6.5-12 gives us the rate of energy transport away from the surface and depends in general upon the ratio α_n/β_n and Θ_s. The solution or solutions to the original problem must lie on both curves and therefore on the intersections of these curves. The particular merit of the graphical method of presentation is that it clearly demonstrates what values of the parameters give rise to multiple steady-state solutions. For the particular case when $\alpha_1 > 1.5\beta_1$, only a single steady-state is possible and that lies in the kinetic-controlled regime. When $\alpha_1 < 1.5\beta_1$, multiple solutions are possible until $\beta_1 \gg \alpha_1$, in which case it is clear that only a diffusion-controlled solution is possible. For intermediate values of the ratio α_1/β_1, three mathematical steady-state solutions are possible. It turns out, however, that the intermediate solution labeled Solution II on Fig. 6.5-1 is not physically realizable because it is unstable. This can be shown mathematically;* however, a physical argument

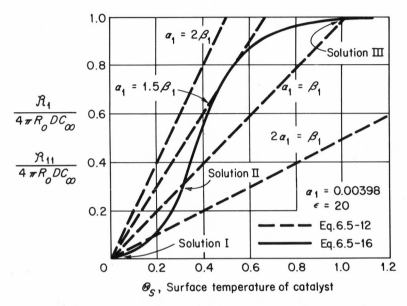

Fig. 6.5-1. Multiple steady-state solutions for heat and mass transfer to a nonporous spherical pellet.

is perhaps sufficient here. Suppose that the system was delicately balanced at the conditions of Solution II. If now a slight upset owing to noise in the system caused the temperature of the surface to be increased by a very small amount, then according to our curves, the rate of heat release would increase faster than the rate of heat transfer from the surface, and the surface temperature would continue to increase up to Solution III. By a similar argument, this latter solution can be shown to be stable. If a slight upset to the system balanced at Solution II causes the surface temperature to decrease, clearly it will continue to decrease until it reaches the conditions of Solution I which is again a stable solution. A system having finite resistances to heat and mass transfer combined with chemical reaction at surfaces is therefore an unusual one in that its state of operation under a rather wide range of conditions

* J. C. Friedly and E. E. Petersen, *Chem. Eng. Sci.* (to appear in 1965).

depends upon how it is initiated. This is very much like the exothermic reactions in the so-called stirred tank reactors having cooling coils. Here again for very much the same reason multiple steady-states are possible.

It should be clear that the preceding discussion can readily be extended to include all systems in which the surfaces are uniformly accessible. That is, for the general case of a uniformly accessible surface, the definition of the parameters α_n and β_n of Eqs. 6.5-4 are generalized to

$$\alpha_n' = \frac{\alpha_n}{\mathrm{Nu}_m} \tag{6.5-17}$$

$$\beta_n' = \frac{\beta_m}{\mathrm{Nu}_h} \tag{6.5-18}$$

where Nu_m and Nu_h are respectively the Nusselt numbers for mass and heat transfer.

6.6 Effect of concentration and temperature gradients in the bulk phase on the rate of reaction at a surface

Owing to conversion, a catalyst pellet in a packed bed is exposed to gradients in the bulk concentration and temperature, whereas in the preceding sections we have assumed that far from the external surface the bulk concentration and temperature approach constant values, C_∞ and T_∞. It is the purpose of this section to show, for an idealized system, how large these gradients must be before rates computed on the basis of constant environmental conditions differ appreciably from the true rates.

The idealized system, again, concerns a single, nonporous spherical catalyst pellet immersed in large reactant medium in which concentration and temperature gradients are maintained—a system wherein no hydrodynamic flow takes place. Such a system is shown in Fig. 6.6-1. In the region $R > R_0$ the two-dimensional Laplace equation applies because the concentration and temperature vary with both the radial coordinate R and the angular coordinate θ. Three equations are needed to describe the concentration and temperature outside the spherical particle and inside the particle. These equations are:

$$\nabla^2 C_i = \nabla^2 T_f = \nabla^2 T_s = 0, \tag{6.6-1}$$

where $C_i =$ concentration of reactant in the region outside the sphere,
$\quad T_f =$ temperature in the region outside the sphere,
$\quad T_s =$ temperature in the region inside the sphere,

$$\nabla^2 \equiv \frac{1}{R^2} \frac{\partial}{\partial R}\left(R^2 \frac{\partial}{\partial R}\right) + \frac{1}{R^2 \sin\theta} \frac{\partial}{\partial \theta}\left[\sin\theta \frac{\partial}{\partial \theta}\right].$$

Boundary conditions

$$C(\infty, \pi/2) = C_\infty; \quad \frac{\partial C(\infty, \theta)}{\partial Z} = -E_C'$$

$$T_f(\infty, \pi/2) = T_\infty; \quad \frac{\partial T_f(\infty, \theta)}{\partial Z} = -E_T'$$

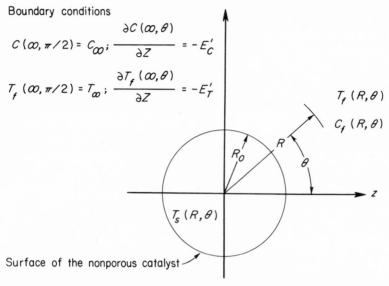

Fig. 6.6-1. Schematic diagram of a spherical catalyst pellet in temperature and concentration gradients.

In writing Eq. 6.6-1 it has been assumed that properties such as the diffusivity and thermal conductivity are not functions of C_i and T. These equations are subject to certain standard boundary conditions at infinity shown on Fig. 6.6-1, and to the kinetic boundary condition at the surface of the sphere. The latter are of the form

$$\left.\begin{array}{l} D_i \dfrac{\partial C_i(R_0, \theta)}{\partial R} = -a_i \mathscr{R}_x \\[2ex] -\lambda_f \dfrac{\partial T(R_0, \theta)}{\partial R} + \lambda_s \dfrac{\partial T_s(R_0, \theta)}{\partial R} = (-\Delta H)\mathscr{R}_x \end{array}\right\} \quad (6.6\text{-}2)$$

where D = diffusivity,

a_i = stoichiometric coefficient of reactant,

λ_f, λ_s = thermal conductivities of fluid and solid phases, respectively,

ΔH = enthalpy of reaction,

$\mathscr{R}_x$ = heterogeneous reaction rate per unit area.

The reaction rate for a single sphere is then found from the concentration profile by the expression

$$\begin{array}{l} \text{Reaction rate} \\ \text{per pellet} \end{array} = 2\pi R_0^2 D_i \int_0^\pi \frac{\partial C_i(R_0, \theta)}{\partial R} \sin\theta \, d\theta. \qquad (6.6\text{-}3)$$

The mathematical problem is therefore similar to a standard problem of mathematical physics: the solution may be expressed in terms of zonal harmonics. However, unlike the classic problem of this type, the coefficients of the harmonics cannot be obtained from the orthogonality property because the boundary condition (Eq. 6.6-2) is nonlinear. The solution to this problem was obtained using an iterative numerical scheme to evaluate the coefficients. However, the mathematical details of this problem have been treated elsewhere* and only the results are of interest here.

For zero and first-order isothermal reactions, the solution can be obtained analytically and it can be shown that while the concentrations vary with position on the pellet surface, the over-all reaction rate as computed from Eq. 6.6-3 is identical with the corresponding one-dimensional problem having a constant bulk concentration equal to C_∞. For a second-order isothermal reaction, the over-all reaction rate is affected by a concentration gradient; however, the gradient $-E_c'$ of Fig. 6.6-1 must be of the order C_∞/R_0 before any appreciable error is made in neglecting the effect of the gradient, e.g., where

$$E_c' < \frac{C_\infty}{2R_0}$$

the error is less than about 10 per cent. The gradient E_c' is defined as $-\partial C(\infty, \theta)/\partial z$, z being the coordinate in the direction of the concentration gradient. The nonisothermal results compare with their corresponding one-dimensional solutions in about the same way as do the isothermal results.

These results allow us to use bulk concentrations and temperatures in the vicinity of a particle in a packed bed without making a correction for the relatively small gradients which exist even for very rapid reactions.

6.7 The general problem of convective diffusion
to catalytic surfaces

In the preceding sections we have discussed both non-flow and flow systems. Although useful for examining the behavior of simple systems and perhaps as a qualitative guide to the behavior of more complex systems, the discussion was somewhat restricted in its application because true non-flow systems are rarely encountered in practice, and the treatment of flow systems was based upon film theories and therefore was approximate.

From a fundamental point of view the analysis of flow systems using film theories is objectionable, and it is worth while to discuss these theories† briefly in order to show why this is true.

* E. E. Petersen, J. C. Friedly, and R. J. DeVogelaere, *Chem. Eng. Sci.*, **19**, 683 (1964).

† For a more complete discussion the reader is referred to V. G. Levich, "Physico-chemical Hydrodynamics," p. 40, Prentice-Hall Inc., Englewood Cliffs, N.J., 1962.

One of the early film theories is due to Nernst* who postulated that a stagnant film of thickness δ existed adjacent to a solid body, and that the resistance to transport is in this thin layer. According to this picture, the steady state equation for diffusion between two infinite planes separated by the distance δ applies. However, the theory does not provide a means of calculating the magnitude of δ *a priori*, thus δ is an adjustable parameter to be evaluated and correlated by experiment. Unfortunately, δ was found to be a function of the diffusivity and did not depend solely upon the hydrodynamics of the system.

Other film theories, which have been so widely used in chemical engineering computations, have postulated that the flow within the film is laminar and is parallel to the surface, and that such motion does not contribute to the transport of material through the film. In this theory, the flux of material is obtained in terms of a concentration difference and a mass transfer coefficient. However, the mass transfer coefficient is really only an adjustable parameter, and in common with the Nernst theory, makes no provision for its determination from first principles.

The film theories are appealing because of their simplicity; however, the basic postulates upon which they are based inadequately describe the details of the processes occurring near surfaces, and as a consequence results based upon them must be regarded as qualitative.

The practice of correlating heat and mass transfer coefficients between fluids and non-reacting solid boundaries is in principle correct when applied to similar systems.† It is also useful because there are only a relatively few geometries which need be studied. This approach cannot be extended to include transport to surfaces at which reactions occur because similarity cannot be maintained and the convective properties depend upon the details of the surface reaction.

These difficulties have caused a number of workers to abandon film theories and seek a more fundamental description of these processes, which includes convective transport parallel and normal to the catalyst surface. In applying this more fundamental description to problems of importance in reactor design, however, we face a difficulty of a different kind—that of solving the corresponding fluid mechanical problem. If the velocity field and the transport properties within the system can be specified, then the solution of the corresponding conservation equations lead to far more reliable results. Unfortunately, application of the method to describe reactions on blunt objects is not yet possible because the flow fields around such objects cannot be determined beyond the separation point. On the other hand, certain geometries do lend themselves readily to this kind of analysis. One class of

* W. Nernst, *Z. Physik. Chem.*, **47**, 55 (1904); W. Nernst and E. S. Merriam, *ibid.*, **53**, 235 (1905).

† Similar in the mathematical sense.

problems which has yielded to fundamental treatment is that of laminar boundary flows around streamlined catalytic surfaces. In this section we shall look at the general approach to the description of these systems. In the following section we shall apply the method to certain simplified cases and show how asymptotic methods may be employed to further simplify the analysis. Finally, the results obtained will be compared with those of less rigorous methods.

This section must of necessity be brief, and only the over-all ideas are treated here. The reader interested in pursuing the subject in greater depth will profit from studying the suggested references.*

At sufficiently large Reynolds numbers, Prandtl showed that a flow field may be divided into two regimes, one close to the surface in which the inertial and viscous forces are of the same order of magnitude and another far from the surface, where inertial forces greatly exceed the viscous forces and the flow can be treated as inviscid. Asymptotically, as the Reynolds number approaches infinity the potential flow equations apply to the latter region, whereas the boundary layer equations are applicable to the former region. The resulting equations are far simpler to solve than the Navier-Stokes equations, and the literature contains the solutions of many hydrodynamic problems based upon the boundary layer approximation. In this section we shall be concerned primarily with the rate of heat and mass transfer to two-dimensional catalytic surfaces in boundary layer flows. Subsequently, these solutions will be compared with those obtained by approximate methods currently used by chemical engineers.

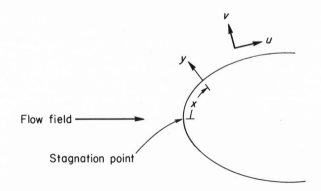

Fig. 6.7-1. Directions of the coordinates x and y and the velocities u and v with respect to a two-dimensional catalytic surface.

Consider the type of geometry shown in Fig. 6.7-1. The reactants establish a flow field around a two-dimensional catalyst surface of arbitrary shape

* H. Schlichting, *Boundary Layer Theory*, Chapters 7 and 8, Pergamon Press, Inc., New York, 1955; V. G. Levich, *Physicochemical Hydrodynamics*, Chapter 2, *op. cit.*

whereupon a simple surface reaction occurs according to the stoichiometric equation

$$\sum_{i=1}^{n} a_i A_i = 0. \tag{6.7-1}$$

As before, if $a_i < 0$, A_i is a reactant; and if $a_i > 0$, A_i is a product. Consider further a rate expression of the form

$$\mathscr{R}_i = \mathscr{R}_i[C_1(x, 0), C_2(x, 0), \ldots, C_n(x, 0), T(x, 0)] \tag{6.7-2}$$

where $\mathscr{R}_i$ is the rate of production of A_i due to reaction per unit time per unit external area of catalyst surface. Clearly then from stoichiometry,

$$\frac{\mathscr{R}_i}{a_i} = \frac{\mathscr{R}_j}{a_j} = \mathscr{R}. \tag{6.7-3}$$

Thus, in Fig. 6.7-1, a surface reaction is occurring at a rate depending upon the local values of $C_1, C_2, \ldots, C_n$ and the temperature. The local magnitudes of these variables depend in turn upon the rate of transport of the species involved in the reaction and energy between the surface and the bulk fluid phase. We can easily visualize qualitatively what happens in this system. The reaction proceeds at a finite rate and removes a part of the reactants from the fluid in the vicinity of the surface and at the same time either liberates or absorbs energy from the system. Therefore, the concentrations and temperature at the surface are functions of the coordinate x and it follows that the local rate of conversion varies with x.

We now present a theory which allows this variation to be predicted quantitatively. The system of equations which describe the hydrodynamics, heat and mass transport are given below. They are subject to the conventional boundary layer assumptions and neglect the variation of properties with the dependent variables.

$$\frac{\partial u}{\partial x} + \frac{\partial v}{\partial y} = 0 \tag{6.7-4}$$

$$u \frac{\partial u}{\partial x} + v \frac{\partial u}{\partial y} = -\frac{1}{\rho} \frac{dp}{dx} + v \frac{\partial^2 u}{\partial y^2} \tag{6.7-5}$$

$$u \frac{\partial T}{\partial x} + v \frac{\partial T}{\partial y} = \frac{\lambda_g}{\rho C_p} \frac{\partial^2 T}{\partial y^2} \tag{6.7-6}$$

$$u \frac{\partial C_i}{\partial x} + v \frac{\partial C_i}{\partial y} = D_i \frac{\partial^2 C_i}{\partial y^2} \qquad (i = 1, 2, 3, \ldots, n). \tag{6.7-7}$$

The usual boundary conditions which apply are

$$\left.\begin{array}{llll} \text{at } y = 0, & u = 0, & v = 0^* \\[2mm] y = \infty, & u = U_\infty(x), & T = T_\infty, & C_i = C_{i\infty} \\[2mm] x = 0, & u = U_\infty(0), & T = T_\infty, & C_i = C_{i\infty} \end{array}\right\} \tag{6.7-8}$$

* We are neglecting large interfacial velocities here. This topic has been discussed by A. Acrivos, *A.I.Ch.E. Journal* **6**, 410 (1960) and A. Acrivos, *J. of Fluid Mech.* **12**, 337 (1962).

The rate expression is introduced as a boundary condition on T and C at $y = 0$ as follows:

$$\lambda_g \frac{\partial T(x, 0)}{\partial y} = \mathcal{R} \sum_{j=1}^{n} a_j \tilde{H}_j = \mathcal{R}(-\Delta H) \tag{6.7-9}$$

$$D_i \frac{\partial C_i(x, 0)}{\partial y} = -a_i \mathcal{R} \tag{6.7-10}$$

where $\tilde{H}_j$ is the partial molal enthalpy of the jth species in the mixture and ΔH is the enthalpy of reaction. Equations 6.7-4 and 6.7-5 govern the hydrodynamics and, in the absence of coupling with Eqs. 6.7-6 and 6.7-7 can be

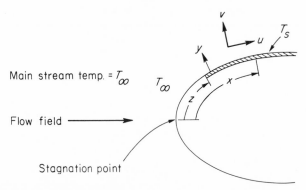

Fig. 6.7-2. Diagram showing the heated and unheated sections of the two-dimensional surface.

solved independently to obtain u and v as functions of x and y. No effort will be made here to develop these solutions. The reader unfamiliar with these methods should consult a comprehensive treatment of the subject.*

Therefore, the problem is to solve the set of linear Equations 6.7-6 and 6.7-7 subject to the boundary conditions given by Eqs. 6.7-8, 6.7-9, and 6.7-10. The difficulty arises in the coupling of the latter boundary conditions through Eq. 6.7-2.

Because the equations are linear the principle of superposition may be used to obtain solutions which satisfy the boundary conditions of Eqs. 6.7-9 and 6.7-10. To do this, we solve the equations subject to a different set of boundary conditions.† Taking Eq. 6.7-6 as an example, consider the problem of heat transfer from the two-dimensional surface shown in Fig. 6.7-2. In this problem we assume that heating begins downstream at some distance z from the stagnation point. For all $x > z$, the solid surface temperature is the free stream value T_∞, and for all $x < z$, the temperature of the

* E.g., Schlichting's *Boundary Layer Theory*, op. cit.

† P. Chambré, *Appl. Sci. Research*, A6, 97 (1956).

heating surface T_s is constant. In the above problem, the dimensionless temperature $\Theta \equiv (T - T_\infty)/(T_s - T_\infty)$ satisfies the following discontinuous conditions:

$$\Theta(z, x, 0) = \begin{cases} 1 & x > z \\ 0 & x < z \end{cases} \Bigg\}$$

and

$$\Theta(z, z, y) = 0 \qquad y \neq 0$$

$$(6.7\text{-}11)$$

At a distance far from the surface and at the entrance plane at the leading edge let $\Theta(z, x, y)$ satisfy Eq. 6.7-6 subject to the boundary conditions of Eq. 6.7-8.

From the function $\Theta(z, x, y)$, one can construct the solution to a problem in which $T(x, 0)$, the temperature profile at the heat transfer surface, is an arbitrary function of x, by the use of Duhamel's theorem.* This is accomplished by summing the solutions $\Theta(z, x, y)$ multiplied by a weighting function $a(z)$. The solution is of the form

$$T(x, y) = T_\infty + \int_0^x a(z)\Theta(z, x, y)\, dz. \qquad (6.7\text{-}12)$$

The form of $a(z)$ follows from recognizing that $T(x, y)$ must reduce to $T(x, 0)$, the arbitrary surface temperature profile.

$$T(x, 0) = T_\infty + \int_0^x a(z)\Theta(z, x, 0)\, dz. \qquad (6.7\text{-}13)$$

But $\Theta(z, x, 0) = 1$ for all $x > z$, hence $a(z) = dT(z, 0)/dz$ satisfies Eq. 6.7-13 where z is the distance from the stagnation point along the x coordinate to a point where the surface temperature is $T(z, 0)$. Therefore:

$$T(x, y) = T_\infty + \int_0^x \Theta(z, x, y)\frac{dT(z, 0)}{dz}\, dz. \qquad (6.7\text{-}14)$$

It follows that the solution to Eq. 6.7-7 may be obtained for an arbitrary surface concentration profile by the same method. This corresponding solution is

$$C_i(x, y) = C_{i\infty} + \int_0^x \psi_i(z, x, y)\frac{dC_i(z, 0)}{dz}\, dz, \qquad (6.7\text{-}15)$$

where ψ_i is a dimensionless concentration which satisfies a set of boundary conditions analogous to those of Eq. 6.7-11.

We now return to the original problem. Since the functional forms of the derivatives $dT(z, 0)/dz$ and $dC_i(z, 0)/dz$ are not known, the formal solution to this system of equations can be formulated by differentiating Eq. 6.7-14 and the n equations analogous to Eq. 6.7-15 and inserting the derivatives

* See, for example, H. S. Carslaw and J. C. Jaeger, *Conduction of Heat in Solids*, 2nd ed. Oxford University Press, Inc., New York, 1959, p. 30.

into Eqs. 6.7-9, 6.7-10, and 6.7-12. We obtain:

$$\mathscr{R}_i[C_1(x, 0), C_2(x, 0), \ldots, C_n(x, 0)]$$

$$= -\int_0^x D_i \left(\frac{\partial \psi_i}{\partial y}\right)_{y=0} \frac{dC_i(z, 0)}{dz} \, dz, \qquad (i = 1, 2, 3, \ldots, n) \qquad (6.7\text{-}16)$$

$$\mathscr{R}_i[C_1(x, 0), C_2(x, 0), \ldots, C_n(x, 0), T(x, 0)](-\Delta H)$$

$$= \int_0^x k \left(\frac{\partial \Theta}{\partial y}\right)_{y=0} \frac{dT_i(z, 0)}{dz} dz. \qquad (6.7\text{-}17)$$

The system is now reduced to a series of $n + 1$ nonlinear Volterra integral equations, and the results of the analysis are valid in systems where laminar boundary layer theory is applicable. Equations 6.7-16 and 6.7-17 satisfy the boundary conditions of Eqs. 6.7-9 and 6.7-10. The former equations are constructed from the functions $\Theta(z, x, y)$ and $\psi_i(z, x, y)$ which satisfy respectively the conservation Eqs. 6.7-6 and 6.7-7 and the conditions of Eq. 6.7-11. The successful application of the method therefore depends upon being able to obtain the functions $\Theta(z, x, y)$ and $\psi_i(z, x, y)$.

In the next section, the methods outlined in this section are applied to simplified cases. However, before proceeding to the applications two comments should be made: First, the method described above can be adapted to any system for which the hydrodynamic fields are specified, e.g., laminar flow inside tubes where the wall is a catalytic surface. Second, the simultaneous solution of Eqs. 6.7-16 and 6.7-17 must in general be obtained by numerical methods.

6.8 Convective diffusion to isothermal catalytic surfaces: Asymptotic methods

This section has a threefold purpose: (1) to illustrate the general method described earlier by carrying a simplified example to a complete solution; (2) to demonstrate the utility of asymptotic methods as a means of simplifying the analysis; and (3) to compare the results of analyses based upon the two-dimensional convective diffusion equations with those obtained assuming a one-dimensional uniformly accessible surface.

We shall discuss first the asymptotic methods for the analysis of convective diffusion. The form of the functions $\psi_i(z, x, y)$ and $\Theta(z, x, y)$, which are needed in Eqs. 6.7-16 and 6.7-17, are obtained from two limiting cases: those obtained for large values of the Prandtl and Schmidt numbers, and those obtained for small Prandtl and Schmidt numbers. Both cases will be treated here.

As the Prandtl number approaches infinity, the thermal boundary layer is developed well within the momentum boundary layer, as suggested by

Fage and Falkner* and rigorously proven by Morgan and Warner,† and essentially all of the temperature change occurs in a narrow region close to the catalytic surface where the actual velocity distribution can be replaced by the first two terms of a power series expansion in y. Lighthill‡ first solved such a system to obtain a closed-form expression for the local rate of heat transfer. We shall derive this expression for mass transfer by a method§ that is somewhat simpler than that originally given by Lighthill. The problem which we shall consider first is that of a boundary layer flow past a two-dimensional catalytic surface immersed in a flow field in which the mass transfer process begins at some distance z along the x coordinate from the stagnation point. At $x = z$ the concentration at the surface is unity and remains constant at this value for all values of $x > z$. This solution may then be used to construct solutions for an arbitrary variation in concentration along x by the method outlined previously in Eq. 6.7-15. It follows from the similarity of the energy and conservation equations that this asymptotic form will also apply to the corresponding heat transfer equations. If we make Eq. 6.7-7 dimensionless by means of the following transformations,

$$x_1 \equiv \frac{x}{L}, \qquad y_1 \equiv [\mathrm{Re}]^{1/2}\frac{y}{L}, \qquad u_1 \equiv \frac{u}{U_\infty}, \qquad v_1 \equiv [\mathrm{Re}]^{1/2}\frac{v}{U_\infty},$$

$$\psi \equiv \frac{C - C_\infty}{C_s - C_\infty}, \qquad z_1 \equiv \frac{z}{L}, \qquad \mathrm{Re} = \frac{U_\infty L}{\nu}, \qquad \mathrm{Sc} \equiv \frac{\nu}{D}, \tag{6.8-1}$$

then Eq. 6.7-7 becomes

$$u_1\frac{\partial\psi}{\partial x_1} + v_1\frac{\partial\psi}{\partial y_1} = \frac{1}{\mathrm{Sc}}\frac{\partial^2\psi}{\partial y_1^2}. \tag{6.8-2}$$

If u_1 is expanded in a power series in y_1 and only the first two terms are retained, we obtain

$$u_1 \equiv \beta(x_1)y_1. \tag{6.8-3}$$

The coefficient $\beta(x_1)$ is determined by solving Eqs. 6.7-4 and 6.7-5 for the particular geometry in question and setting $\beta(x_1) = (\partial u_1/\partial y_1)_{y_1=0}$. Substitution of Eq. 6.8-3 into 6.8-2 gives

$$\beta y_2\frac{\partial\psi}{\partial x_1} - \frac{\beta'}{2}y_2^2\frac{\partial\psi}{\partial y_2} = \frac{\partial^2\psi}{\partial y_2^2}, \tag{6.8-4}$$

where β' is the derivative of β with respect to x_1 and

$$y_2 \equiv (\mathrm{Sc})^{1/3}y_1. \tag{6.8-5}$$

---

* A. Fage and Y. M. Falkner, *Rept. Mem. Aeronaut. Res. Com.*, London, No. 1314 (1931).
† G. W. Morgan and H. W. Warner, *J. Aero Sci.* **23**, 937 (1956).
‡ M. J. Lighthill, *Proc. Roy. Soc.* (London), **A202**, 359 (1950).
§ A. Acrivos, M. J. Shah and E. E. Petersen, *A.I.Ch.E. J.* **6**, 312 (1960). See also A. Acrivos, *Phys. Fluids* **3**, 657 (1960).

Equation 6.8-4 can be reduced to an ordinary differential equation by a similarity transformation of the form:

$$\mathcal{y} \equiv \frac{\beta(x_1)}{2t^{2/3}} \, y_2^2,$$

where

$$t(x_1) \equiv \int_0^{x_1} \sqrt{2\beta(\alpha)} \, d\alpha - \int_0^{z_1} \sqrt{2\beta(\alpha)} \, d\alpha \equiv \sqrt{2}[\zeta(x_1) - \zeta(z_1)],$$

and where

$$\zeta(x_1) \equiv \frac{1}{\sqrt{2}} \int_0^{x_1} \sqrt{2\beta(\alpha)} \, d\alpha. \tag{6.8-6}$$

Substituting, Eq. 6.8-4 reduces to

$$\frac{d^2\psi}{d\mathcal{y}^2} + \frac{1}{2\mathcal{y}} + \frac{2\mathcal{y}^{1/2}}{3} \frac{d\psi}{d\mathcal{y}} = 0. \tag{6.8-7}$$

Equation 6.8-7 is subject to the boundary conditions:

$$\psi = 0 \quad \text{at} \quad \mathcal{y} = \infty, \qquad \psi = 1 \quad \text{at} \quad \mathcal{y} = 0. \tag{6.8-8}$$

The solution satisfying the boundary conditions is

$$\psi = \frac{1}{\Gamma(1/3)} \int_{\frac{4\mathcal{y}^{3/2}}{9}}^{\infty} x^{-2/3} e^{-x} \, dx. \tag{6.8-9}$$

Substituting back to the original variables,

$$-\left(\frac{\partial\psi}{\partial y_1}\right)_{y_1=0} = \frac{1}{0.893} \left(\frac{\mathrm{Sc}}{9}\right)^{1/3} \frac{\sqrt{\beta(x_1)}}{[\zeta(x_1) - \zeta(z_1)]^{1/3}}. \tag{6.8-10}$$

To generalize this expression to the case of an arbitrary variation of surface concentration, Eq. 6.7-15 is differentiated with respect to y_1 and Eq. 6.8-10 is substituted for $(\partial\psi/\partial y_1)_{y_1=0}$ to obtain

$$-\left(\frac{\partial C}{\partial y_1}\right)_{y_1=0} = \frac{1}{0.893} \left(\frac{\mathrm{Sc}}{9}\right)^{1/3} \sqrt{\beta(x_1)} \int_0^{x_1} [\zeta(x_1) - \zeta(z_1)]^{-1/3} \frac{dC(z_1, 0)}{dz_1} \, dz_1. \tag{6.8-11}$$

Equation 6.8-11 is an expression for the rate of mass transfer from a surface when the surface concentration $C(z, 0)$ is known. Normally when Eq. 6.8-11 is used to describe a catalytic reaction at the solid fluid interface, $C(z, 0)$ is not known. However, one may now use Eq. 6.7-10 which for an isothermal surface becomes

$$\mathscr{R}_i[C(x_1, 0)] = D_i\left(\frac{\text{Re}^{1/2}}{L}\right)\left(\frac{\partial C}{\partial y_1}\right)_{y=0}$$

$$\mathscr{R}_i[C(x_1, 0)] = \frac{D\,\text{Re}^{1/2}}{0.893L}\left(\frac{\text{Sc}}{9}\right)^{1/3}\sqrt{\beta(x_1)}\int_0^{x_1}[\zeta(x_1) - \zeta(z_1)]^{-1/3}\frac{dC(z_1, 0)}{dz_1}\,dz_1$$

$$(6.8\text{-}12)$$

or in a different form:

$$\mathscr{R}_i[C(x, 0)] = \frac{D}{0.893}\left(\frac{\rho\,\text{Sc}}{9\mu^2}\right)^{1/3}\sqrt{\tau(x)}\int_0^{x_1}[\phi(x) - \phi(z_1)]^{-1/3}\frac{dC(z_1,0)}{dz_1}\,dz_1,$$

$$(6.8\text{-}13)$$

where

$$\tau(x) \equiv \mu(\partial u/\partial y)_{y=0}$$

$$\phi(x) \equiv \int_0^x \sqrt{\tau(\alpha)}\,d\alpha.$$

Equation 6.8-12 is an integral equation in $C(x_1, 0)$ and is a special case of Eqs. 6.7-15 and 6.7-16 because it is restricted to isothermal surfaces and to high Schmidt numbers. As written, Eq. 6.8-12 may be used to predict the behavior of a surface catalyzed reaction for any functional form of $\mathscr{R}_i$, provided the integral is interpreted as a Steltjes* integral.

The question might well be raised at this point as to how reliable Eq. 6.8-12 may be. First of all, it is based upon boundary layer theory. Suffice it to say that the successful applications of this theory have been numerous throughout several branches of engineering and its appropriate application here will be assumed. The use of the Lighthill approximation deserves more attention however. The reader will recall that Eq. 6.8-4 is asymptotically correct as the Schmidt number becomes very large, but it is not at all obvious over what range of numerical values of the Schmidt number this formula may be applied for engineering purposes as a useful and accurate approximation. Although this will not be answered in a general way, some insight as to the range of usefulness of this asymptotic solution will be revealed by an analysis of a first-order isothermal reaction on a flat plate. This case will be analyzed by a method similar to that used by Chambré and Acrivos.†

To carry out this analysis we need first the value of $\beta(x_1)$, which from its definition in Eq. 6.8-3 is

$$\beta(x_1) = \left(\frac{\partial u_1}{\partial y_1}\right)_{y_1=0}.$$

$$(6.8\text{-}14)$$

---

* Note that Eq. 6.8-12 must reduce to Eq. 6.8-10 for constant surface concentration. See for example E. W. Hobson, *The Theory of Functions of a Real Variable*, Vol. I, Dover Publications, Inc., New York, 1957.

† P. L. Chambré and A. Acrivos, *J. Appl. Phys.* **27**, 1322–28 (1956). See also V. G. Levich and N. N. Meiman, *Doklady Akad. Nauk* SSSR **79**, 97 (1951).

The solution to Eqs. 6.7-4 and 6.7-5 for a flat plate was first given by Blasius.*
Using the transformation

$$u_1 \equiv f'(\omega), \tag{6.8-15}$$

where $\omega \equiv y_1/x_1^{1/2}$ and where the prime indicates differentiation of the function f with respect to ω, the boundary layer equations were reduced to a nonlinear ordinary differential equation in the functions f, f'', and f'''. The solution to this equation as obtained by Howarth† is tabulated in Schlichting.‡ It is clear from Eq. 6.8-15 that

$$\left(\frac{\partial u_1}{\partial y_1}\right)_{y_1=0} = \frac{1}{x_1^{1/2}}\, f''(0), \tag{6.8-16}$$

from which it follows that

$$\beta(x_1) = \frac{0.332}{x_1^{1/2}}. \tag{6.8-17}$$

If we replace $k_1 C(x_1, 0)$ for $\mathscr{R}_i[C(x_1, 0)]$ and substitute Eq. 6.8-17 into Eq. 6.8-12, we obtain a description of the first-order isothermal reaction on a flat plate.

It is convenient now to define a new variable:

$$\xi \equiv \frac{k_1}{0.339\, \mathrm{Sc}^{1/3} D}\left(\frac{\nu x}{U_\infty}\right)^{1/2} \tag{6.8-18}$$

and an analogous quantity ξ_z based upon the variable z. As we shall see later in this section (Eq. 6.8-42) the variable ξ is the ratio of k_1 and the local mass transfer coefficient. The use of this variable is best justified at this time on physical grounds. Consider the behavior of the system as ξ approaches the limiting values $\xi \to 0$ and $\xi \to \infty$. As $\xi \to 0$, the system is kinetic controlled, that is, the local mass transfer coefficient is very large and the concentration of reactant at the surface approaches the bulk stream value. The local rate is determined therefore only by the kinetics of the reaction at the catalyst surface. When $\xi \to \infty$, the system is mass transfer controlled, that is, the local rate is determined by how fast reactants can be transported to the catalyst surface and the reactant concentration at the surface approaches zero. This variable therefore is very useful because in its two limits, $\xi \to 0$ and $\xi \to \infty$, the system reduces to cases which are easily identified and analyzed.

When Eq. 6.8-18 is substituted into Eq. 6.8-12 one obtains for a first-order isothermal surface reaction:

$$C(\xi) = -\frac{1}{\xi^{\frac{1}{2}}}\int_0^{\xi}(\xi^{3/2} - \xi_z^{3/2})^{-1/3}\frac{dC(\xi_z, 0)}{d\xi_z}\, d\xi_z. \tag{6.8-19}$$

* H. Blasius, *Z. Math. u. Physik* **56**, 1 (1908).
† L. Howarth, *Proc. Roy. Soc.* (London), **A164**, 547 (1938).
‡ Schlichting, *op. cit.*, pp. 107, 108

Equation 6.8-19 is a linear Volterra integral equation. It may be solved for small values of ξ by a Maclaurin series expansion of the form

$$\psi(\xi) = 1 + \sum_{n=1}^{\infty} a_n (-1)^n \xi^n, \tag{6.8-20}$$

and for large values of ξ

$$\psi(\xi) = \frac{1}{\xi} \tag{6.8-21}$$

The solution to Eq. 6.8-19 for the surface concentration is shown by the dashed line on Fig. 6.8-1 marked $Sc = \infty$ as computed by Chambré and

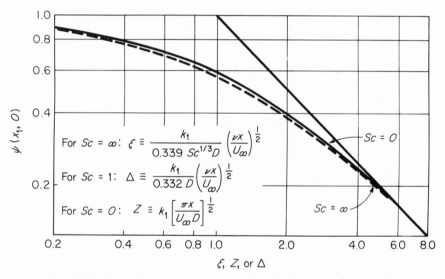

For $Sc = \infty$: $\quad \xi \equiv \dfrac{k_1}{0.339\, Sc^{1/3} D} \left(\dfrac{\nu x}{U_\infty} \right)^{\frac{1}{2}}$

For $Sc = 1$: $\quad \Delta \equiv \dfrac{k_1}{0.332\, D} \left(\dfrac{\nu x}{U_\infty} \right)^{\frac{1}{2}}$

For $Sc = 0$: $\quad Z \equiv k_1 \left[\dfrac{\pi x}{U_\infty D} \right]^{\frac{1}{2}}$

Fig. 6.8-1. Rate of reaction of a first-order reaction at the surface of a flat plate of catalyst. Laminar boundary layer solution.

Acrivos. This asymptotic solution has limiting asymptotes of $\psi = 1$ as $\xi \to 0$ and $\psi = 1/\xi$ as $\xi \to \infty$. The local rate of the reaction is readily computed from values of the dimensionless concentration.

$$\psi(x_1, 0) \equiv \frac{C(x_1, 0)}{C_\infty} \tag{6.8-22}$$

The other solution on Fig. 6.8-1 corresponds to the asymptotic solution to this problem for the case of very small Schmidt numbers. Although of no practical importance in mass transfer,* this problem is important because the solution is almost identical in its relationship to its limiting asymptotes.

* Small Prandtl numbers are observed for liquid metals and the corresponding heat transfer solution is useful for these cases.

The physical argument is similar to the high Schmidt number case. As the Schmidt numbers tend toward zero, the momentum boundary layer is well inside the concentration boundary layer. Under these conditions, the velocity field may be considered the value at the edge of the boundary layer which is a constant for a flat plate. The region of the momentum boundary layer can be disregarded. Equation 6.7-7 therefore becomes:

$$U_\infty \frac{\partial C}{\partial x} = D \frac{\partial^2 C}{\partial y^2}. \tag{6.8-23}$$

Subject to the boundary conditions

$$C = C_\infty \quad \text{at } y = \infty \text{ and } x = 0,$$

$$\frac{\partial C(x, 0)}{\partial y} = \frac{k}{D} C(x, 0). \tag{6.8-24}$$

Let

$$\psi \equiv \frac{C}{C_\infty}, \quad x_1 \equiv \frac{U_\infty x}{\nu}, \quad y_2 \equiv \frac{U_\infty}{\nu} \sqrt{Sc}\, y, \quad \kappa \equiv \frac{k}{U_\infty} \sqrt{Sc}, \quad Sc \equiv \frac{\nu}{D}. \tag{6.8-25}$$

Since we are primarily interested in the concentration gradient normal to the catalyst surface, we shall use the method of Laplace transforms to solve the system. Let

$$\Psi \equiv \mathscr{L}(\psi) = \int_0^\infty \psi(x_1, y_2) e^{-p x_1}\, dx_1.$$

Then Eq. 6.8-23 in dimensionless coordinates becomes

$$p\Psi - 1 = \frac{d^2\Psi}{dy_2^2}$$

and the solution is

$$\Psi = \frac{1}{p} + \mathscr{A} e^{\sqrt{p} y_2}.$$

But

$$\frac{d\Psi}{dy_2} = \kappa\Psi \quad \text{at} \quad y_2 = 0.$$

Therefore

$$\mathscr{A} = \frac{\kappa}{p(\kappa + \sqrt{p})},$$

$$\Psi(0) = \frac{1}{\sqrt{p}(\kappa + \sqrt{p})},$$

$$\psi(x_1, 0) = e^{\kappa^2 x_1} \operatorname{erfc} \kappa x_1^{1/2}.$$

If we let

$$Z \equiv \kappa x_1^{1/2}\sqrt{\pi}, \qquad (6.8\text{-}26)$$

$$\psi(Z) = e^{Z^2/\pi} \operatorname{erfc} \frac{Z}{\sqrt{\pi}}, \qquad (6.8\text{-}27)$$

where

$$Z = k\sqrt{\frac{\pi x}{U_\infty D}}. \qquad (6.8\text{-}28)$$

The solution to this problem as given by Eq. 6.8-27 is represented by the solid curve on Fig. 6.8-1 labeled $Sc = 0$. The equations of the asymptotes are $\psi(Z) \to 1/Z$ as $Z \to \infty$ and $\psi(Z) \to 1$ as $Z \to 0$. Note that the exact solution to each of the limiting cases lies in almost the identical position with respect to its asymptotes. It seems, therefore, reasonable to expect that this same situation would also be true for all Schmidt numbers between zero and infinite values. If this is actually the case, then it becomes possible to obtain the complete solution for an intermediate value of the Schmidt number by evaluating only its limiting asymptotes as κ, the rate constant, becomes very large and very small. However, from the boundary condition Eq. 6.7-10, it is clear that as $\kappa \to \infty$, $C(x_1, 0) \to 0$, and the problem we want to solve is the case of mass transfer in boundary layer flows to a flat plate with a zero concentration maintained at its surface throughout its length. This, of course, also corresponds to the problem of heat transfer from an isothermal flat plate.

Let us now show how an expression for the asymptotes can be formulated in two cases without solving the complete problem. Return again to the $Sc \to 0$ case. We wish to solve Eq. 6.8-23 subject to the boundary conditions of Eq. 6.8-24. However, the second boundary condition is to be replaced by the boundary condition $\psi(x_1, 0) = 0$, because κ is so large that the surface concentration is reduced to a very small value. As before, let

$$\Psi = \mathscr{L}(\psi) = \int_0^\infty \psi(x_1, y_2) e^{-px_1} dx_1.$$

Then

$$p\Psi - 1 = \frac{d^2\Psi}{dy_2^2}$$

and

$$\Psi = \frac{1}{p} + \mathscr{A} e^{\sqrt{p} y_2}.$$

Now at $y_2 = 0$, $\Psi = 0$. Therefore

$$\mathscr{A} = -\frac{1}{p} \quad \text{and} \quad \frac{d\Psi}{dy_2} = \frac{e^{-\sqrt{p} y}}{\sqrt{p}}.$$

Inverting the transform,

$$\left(\frac{d\psi}{dy_2}\right)_{y_2=0} = \frac{1}{\sqrt{\pi x_1}}.$$

Going back to the original boundary conditions of Eq. 6.8-25,

$$\left(\frac{d\psi}{dy_2}\right)_{y_2=0} = k\psi, \qquad \psi = \frac{1}{\kappa\sqrt{\pi x_1}} = \frac{U_\infty}{k\sqrt{\text{Pe}}\,\sqrt{\pi}}\left(\frac{L}{X}\right)^{1/2},$$

where $\text{Pe} = U_\infty L/D$, or

$$\psi = \frac{1}{Z}, \tag{6.8-29}$$

where

$$Z \equiv k\sqrt{\frac{\pi x}{U_\infty D}}, \tag{6.8-30}$$

which is, of course, the same asymptote as that found from Eq. 6.8-27. Thus an excellent approximation of the solution to the first-order reaction on a flat surface in boundary layer flow for $\text{Sc} \to 0$ could have been obtained from the $\text{Sc} \to \infty$ solution if the abscissa ξ is replaced by Z above and the curve of ψ vs. ξ is used.

This example is trivial because the entire solution may be obtained with very little more effort than the asymptote. However, suppose now that we desired a solution to the case of a first-order reaction on a flat plate when $\text{Sc} = 1$. For this case, Eq. 6.8-2 becomes:

$$u_1\frac{\partial\psi}{\partial x_1} + v_1\frac{\partial\psi}{\partial y_1} = \frac{\partial^2\psi}{\partial y_1^2} \tag{6.8-31}$$

Subject to the boundary conditions

$$\psi(0, y_1) = 1, \qquad \psi(x_1, \infty) = 1,$$

$$\left(\frac{\partial\psi}{\partial y_1}\right)_{y_1=0} = \left(\frac{k_1\nu}{DU_\infty}\right)\psi(x_1, 0). \tag{6.8-32}$$

This is not a trivial problem. However, if one assumes that the true solution to Eq. 6.8-31 and 6.8-32 lies in the *same* position with respect to its two asymptotes, i.e., $\kappa \to 0$ and $\kappa \to \infty$, as do the true solutions to the cases of $\text{Sc} \to 0$ and $\text{Sc} \to \infty$, which seems reasonable from Fig. 6.8-1, the problem is enormously simplified. The $\kappa \to 0$ case is the same as before, i.e., $\psi(x_1, 0) = 1$. As $\kappa \to \infty$, the concentration at the surface approaches zero and we can replace the last boundary condition of Eq. 6.8-32 by

$$\psi(x_1, 0) = 0 \tag{6.8-33}$$

Clearly, now the solution for

$$\left(\frac{\partial \psi}{\partial y_1}\right)_{y_1=0}$$

is the same as for

$$\left(\frac{\partial u_1}{\partial y_1}\right)_{y_1=0}$$

as found from the Blasius solution of the boundary layer equations on a flat plate. According to Eq. 6.8-16, then,

$$\left(\frac{\partial u_1}{\partial y_1}\right)_{y_1=0} = \left(\frac{\partial \psi}{\partial y_1}\right)_{y_1=0} = \frac{f''(0)}{x_1^{1/2}}. \tag{6.8-34}$$

From Eqs. 6.8-34 and 6.8-32, the asymptotic behavior of the surface concentration as $\kappa \to \infty$ is

$$\psi(x_1, 0) = \frac{DU_\infty}{k_1\nu} \frac{f''(0)}{x_1^{1/2}} \tag{6.8-35}$$

or

$$\psi(\Delta) = \frac{1}{\Delta}, \tag{6.8-36}$$

where

$$\Delta \equiv \frac{k_1}{0.332 D}\left(\frac{\nu x}{U_\infty}\right)^{1/2}. \tag{6.8-37}$$

The implication of these results is that the curve obtained from the solution to the boundary layer equation for a first-order reaction on a flat plate for $Sc \to \infty$, $\psi(\xi)$ vs. ξ of Fig. 6.8-1, may be used for $Sc = 1$ when the abscissa ξ is replaced by Δ. Note that when $Sc = 1$, $\xi \approx \Delta$, which is evidence that the solution obtained by the Lighthill method is useful even for values of Sc as small as unity.

The method described above suggests that under conditions where boundary layer theory is applicable, the designer can obtain the general behavior of a system from the form of two or perhaps three asymptotic solutions instead of the numerical solution of the single problem under the conditions of interest. Although the suggested procedure may at first appear to involve more labor, in reality less labor is usually involved. Moreover, the solutions are in general more reliable, and the designer has the decided advantage of knowing how the solution depends *functionally* on the various parameters of the equations. He thereby gains a familiarity with the general behavior of the system which is far more intimate than he would from the results of numerical solutions.

Attention is again drawn to the last of our objectives, namely: to see how variations in the detailed surface kinetics influence the solution. These results will then be compared with methods based upon the uniformly accessible surface.

To apply the method of the uniformly accessible surface, we need a value for the over-all mass transfer coefficient $\bar{\beta}_m$. This in principle would be an experimental value found from a mass transfer experiment carried out in the absence of a chemical reaction. We do not have such a value for a flat plate; however, we can calculate it from Eq. 6.8-10. The local mass transfer coefficient β_m is, by definition,

$$\beta_m[C_\infty - C(x, 0)] \equiv -D\left(\frac{\partial C}{\partial y}\right)_{y=0} \tag{6.8-38}$$

where on the right-hand side of the equation, $-D(\partial C/\partial y)_{y=0}$ is the true local rate of mass transfer. Substituting Eq. 6.8-10 into Eq. 6.8-38 we obtain

$$\frac{\beta_m}{D} = -\frac{\text{Re}_L^{1/2}}{L}\left(\frac{\partial \psi}{\partial y_1}\right)_{y_1=0} = \text{Re}_L^{1/2}\text{Sc}^{1/3}\left(\frac{1}{(0.893)(9)^{1/3}}\right)\frac{\sqrt{\beta(x_1)}}{[\zeta(x_1)]^{1/3}}.$$
$$\tag{6.8-39}$$

From Eq. 6.8-17

$$\beta(x_1) = \frac{0.332}{x_1^{1/2}}, \tag{6.8-40}$$

and from Eq. 6.8-6 we obtain

$$[\zeta(x_1)]^{1/3} = \frac{x_1^{1/4}}{0.91}. \tag{6.8-41}$$

Therefore we may obtain upon substitution:

$$\frac{\beta_m x}{D} = 0.339\,\text{Sc}^{1/3}\left[\frac{U_\infty}{\nu x}\right]^{1/2}. \tag{6.8-42}$$

However, the definition of the over-all mass transfer coefficient is:

$$\bar{\beta}_m = \frac{1}{L}\int_0^L \beta_m x\,dx.$$

Carrying out the indicated integration, we get

$$\frac{\bar{\beta}_m L}{D} = 0.678\,\text{Re}_L^{1/2}\text{Sc}^{1/3}. \tag{6.8-43}$$

This expression for the mass transfer coefficient is based upon the Lighthill approximation. The coefficient 0.678 becomes 0.664 for $\text{Sc} = 1$.

Let us use the mass transfer coefficient $\bar{\beta}_m$ to predict the rate of over-all chemical reaction on a flat plate. To do this, we equate the rates of mass transfer and surface chemical reaction. The latter statement corresponds to the equation below.

$$\mathcal{R} = Lb\bar{\beta}_m(C_\infty - C_s) = Lbk_1 C_s, \tag{6.8-44}$$

where L = the length of the flat plate,

    b = the width of the flat plate,

    k_1 = first-order rate constant.

Solving Eq. 6.8-44 for C_s, and expressing the rate of the surface chemical reaction,

$$\mathcal{R} = \frac{Lbk_1C_\infty}{1 + (k_1/\bar{\beta}_m)} \tag{6.8-45}$$

Eq. 6.8-45 is the expected value of the rate of reaction based upon the lumped parameter $\bar{\beta}_m$.

The rate of reaction based upon the boundary layer solution is

$$\mathcal{R} = Lbk_1 \int_0^L C(x, 0) \, dx. \tag{6.8-46}$$

Transforming Eq. 6.8-46 and

$$\mathcal{R} = \frac{bk_1 2L}{\xi^2 L} \int_0^{\xi L} C(\xi)\xi \, d\xi \tag{6.8-47}$$

where

$$\xi(x) \equiv \frac{k_1}{0.339 \, Sc^{1/3} D} \left(\frac{\nu x}{U_\infty}\right)^{1/2}$$

Now for small values of ξ, Chambré and Acrivos* developed a series solution to Eq. 6.8-19 which is:

$$C(\xi) = C_\infty(1 - 0.731\xi + 0.453\xi^2 - 0.252\xi^3 + \ldots). \tag{6.8-48}$$

Substitution of Eq. 6.8-48 into 6.8-47, carrying out the integration and simplifying, yields

$$\mathcal{R} = Lbk_1 C_\infty[1 - 0.4873\xi(L) \\ + 0.2265\xi^2(L) - 0.1008\xi^3(L) + \ldots]. \tag{6.8-49}$$

We can now compare Eq. 6.8-49 with 6.8-45 noting that the latter can be written alternately as

$$\mathcal{R} = \frac{Lbk_1 C_\infty}{1 + \dfrac{\xi(L)}{2}}, \tag{6.8-50}$$

which when expanded as a series becomes

$$= Lbk_1 C_\infty[1 - 0.5\xi(L) + 0.25\xi^2(L) - 0.125\xi^3(L) + \ldots]. \tag{6.8-51}$$

A comparison of Eqs. 6.8-49 and 6.8-51 shows that numerical values computed from each of the series are extremely close in magnitude. In fact, the error made using the simplified treatment is probably much smaller than

* P. L. Chambré and A. Acrivos, *J. Appl. Phys.* **27**, 1322 (1956).

the error in the kinetic information. On the other hand, there is no way of knowing the magnitude of the error involved in using the simplified method except by comparing the results with those obtained by more rigorous methods. Thus we face the dilemma: (1) a simplified treatment which is powerful in general and almost always leads to an answer (but an approximate answer) and where an estimate of the closeness of the approximation is impossible owing to the nature of the method; or (2) a rigorous treatment which is fundamentally correct but is limited in its application to systems wherein the corresponding fluid mechanical problem can be solved. As a result, many important systems cannot be satisfactorily treated.

Theoretical investigations of isothermal reactions of greater kinetic complexity on a catalytic flat plate were reported by Acrivos and Chambré.* They studied the following first-order reactions:

Case 1: $A_1 \rightleftarrows A_2$

Case 2: $A_1 \rightarrow A_2 \rightarrow A_3$

and the second-order reaction

Case 3: $A_1 + A_2 \rightarrow A_3$

by the rigorous method outlined in this section. They compared the corresponding local rates of reaction with those based upon Eq. 6.8-44 with β_m of Eq. 6.8-42 substituted in place of $\bar{\beta}_m$. The magnitude of the discrepancy between their solutions should be greater than that found in our earlier comparison; nevertheless, the maximum error found was about 37 per cent and it occurred at the leading edge of the plate for Case 2. Downstream of the leading edge, the error decreased and even changed sign. An integration of the local rates to obtain the over-all rates as presented earlier would have given errors for these cases of the order of 15 to 20 per cent.

From these results there is a temptation to accept the simplified treatment using the argument that we cannot fuss over 15–20 per cent error when the error in the rate expressions themselves are usually greater. We must accept such a generalization with caution because it is based on results using highly simplified rate expressions in idealized systems. Acrivos and Chambré point out that in a series of consecutive reactions the errors can reach values greater than 120 per cent. Moreover, as we have shown in Chapter 4, the sensitivity of rate expressions to product inhibition might render the simplified treatment invalid. Therefore, while we may be forced to use the method of uniformly accessible surfaces in a kinetic analysis, we should bear in mind the possibility that the method will mask certain kinetic complications, making them more difficult to assess.

---

* A. Acrivos and P. L. Chambré, *Ind. Eng. Chem.* **6**, 1025 (1957).

NOTATION FOR CHAPTER 6

A_n	Defined by Eq. 6.5-3
A_i	ith species in a reaction mixture
A_n', B'	integration constants
$\mathscr{A}_1$, $\mathscr{A}_2$	integration constants
a	external surface area per unit volume of the catalytic pellet
a_i	stoichiometric coefficients
b	width of a flat plate
C	concentration
C_0	concentration of reactant at the external surface of a catalyst pellet
C_∞	concentration of reactant at large distances from the catalyst surface
D	diffusivity
D_e	effective diffusivity
ΔE	activation energy
E_c'	concentration gradient, $C_\infty/2R_0$
$\hat{h}_p$	generalized Thiele parameter for a pellet (see Chapter 4)
ΔH	enthalpy of reaction
k_n	true heterogeneous rate constant
k_n'	heterogeneous rate constant based upon a unit of external surface
f	defined by the relationship that $u_1 = f'(\omega)$ where primes indicate differentiation with respect to ω
L	characteristic dimension of the catalyst surface
n	exponent on order of the concentration in reaction rate expression
Nu_m	Nusselt number, $\beta_m R_0/D$
Nu_h	Nusselt number, $\beta_h R_0/\lambda_g$
p	Laplace transform variable
x_1, y_1, u_1, v_1, z_1	dimensionless quantities defined in Eq. 6.8-1
R	radial coordinate
R_0	radius of a spherical pellet
R_g	gas constant

Sc	Schmidt number
S	surface area per unit mass of catalyst
t	$\sqrt{2}[\xi(x_1) - \xi(z_1)]$
T	temperature
T_0	temperature at the external surface of a catalyst pellet
T_∞	temperature in the fluid phase far from catalyst external surface
T_f	fluid temperature
u	velocity component parallel to the catalyst surface
v	velocity component perpendicular to the catalyst surface
U_∞	velocity far from catalyst surface
x_1, y_1, u_1, v_1, z_1	dimensionless quantities defined in Eq. 6.8-1
x	coordinate along the catalyst surface
y	coordinate normal to the catalyst surface
y_2	defined by Eq. 6.8-5
z	$\beta(x_1)y_2^2/2t^{2/3}$
Z	defined by Eq. 6.8-27

GREEK

α_n	defined by Eq. 6.5-4
α_n'	defined by Eq. 6.5-17
β_m	mass transfer coefficient
β_h	heat transfer coefficient
$\beta(x_1)$	defined by Eq. 6.8-3
β'	derivative of $\beta(x_1)$
β_n	defined by Eq. 6.5-4
β_n'	defined by Eq. 6.5-18
$\bar{\beta}_m$	over-all mass transfer coefficient, see Eq. 6.8-43
γ_n	$= \dfrac{k_n R_0 C_\infty^{n-1}}{D}$
$\hat{\gamma}_n$	$= \gamma_n/\mathrm{Nu}$
Γ	gamma function
Δ	defined by Eq. 6.8-37
ϵ	defined by Eq. 6.5-4

ζ	defined by Eq. 6.8-6
η	$\equiv R/R_0$
κ	defined in Eq. 6.5-4
λ	effective thermal conductivity of catalyst pellet
λ_g	thermal conductivity of fluid phase surrounding pellet
μ	viscosity of the fluid
ν	kinematic viscosity of the fluid
ξ	defined by Eq. 6.8-18
ρ	fluid density
ρ_p	apparent density of a catalyst pellet
$\tau(x)$	$\mu\left(\dfrac{\partial u}{\partial y}\right)_{y=0}$, the shear stress
ϕ	$\equiv \displaystyle\int_0^x \sqrt{\tau(\alpha)}\, d\alpha$
ψ	dimensionless concentration
Ψ	$\mathscr{L}(\psi)$, the Laplace transform of ψ
ω	$y_1/x_1^{1/2}$
Θ	dimensionless temperature

SCRIPT

$\mathscr{E}$	effectiveness factor
$\mathscr{L}$	Laplace transform operator
$\mathscr{R}$	defined by Eq. 6.7-3
$\mathscr{R}_i$	defined by Eq. 6.7-2
$\mathscr{R}_n$	nth-order heterogeneous rate of reaction per unit area of external surface
$\mathscr{R}_x$	defined by Eq. 6.4-2
$\mathscr{T}$	transport factor

Conservation Equations

7

A huge gap appeared in the side of the mountains.
At last a tiny mouse poked its little head out
of the gap . . . . Much outcry, little outcome.

AESOP

7.1 Introduction

The prediction of the performance of a given catalytic reactor under a particular set of reaction conditions is rather easily stated in words—it involves the incorporation of the heterogeneous rate expression as a boundary condition to an appropriate set of conservation equations for each species present and a conservation equation for energy. When the flow conditions and the geometry of the system are extremely simple, as was the case in the example considered in Section 6.8, this approach may be feasible. The set of equations describing the system is generally linear and the nonlinearities appear only in the boundary conditions.

This is the correct way to analyze heterogeneous reactors. Unfortunately, we rarely can describe the catalytic surface geometrically and are forced therefore to abandon this approach. In its place we adopt a method based upon the pseudo-homogeneous rate expression as discussed in Sections 2.4 and 4.1. Now, the rate expression appears as a source term in the conservation equations, and although it is generally highly nonlinear, an enormous geometric simplification is affected. But there is a price for this simplification, and not an insignificant one, for there are conceptual difficulties as to how to describe all of the phenomena which arise owing to the presence of the solid phase. Only those properties which relate to the pseudo-homogeneous rate expression appear directly and, as we might expect, the other effects must be approximated by introducing phenomenological parameters whose numerical values are often estimated from models of the idealized behavior of the system. Since we cannot make the pseudo-homogeneous system correspond exactly to the real heterogeneous system, we must be in a position to decide which details of the system may be neglected and which must be retained in order to describe the essential features of the reacting system for the purpose at hand. Although this is not possible in a quantitative fashion, we shall qualitatively concern ourselves with this problem and show, when possible, the approximate magnitude of errors introduced by neglecting certain details.

7.2 Conservation equations

A completely general set of equations capable of describing any reactor would be exceedingly complex and would of necessity be symbolic in character. Moreover their abstractness and complexity would serve to confuse rather than illustrate the physical meaning and mathematical form of the various kinds of terms, of which the design equations are composed. Accordingly, we shall develop a more restricted set which is sufficiently general to contain representative types of terms and at the same time simple enough so that most of our attention can be given to the physical significance of each term.

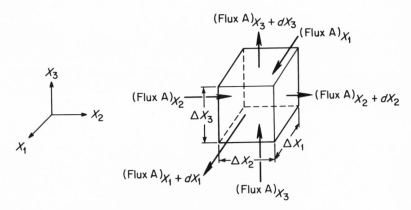

Fig. 7.2-1. Differential volume element within a reactor.

Figure 7.2-1 depicts a differential volume element within a heterogeneous reactor. Although the drawing is represented in Cartesian coordinates, the discussion to follow will be applicable to any orthogonal set of coordinates.*

---

* An elementary discussion of coordinate systems and vectors is given in Appendix I.

Within the control volume element a reaction is presumed to take place at a rate given by the pseudo-homogeneous rate law described earlier. This rate depends in general upon an impressive list of intensive properties and constants including the concentrations of the reactants and products, some characteristic temperature, the activity and concentration of the catalyst, and a series of parameters which account for transport phenomena, adsorption-desorption rate constants, kinetic rate constants and the like. The detailed dependence of the rate on each of the above variables and parameters is known when the design stage is reached and can be expressed as the function $\bar{\bar{\mathscr{R}}}$, the pseudo-homogeneous rate expression. Assume now that we know the nature of the function $\bar{\bar{\mathscr{R}}}$ for the simple reaction

$$\sum_{i=1}^{n} a_i A_i = 0 \tag{7.2-1}$$

A conservation equation for the ith species can now be set up. In words the familiar conservation equation is

$$\begin{pmatrix} \text{rate of accumulation} \\ \text{of the } i\text{th species in} \\ \text{the volume element} \end{pmatrix} = \begin{pmatrix} \text{net rate of inward flow} \\ \text{of the } i\text{th species through} \\ \text{the area enclosing the} \\ \text{volume element} \end{pmatrix} + \begin{pmatrix} \text{rate of genera-} \\ \text{tion of the } i\text{th} \\ \text{species in the} \\ \text{volume element} \end{pmatrix} \tag{7.2-2}$$

Before translating this word equation into its equivalent mathematical formulation, attention should be called to the fact that equations of this type are customarily set up on a unit volume basis. We shall adopt this custom here in setting up the conservation equations and when necessary transform them to other bases. Also, some remarks are in order with regard to the first term on the right-hand side of Eq. 7.2-2. In general, several terms in the final equation stem from this term. Material may flow into the control volume by various transport mechanisms and there will be a term in Eq. 7.2-2 corresponding to each. Thus, it is necessary to identify the various modes of material transport before the form of the conservation equation can be established.

Transport phenomena are always based upon the concept of a flux, that is the net amount which passes through a unit area per unit time. By definition, a flux is a vector quantity. Thus the amount of material passing through a unit area of a given orientation is equal to the scalar product of the flux vector and a unit vector normal to the unit area as shown on Fig. 7.2-2. If now by an integration process, we sum up all the scalar products of the flux and the unit vector normal to and pointing away from the surface enclosing the volume element, we obtain a quantity which is equal to the net *outward* flow of material from the volume element. In mathematical form

$$\begin{pmatrix} \text{net outward flow of} \\ \text{material from the} \\ \text{volume element per} \\ \text{unit time} \end{pmatrix} = \iint_{S} (\text{flux } A) \cdot n \, ds, \tag{7.2-3}$$

where (flux A) and n are the vectors shown in Fig. 7.2-2 and the limit S signifies integration over the area enclosing the volume element. From the divergence theorem, we learn that

$$\iint_S \text{flux } A \cdot \text{nds} = \iiint_V \text{div (flux } A) \, dV. \qquad (7.2\text{-}4)$$

Since Eq. 7.2-4 is true for any volume, including the elemental volume of Fig. 7.2-1, it follows that the integrands are identical leading to the useful result that the

$$\left. \begin{array}{l} \text{net outward flow of} \\ \text{material from the} \\ \text{volume element per} \\ \text{unit time per unit} \\ \text{volume} \end{array} \right\} = \text{div (flux).} \qquad (7.2\text{-}5)$$

It should be clear then that the first term on the right-hand side of Eq. 7.2-2 is made up of terms of the type $-\text{div (flux}_j)$. The index j refers to one

Fig. 7.2-2. Flow of material from a volume element.

of ℓ modes of transport in the system. Thus, Eq. 7.2-2 takes the form for component A_i

$$\frac{\partial C_i}{\partial t} = -\sum_{j=1}^{\ell} \text{div (flux}_j \, A_i) + a_i \bar{\mathscr{R}}, \qquad (7.2\text{-}6)$$

where the sign of the term $a_i \bar{\mathscr{R}}$ is positive to conform to the definitions of a_i and $\bar{\mathscr{R}}$ previously used in Section 2.2. For independent components one would obtain independent equations of the form of Eq. 7.2-6—for each species.

The general form of an energy equation may be also developed by parallel reasoning to obtain

$$\frac{\partial(\rho E)}{\partial t} = -\sum_{j=1}^{\ell'} \text{div (flux}_j \text{ of energy)} + (-\Delta H) \bar{\mathscr{R}}, \qquad (7.2\text{-}7)$$

where E is the energy, and ΔH is the enthalpy of reaction—negative for an exothermic reaction. From the simultaneous solution of k equations of the form of Eq. 7.2-6 and Eq. 7.2-7, it will in general be possible to determine the concentration and temperature profiles within the reactor.

The rate term $\mathscr{R}$ depends upon the concentration of the catalyst and its activity. In some cases, these are constant throughout the reactor. In other cases, the catalyst may be in motion and its activity may change appreciably during its residence within the reactor. Or the density, i.e., the mass of catalyst per unit of reactor volume, may vary within the reactor. When it is evident that these complications are present in the system, two additional equations are necessary: One which describes the point density and one which accounts for changes in the point value of the activity.

The first equation is

$$\frac{\partial \rho_B}{\partial t} = -\sum_{j=1}^{\ell''} \mathrm{div}\,(\mathrm{flux}_j \text{ of particles}), \qquad (7.2\text{-}8)$$

where ρ_B is the mass of catalyst per unit volume within the reactor.

Writing an equation for activity changes is not as easy, because in general the activity change is related to the detailed environmental conditions to which the catalyst has been exposed. One cannot, therefore, set up a general equation for activity change. One limiting case, which will be treated in more detail in Chapter 10, is based upon the assumption that the activity decline depends only on the time the catalyst resides in the reactor. This assumption obviously makes the activity equation independent of Eqs. 7.2-6, 7.2-7, and 7.2-8 and it may be solved separately.

7.3 Macroscopic transport phenomena in reactors

In order to use the equations of Section 7.2 for the design of reactors, we must specify the form of the various flux terms in the reactor. Since the effects of microscopic transport processes between the bulk fluid phase and the catalyst surface are already included in the pseudo-homogeneous rate expression, we shall concern ourselves here only with the macroscopic transport processes. We shall consider only two examples of fluxes for the purpose of illustrating the form of the summation term in Eq. 7.2-6.

The most commonly encountered transport mechanism, and generally the most important, is caused by convective flow. Material and energy are moved from point to point by convective processes in an amount depending on the product of the numerical magnitudes of some scalar intensive property and the velocity. For example, the magnitude of the flux of a component A in the x-direction is equal to

$$[\text{flow flux}_x\,A] = \bar{U}_x C_A \qquad (7.3\text{-}1)$$

where C_A is the concentration of A at the point x and $\bar{U}_x$ is the component of the average velocity in the x-direction. In the first part of Chapter 8, we shall deal with reactors in which it is only necessary to include this flux term in the conservation equation.

Another type of transport results from an *eddy diffusion* process, a process so named because of the apparent similarity between the mathematical forms of the eddy diffusive and molecular diffusive fluxes. Although this process will be considered in detail for fixed beds in Chapter 9, the final result for constant fluid density systems is written here to show its form.

$$[\text{eddy diffusive flux}_R \, A] = -E_{DR} \operatorname{grad} C_A \qquad (7.3\text{-}2)$$

An analogous form applies to the transport of energy.

Using the above modes of transport as examples, we take the negative divergences of Eqs. 7.3-1 and 7.3-2 and obtain two terms making up a part of the summation term in Eq. 7.2-6. Other modes of transport would be handled in a similar way.

Equations 7.2-6, 7.2-7, and 7.2-8 are certainly not in a usable form as yet; in fact the remainder of this book will be largely devoted to the application of these equations to particular types of reactors and the methods for their solution.

7.4 Remarks

The design equations of Section 7.2 are based upon rigorous concepts for smoothly varying fields. A careful look at the derivation of the divergence theorem in Appendix I will reveal that the differential volume chosen as the basis for the conservation equation must be small enough so that the field variation is smooth and to allow us to neglect second order terms in the Taylor's series expansion of the field variation over the length of the differential volume. In the discussion of the pseudo-rate expression, however, we decided that in order for such an expression to have meaning, the differential volume for reactor analysis should contain a "statistical" number of catalytic pellets and at the same time be small compared to the reactor. Smooth variation is incompatible with these latter requirements, for as we have already seen, large external and internal diffusion resistances tend to make large changes in the concentration as we approach and enter the solid porous structure.

Clearly then, the conservation equations which we have do not rigorously apply to reactors when the differential volume contains a statistical number of particles. Alternately, if these equations are forced to apply, by definition as it were, then the concentrations and temperatures which they contain as dependent variables are no longer the measurable point values, nor are they the simple space average of the point variable. In fact, the difficulties we face in trying to decide how to formulate the new average dependent variables are conceptual ones which we have already discussed at the end of Chapter 2.

This situation should not surprise the reader because it is for this very reason that the pseudo-homogeneous rate expression is used, and it is a part of the price for invoking this simplification. Clearly, we could not solve this problem before, and there is no reason to suppose that we can now. However, concern over this point seems to be more philosophical than practical.

NOTATION FOR CHAPTER 7

a_i	stoichiometric coefficient $a_i < 0$ is a reactant
	$a_i > 0$ is a product
A_i	ith species in a reaction mixture
C_i	concentration of ith species
E	internal energy
E_{DR}	radial eddy diffusivity
ΔH	enthalpy of reaction
n	vector normal to surface enclosing a differential volume element
$\bar{\mathscr{R}}$	pseudo-homogeneous rate
S	area
t	time
$\bar{U}_x$	component of the average velocity in the x-direction
V	volume
x_1, x_2, x_3	Cartesian coordinates

GREEK

ρ_B	mass of catalyst per unit volume of reactor space

Fixed-bed Reactors

8

"The time has come," the Walrus said, "To talk of
many things; Of shoes—and ships—and sealing wax
—Of cabbages—and Kings—And why the sea is
boiling hot—And whether pigs have wings."

LEWIS CARROLL

8.1 Introduction

In its simplest form a fixed-bed reactor consists of a cylindrical tube
packed with pellets of catalyst. Reactants are passed through the bed of
catalyst and converted into products in an amount depending upon the
parameters of the system such as the flow rate, concentrations, temperature,
length of the reactor, etc. The difficulty which the designer will experience
in calculating the performance of a reactor will depend upon the nature of
the reaction and the physical requirements necessary to maintain steady
operation. For example, when the heat of reaction is very small, the resulting
system may be viewed as isothermal, and it is often possible to obtain a
closed-form expression for the conversion in terms of the parameters of the
system. On the other hand, when reactions are either highly exothermic or
endothermic, large amounts of heat must frequently be transferred between
the surroundings and the reactor to keep the temperature within prescribed
bounds. In the latter case an analytical solution is in general out of the question and it is necessary to integrate each case numerically for a given set of
parameters.

We shall consider the design equations for fixed-bed reactors of increasing
mathematical difficulty in terms of the pseudo-homogeneous rate expression
and averaged values of the dependent variables in the reactor space.

175

8.2 The isothermal reactor

The simplest fixed-bed reactor is isothermal. When the average velocity $\bar{U}$ and the temperature in the bed are independent of radial position, the reactor is one-dimensional. Radial transport processes can be neglected because no *net* exchange of material and energy occurs along the radial coordinate. The conservation equation applicable to reactors of this type contains only the flow flux term if axial diffusion is neglected.

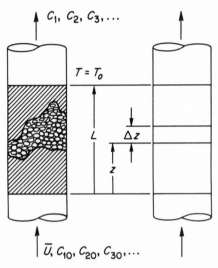

Fig. 8.2-1. Fixed bed reactor.

Consider a reactor of this type, shown schematically in Fig. 8.2-1, wherein a simple reaction occurs of the form

$$\sum_{i=1}^{n} a_i A_i = 0, \tag{8.2-1}$$

where as before $a_i < 0$ is a reactant and $a_i > 0$ is a product. The initial concentration of A_i is C_{i0}. For uniformly packed beds of particles, $C_i(Z)$ and $\bar{U}(Z)$ are averaged concentrations and averaged velocity in the differential volume per unit cross-section ΔZ. The conservation equation, 7.2-6 may be simplified to

$$-\frac{d(\bar{U}C_i)}{dZ} = \bar{\mathcal{R}}_i(C_1, C_2, C_3, \ldots, C_n) = a_i \bar{\bar{\mathcal{R}}} \qquad (i = 1, 2, 3, \ldots, n). \tag{8.2-2}$$

Equations 8.2-2 are identical in form to Eq. 2.2-8 previously developed. As before they may be transformed to

$$-\frac{G_0}{\bar{M}}\frac{dY_i}{dZ} = \bar{\mathcal{R}}_i(Y_1, Y_2, Y_3, \ldots, Y_n) = a_i \bar{\bar{\mathcal{R}}} \qquad (i = 1, 2, 3, \ldots, n), \tag{8.2-3}$$

where $Y_i \equiv$ moles of A_i per mass of fluid numerically equal to the average
molecular weight of the feed, thus the variable Y in the feed is
numerically equal to the mole fraction.

G_0 = mass velocity.

$\bar{M}$ = average molecular weight of feed.

For the system described above, the solution to Eq. 8.2-3 is obtained from
the quadrature

$$\int_{Y_{i0}}^{Y_{iL}} \frac{dY_i}{a_i \bar{\mathscr{R}}} = -\frac{\bar{M}L}{G_0}. \qquad (8.2\text{-}4)$$

In the design of reactors the designer generally asks one of the following
questions: What length of reactor, L, is needed to obtain a desired conversion

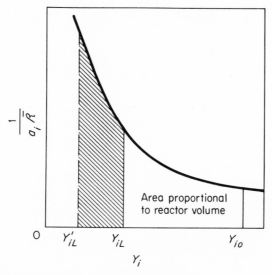

Fig. 8.2-2. Method for the graphical solution to Eq. 8.2-4 from
which the length of reactor is computed.

Y_i? Or, what conversion Y_i does one obtain from a reactor of length L?
The answer to either question is obtained in a straightforward way from
Eq. 8.2-4. Figure 8.2-2 is a graphical representation of the quadrature and
of course the area on the graph is proportional to the length of the reactor
required to obtain a given conversion Y_{iL}. Note that additional conversion
corresponding to an output conversion of Y'_{iL} requires an additional length
of reactor proportional to the cross-hatched area on the figure.

Note also that scale-up of this type of reactor is extremely simple in that
the conversion is independent of the cross-sectional area of the fixed bed.
But more than this can be inferred. Equation 8.2-4 would predict the same

conversion if the ratio $\bar{M}L/G_0$ remains constant. The volume of the catalyst bed V and the mass flow rate F are related to this ratio, i.e.,

$$\frac{V}{F} = \frac{L(\text{cross-sectional area of the reactor})}{G_0(\text{cross-sectional area of the reactor})}$$

Accordingly the reactors shown in Fig. 8.2-3 are identical in performance *provided $\bar{\mathcal{R}}$ is not a function of G_0*. For example, $\bar{\mathcal{R}}$ will be a function of G_0 when external mass transfer offers appreciable resistance to the transport of reactants to the reaction center as discussed in Chapter 6. Under these conditions the conversion is not a unique function of V/F. These points become relevant in the design of experiments to obtain kinetic information.

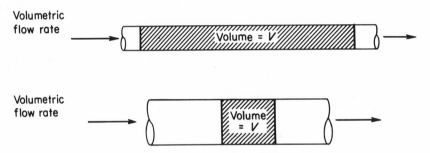

Fig. 8.2-3. Isothermal reactors giving identical conversions.

The analysis of a set of complex reactions introduces additional complications in that a set of differential equations must be solved simultaneously. This set has already been developed in Eq. 2.3-24:

$$\frac{G_0}{\bar{M}}\frac{dY_i}{dZ} = \sum_{j=1}^{k} a_{ij}\bar{\mathcal{R}}_j \qquad (i = 1, 2, 3, \ldots, n). \tag{8.2-5}$$

In the previous reference to this equation, the problem was to develop the functional form of the rate expressions $\bar{\mathcal{R}}_j$ from information on the integral conversion under various conditions. The problem here is simpler in that we now presume a knowledge of the functions $\bar{\mathcal{R}}_j$ and desire conversion information with a prescribed set of parameters. In general, the functional form of the right-hand side of Eq. 8.2-5 precludes the possibility of an analytical solution, and we must normally resort to numerical procedures. The form of Eq. 8.2-5 suggests a number of standard techniques which may be modified to serve as the basis of the numerical method. However, the method which we shall develop here is an integral method somewhat analogous to that suggested by Schilson and Amundson* and can be readily programmed for

* R. E. Schilson and N. R. Amundson, *Chem. Eng. Sci.* **17**, 674 (1962). See also Z. Kopal, *Numerical Analysis*, John Wiley & Sons, Inc., New York, 1955, p. 465.

a digital computer. Although the method is illustrated here by a system of two equations, it may be readily generalized.

Consider the following set of equations:

$$\left.\begin{array}{l} \dfrac{dY_1}{dZ} = -\dfrac{\bar{M}}{G_0}[a_{11}\bar{\mathscr{R}}_1 + a_{12}\bar{\mathscr{R}}_2] = \imath_1(Y_1, Y_2) \\[4mm] \dfrac{dY_2}{dZ} = -\dfrac{\bar{M}}{G_0}[a_{21}\bar{\mathscr{R}}_1 + a_{22}\bar{\mathscr{R}}_2] = \imath_2(Y_1, Y_2) \end{array}\right\} \qquad (8.2\text{-}6)$$

Since Y_1 and Y_2 are unknown, but nevertheless are functions of Z, it is possible to write

$$\left.\begin{array}{l} \imath_1(Y_1, Y_2) \equiv \digamma_1(Z)Y_1 + \digamma_2(Z) \\[2mm] \imath_2(Y_1, Y_2) \equiv \digamma_3(Z)Y_2 + \digamma_4(Z) \end{array}\right\} \qquad (8.2\text{-}7)$$

Therefore:

$$\frac{dY_1}{dZ} - \digamma_1(Z)Y_1 = \digamma_2(Z). \qquad (8.2\text{-}8)$$

The solution to Eq. 8.2-8 is formally:

$$Y_1(Z) = e^{\int \digamma_1(Z)\,dZ}\left[\int e^{-\int \digamma_1(Z)\,dZ} \digamma_1(Z)\,dZ + \text{const}\right]. \qquad (8.2\text{-}9)$$

Similarly for $Y_2(Z)$:

$$Y_2(Z) = e^{\int \digamma_3(Z)\,dZ}\left[\int e^{-\int \digamma_3(Z)\,dZ} \digamma_4(Z)\,dZ + \text{const}\right]. \qquad (8.2\text{-}10)$$

The proposal here is to solve this set by consecutive iterations, as follows: For the first iteration, write an approximation for $\imath_1$, designated as $\imath_1^{(1)}$, such that

$$\imath_1^{(1)}(Y_1, Y_2) = \digamma_1(Y_{10}, Y_{20})Y_1 + \digamma_2(Y_{10}, Y_{20}), \qquad (8.2\text{-}11)$$

where Y_{10} and Y_{20} are the initial values of Y_1 and Y_2. Thus

$$\imath_1^{(1)}(Y_1, Y_2) = \digamma_1^{(1)}Y_1 + \digamma_2^{(1)}, \qquad (8.2\text{-}12)$$

where $\digamma_1^{(1)}$ and $\digamma_2^{(2)}$ are constants. Therefore, the first approximation for Y_1, $Y_1^{(1)}$, comes from Eq. 8.2-9 and upon integration is equal to

$$Y_1^{(1)}(Z) = Y_{10}e^{\digamma_1^{(1)}Z} - \frac{\digamma_2^{(1)}}{\digamma_1^{(1)}}(1 - e^{\digamma_1^{(1)}Z}). \qquad (8.2\text{-}13)$$

From Eq. 8.2-13 we can obtain an approximate idea of the conversion as a function of reactor length which is valuable in knowing how far to carry out the numerical integrations which appear in the remaining iterations. Next $\imath_2^{(1)}(Y_1, Y_2)$ is obtained by substituting Y_{20} and $Y_1^{(1)}$ for Y_1 and Y_2 in $\digamma_3$ and $\digamma_4$. In general then, $\digamma_3^{(1)}$ and $\digamma_4^{(1)}$ are functions of Z and are known. These are substituted into Eq. 8.2-10 to obtain an estimate of $Y_2^{(1)}(Z)$. The procedure is now repeated using both $Y_1^{(1)}$ and $Y_2^{(1)}$ to obtain $\digamma_1^{(2)}$ and $\digamma_2^{(2)}$.

The iterative procedure is continued until no appreciable difference is found between $Y_1^{(n)}$ and $Y_1^{(n-1)}$, and $Y_2^{(n)}$ and $Y_2^{(n-1)}$. Experience with this type of calculation shows rapid convergence in a few iterations.

8.3 The adiabatic reactor

The adiabatic reactor is more commonly encountered in practice than the isothermal reactor. In steady-state operation, as the name implies, all of the heat generated or adsorbed as a result of the heat of reaction manifests itself in a change in enthalpy of the fluid stream. For simple reactions the temperature changes monotonically throughout the reactor length. In principle, very few additional complications are introduced in the analysis of this type of reactor over those already considered for isothermal reactors. To the extent that heat transfer between the catalyst and the fluid phase is very rapid, we can write an energy equation which expresses the condition that all of the energy released or absorbed at a point within a reactor goes to or comes from the fluid phase instantaneously. Thus, to describe the progress of a simple reaction in an adiabatic reactor, we need the energy equation shown below in addition to Eq. 8.2-3.

$$G_0 \bar{C} \frac{dT}{dZ} = \bar{\mathscr{R}}(Y_1, Y_2, Y_3, \ldots, Y_n, T) \sum_{i=1}^{n} a_i \bar{H}_i, \qquad (8.3\text{-}1)$$

where $\bar{H}_i$ is the enthalpy per mole of the ith species in the mixture and $\bar{C}$ is the mean heat capacity of the mixture. If ΔH_R is the enthalpy change for the reaction

$$\sum_{i=1}^{n} a_i A_i = 0,$$

then Eq. 8.3-1 becomes

$$G_0 \bar{C} \frac{dT}{dZ} = -\Delta H_R \bar{\mathscr{R}}. \qquad (8.3\text{-}2)$$

Equation 8.2-3 for an adiabatic reactor is

$$\frac{G_0}{\bar{M}} \frac{dY_i}{dZ} = a_i \bar{\mathscr{R}}. \qquad (8.3\text{-}3)$$

Dividing Eqs. 8.3-2 by 8.3-3,

$$\frac{dT}{dY_i} = \frac{-\Delta H_R}{\bar{M} \bar{C} a_i}. \qquad (8.3\text{-}4)$$

When the parameters on the right-hand side of Eq. 8.3-4 are constants,

$$T - T_0 = \frac{-\Delta H_R}{\bar{M} \bar{C} a_i} [Y_i - Y_{i0}], \qquad (8.3\text{-}5)$$

where T_0 and Y_{i0} are, respectively, the initial temperature and initial concentration of A_i. The temperature and all other species are unique functions of Y_i, and the solution to the adiabatic reactor may be obtained by the same method used for the isothermal reactor. Note that the design equations again predict a unique conversion for a given ratio L/G_0. This follows from the assumption of instantaneous heat transfer and a neglect of axial temperature gradients in the bed. These effects will be discussed in greater detail later in this chapter.

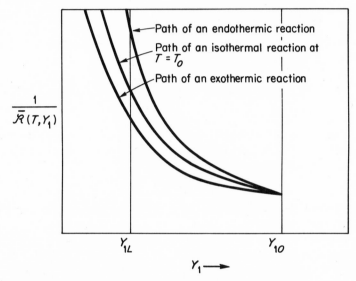

Fig. 8.3-1. Graphical solution to determine the volume of an adiabatic reactor.

Figure 8.3-1 shows a qualitative and hypothetical comparison of the paths of integration of exothermic and endothermic adiabatic reactions and an isothermal reaction. As we should expect, a given conversion is obtained in a shorter reactor for an exothermic reaction than for either the isothermal or endothermic reaction.

Complex reactions carried out adiabatically are a little more difficult to handle than are simple reactions. However, the method of treatment is similar and again, fortunately, the system reduces to the same number of equations to be solved simultaneously as for the isothermal case.

The energy equation which must be added to the set of Eqs. 8.2-6 in order to analyze the adiabatic case is

$$G_0 \bar{C} \frac{dT}{dZ} = \sum_{i=1}^{n} \bar{H}_i P_i, \qquad (8.3\text{-}6)$$

where $\tilde{H}_i$ is the partial molal enthalpy of the ith species in the mixture and P_i is the production of the ith species as a result of k reactions as defined by Eq. 2.3-7. Since P_g, $k + 1 \leq g \leq n$, are not independent, the right-hand term of Eq. 8.3-6 may be rewritten in terms of Eq. 2.3-15 as follows:

$$\sum_{i=1}^{n} \tilde{H}_i P_i = \sum_{i=1}^{k} \tilde{H}_i P_i + \sum_{g=k+1}^{n} \tilde{H}_g \sum_{i=1}^{k} \gamma_{gi} P_i. \tag{8.3-7}$$

Then from Eq. 2.3-25 we obtain

$$G_0 \bar{C} \frac{dT}{dZ} = \sum_{i=1}^{k} \tilde{H}_i \frac{G_0}{\bar{M}} \frac{dY_i}{dZ} + \sum_{g=k+1}^{n} \left[\tilde{H}_g \sum_{i=1}^{k} \gamma_{gi} \frac{G_0}{\bar{M}} \frac{dY_i}{dZ} \right], \tag{8.3-8}$$

which can be immediately integrated to give upon rearrangement and simplification

$$(T - T_0) = \frac{1}{\bar{C}\bar{M}} \sum_{i=1}^{k} (Y_i - Y_{i0}) \left[\tilde{H}_i + \sum_{g=k+1}^{n} \gamma_{gi} \tilde{H}_g \right]. \tag{8.3-9}$$

Defining ΔH_i now as

$$\Delta H_i \equiv \tilde{H}_i + \sum_{g=k+1}^{n} \gamma_{gi} \tilde{H}_g, \tag{8.3-10}$$

we obtain

$$T - T_0 = \overline{M} \bar{C} \sum_{i=1}^{k} (Y_i - Y_{i0})(\Delta H_i) \tag{8.3-11}$$

Thus, as before, the temperature may be calculated directly from the concentrations of the k dependent variables Y_i. The method of integration suggested for isothermal reactions therefore applies with the modification that temperature affects the rate expressions.

8.4 The nonisothermal reactor

The most commonly encountered fixed-bed reactor is nonisothermal. In this kind of reactor, as with the adiabatic reactor, the temperature changes with the extent of reaction; however, unlike the adiabatic reactor, there is an exchange of energy with its surroundings during the course of reaction. The temperature drop associated with an endothermic reaction is partly offset by heating the reactor; thus the reactor size is reduced. A highly exothermic reaction raises the temperature of the system as conversion progresses which is desirable from the standpoint of decreasing the reactor size, but for other reasons is undesirable. For example, excessively high temperatures are often deleterious to the catalyst activity as well as to the unit. In these cases provision is made to remove heat to reduce the maximum temperature in the system, the so-called hot-spot temperature, to a value below which no rapid catalyst deterioration occurs. Heat exchange equipment, which may be necessary from the operational point of view, greatly increases the difficulty in designing the reactor, because of the appearance of temperature gradients perpendicular to the direction of flow. Accompanying the temperature gradients are also concentration gradients. As a result, we lose the one-dimensional character of the reactor. Temperatures and concentrations are now functions of radial as well as axial position. It follows then that there is, in reality, no one-dimensional nonisothermal counterpart of the isothermal or adiabatic reactors. However, it is possible in some instances to approximate the performance of a nonisothermal reactor by a one-dimensional model which is useful to obtain the approximate size and performance of a reactor for a preliminary survey or may be quite accurately applicable in reactors of small diameter. It is with these objectives in mind that a presentation of the one-dimensional nonisothermal reactor is made.

Two equations are needed to describe the simple reaction given in Eq. 8.2-1; one similar to Eq. 8.2-3, and an energy equation similar to Eq. 8.3-2 to which is added a term accounting for heat exchange with the surroundings. These equations are

$$\frac{G_0}{\bar{M}}\frac{dY_1}{dz} = a_1\bar{\mathscr{R}} \tag{8.4-1}$$

and

$$G_0\bar{C}\frac{dT}{dz} = (-\Delta H_R)\bar{\mathscr{R}} - \bar{h}_T a(T - T_w) \tag{8.4-2}$$

where $\bar{\mathscr{R}} = \bar{\mathscr{R}}(Y_1, Y_2, Y_3, \ldots, Y_n)$ and $\bar{h}_T$ is a heat transfer coefficient expressing a resistance to heat transfer between the wall of the reactor and the reactor volume. The factor a is the surface area for heat transfer per unit volume of reactor. The wall temperature is assumed constant and equal to T_w. It is important to recognize that $\bar{h}_T$ is *not* a heat transfer coefficient in the ordinary sense, but rather a phenomenological parameter dependent upon the nature of the rate term in addition to the usual fluid properties and flow conditions. Although the value of this parameter will be considered as known in this treatment, it must be admitted that this situation is rarely true. We shall amplify this point in a little more detail in Chapter 9.

Equations 8.4-1 and 8.4-2 can be solved by a numerical scheme. However, it is more instructive as well as in better keeping with our objectives if we first attempt to learn as much as possible before becoming involved in extensive numerical work.

In the design of reactors wherein heat exchange with the surroundings continuously occurs during conversion, the important considerations are the hot-spot temperature, $T_{\max}$ in the case of exothermic reactions and the cold-spot temperature, $T_{\min}$ in the case of endothermic reactions. To this end it would be valuable to have a rapid method whereby the numerical values of the parameters needed to keep the temperature changes within prescribed bounds could be estimated.

Let us consider the case of an exothermic reaction in a piston-flow reactor. Inspection of Eqs. 8.4-1 and 8.4-2 reveals that the hot-spot temperature, i.e., where $dT/dZ = 0$, gives an equality between the rate of generation of energy from the reaction and the rate of heat removal. Direct use of this relationship is prevented, because the values of Y_i are unknown functions of T. However, experience shows that the operation is very close to adiabatic near the reactor entrance when the inlet temperature is close to T_w, i.e., $T_0 - T_w$ is small. As the reaction progresses, $T - T_w$ grows and the heat transferred from the system increases. However, $\bar{\mathscr{R}}$ increases exponentially during the stage where Y_i is close to Y_{i0} and therefore grows much faster than $T - T_w$. Then as Y_i is consumed, the quantity $(-\Delta H_R)\bar{\mathscr{R}}$ decreases even though the temperature increases and eventually this curve intersects the heat transfer rate curve.

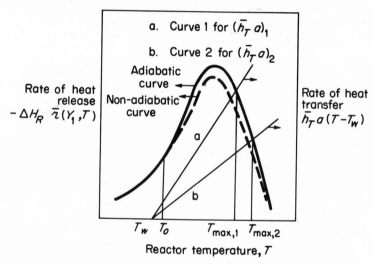

Fig. 8.4-1. A comparison of chemical reaction heat release rate and heat transfer rate as a function of reactor temperature.

A plot of the form of $(-\Delta H_R)\bar{\mathscr{R}}$ based upon the adiabatic reactor versus T is shown on Fig. 8.4-1 and is labeled the adiabatic curve. Curves 1 and 2 represent the heat transfer rates from the reactor for two values of $(h_T a)_1$ and $(h_T a)_2$, respectively. The intersection of these curves is an estimate of $T_{\max}$, the hot-spot temperature. It will be higher than the true $T_{\max}$ for the system because the nonadiabatic curve is lower than the adiabatic curve as sketched in Fig. 8.4-1, and the intersection occurs at a lower temperature. Note that the position of the nonadiabatic curve depends upon the magnitude of $h_T a$. Obviously, the greater the numerical value of $h_T a$, the lower this curve will be. Correspondingly, the position of the estimated value of $T_{\max}$

will be at a smaller value of z than the true position; however, this is rarely of concern.

The reactor length needed to obtain a given conversion can be estimated if the approximate temperature profile through the reactor is known. Following the development above, the temperature is assumed to be the adiabatic temperature from T_0 to the estimated T_{max}, where the latter is obtained from Fig. 8.4-1 or its algebraic equivalent obtained by setting the right-hand side of Eq. 8.4-2 equal to zero. In this way we can obtain Y_1 and T as a function of Z using Eq. 8.4-1.* This is shown on Fig. 8.4-2.

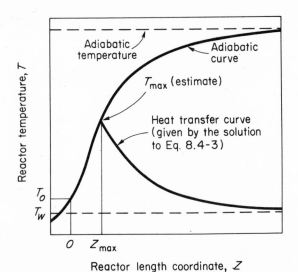

Reactor length coordinate, Z

Fig. 8.4-2. Estimated temperature profile in a nonisothermal one-dimensional reactor.

The temperature profile at greater values of Z is estimated from Eq. 8.4-2 assuming that the reaction term is negligible, i.e.,

$$G_0 \bar{C} \frac{dT}{dz} = -h_T a(T - T_w), \qquad (8.4\text{-}3)$$

where the boundary condition is at

$$Z = Z_{max}; \qquad T = T_{max}. \qquad (8.4\text{-}4)$$

The desired estimate of the conversion as a function of reactor length L is obtained numerically from Eq. 8.4-1:

$$\int_{Y_{1_0}}^{Y_{1_L}} \frac{dY_i}{f(Y_i)} = \frac{\bar{M} a_1 k_0}{G_0} \int_0^L e^{-\frac{\Delta E}{R_g T^{(0)}(Z)}} \, dZ, \qquad (8.4\text{-}5)$$

* Or Eq. 8.3-3.

where $\quad\bar{\mathscr{R}}(Y_1, T) = e^{-(\Delta E/R_g T)}f(Y_1)$,

$\qquad k_0 = $ pre-exponential factor, and

$\qquad T^{(0)}(Z) = $ estimated temperature as a function of Z shown on Fig. 8.4-2.

Although it may be useful for certain purposes, this estimate of the conversion for various reactor lengths is very crude, and there is no really good way of knowing how much error has been made. This solution, however, is a good starting point for an iterative method similar to that used to solve Eqs. 8.2-6. To summarize the method, Eq. 8.4-2 may be written:

$$G_0\bar{C}\frac{dT}{dZ} + \bar{h}_T a(T - T_w) = f_1(Z), \qquad (8.4\text{-}6)$$

where $f_1(Z) = (-\Delta H_R)\bar{\mathscr{R}}[Y_1(Z), T(Z)]$.

If a first estimate of $f_1(Z)$, $f_1^{(1)}(Z)$, is obtained by substituting the value of $Y_1(Z)$ from Eq. 8.4-5 and $T^{(0)}(Z)$, then Eq. 8.4-6 is a homogeneous linear equation and its solution is

$$T^{(1)}(Z) - T_w = e^{-\beta Z}\int_0^Z \frac{e^{\beta Z}f_1(Z)}{G_0\bar{C}}\,dZ + T_0 - T_w, \qquad (8.4\text{-}7)$$

where $\beta \equiv \bar{h}_T a/G_0\bar{C}$.

The new profile $T^{(1)}(Z)$ is then substituted into Eq. 8.4-5 in place of $T^{(0)}(Z)$ and a new value of Y_1 computed as a function of Z from Eq. 8.4-1. The process can be repeated until successive iterations are within the precision of the desired result. This method is easily programmed for digital computers. Although somewhat more involved, similar methods can be adapted to the analysis of complex reactions.

A discussion of the more realistic two-dimensional reactor will be taken up in Section 8.8.

8.5 Autothermal and counter-current one-dimensional reactors

One important use of the one-dimensional treatment of reactors is the prediction of the general performance and stability characteristics of autothermal and counter-current reactors.

Figure 8.5-1 illustrates schematically some examples of this kind of reactor system. In the commercial manufacture of ammonia* and sulfuric acid, autothermal reactors represented by the flow schemes of Fig. 8.5-1(a), (b) are used as well as combinations and variations of this general idea. The

---

* See for example: L. B. Hein, *Chem. Eng. Progr.* **48**, 412 (1956); E. W. Comings, *High Pressure Technology*, McGraw-Hill Book Company, New York, 1956; Jorgen Kjaer, *Measurement and Calculation of Temperature and Conversion in Fixed Bed Catalytic Reactors*, Jul. Gjellerups Forlag Copenhagen, 1958.

counter-current reactor system shown in Fig. 8.5-1(c) is really a variation of the nonisothermal reactor discussed in the previous section except that the coolant flow rate is no longer great enough to permit the assumption of a constant wall temperature. In autothermal reactor systems, the heat liberated

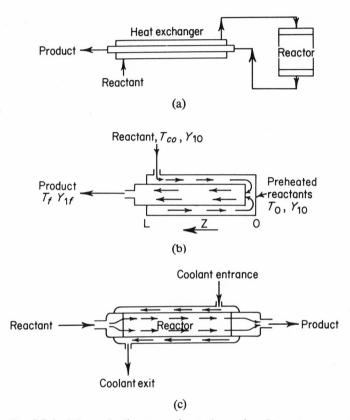

Fig. 8.5-1. Schematic diagrams of autothermal and counter-current reactor systems (a) reactor and heat exchanger, (b) autothermal reactor, (c) counter-current reactor.

as a result of chemical reaction is utilized to heat the reactants to suitable temperatures by providing heat exchange surfaces between the reactor bed and preheat zone. The operating temperature levels in the reactor are thereby raised. Although not as immediately apparent, under certain conditions a similar behavior is predicted for counter-current systems. The parametric sensitivity characteristics of these reactors has been discussed by Grens and McKean* [Fig. 8.5-1(c)] and van Heerden† [Fig. 8.5-1(a), (b)]. These authors

* E. A. Grens II and R. A. McKean, *Chem. Eng. Sci.* **18**, 291 (1963).
† C. van Heerden, *Ind. Eng. Chem.* **45**, 1242 (1953); *Ind. Chem. Belge* **27**, 910 (1962).

have shown that for certain values of the parameters, the temperatures in these systems can become very high.

Although it shows these same characteristics, the combination of a heat exchanger and an adiabatic reactor shown in Fig. 8.5-1(a) will not be discussed as the analysis to obtain the maximum temperature can be made from the discussion in Section 8.3 and a knowledge of the performance of the heat exchangers.

The exchanger-reactor systems shown in Fig. 8.5-1(b), (c) as well as modifications and combinations of them, are not so readily analyzed. They are partially described, in the one-dimensional approximation, by Eqs. 8.4-1 and 8.4-2. However, an additional equation must be written for the variation in wall temperature T_w which changes with position, owing to heat transfer and to the fact that the coolant* maximum flow rate is finite. This analysis is generally carried out by a generalization of the methods used to predict the performance of heat exchangers.

In place of the $h_T a(T - T_w)$ term of Eq. 8.4-2, we substitute $U a_R(T - T_C)$ to give

$$G_0 \bar{C} \frac{dT}{dZ} = (-\Delta H)\,\bar{\mathcal{R}} - U_h a_R(T - T_C), \qquad (8.5\text{-}1)$$

where U_h† = overall heat transfer coefficient between the reactor stream and the coolant stream,

a_R = heat transfer area per unit length of exchanger divided by the cross-sectional area for flow on the reactor side of the exchanger, and

T_C = temperature of the coolant at the position in the exchanger-reactor where the temperature of the reactants is T.

To describe the variation in the coolant temperature the following conservation equation is added.

$$G_{0c} \bar{C}_c \frac{dT_C}{dZ} + U_h a_c(T - T_c) = 0, \qquad (8.5\text{-}2)$$

where G_{0c} = mass flux of coolant through system,

$\bar{C}_c$ = mean heat capacity of the coolant stream, and

a_c = heat transfer area per unit length divided by the cross-sectional area for flow on the coolant side of the exchanger.

The combination of Eqs. 8.4-1, 8.5-1, and 8.5-2 complete the description of the system except for the boundary conditions. The boundary conditions corresponding to the systems of Fig. 8.5-1(c) are simply the inlet concentration and temperature of the reacting stream and the inlet temperature of

---

* The inlet reactant is referred to as the coolant for the system of Fig. 8.5-1(b).

† Refer to any standard text on unit operations. See for example Coulson and Richardson, "Unit Operations," Vol. I, McGraw-Hill Book Company, New York, 1954.

the coolant stream. For the system shown in Fig. 8.5-1(b) we specify the inlet coolant temperature, the inlet reactant concentration, and that the outlet coolant temperature be equal to the inlet reactant temperature.

Owing to the highly nonlinear function $\bar{\mathscr{R}}$ in Eq. 8.5-1, a general analysis of these systems cannot be carried out analytically. We shall consider two cases which give some insight into the behavior of this kind of system. The first is an example of an ammonia converter which is represented by Fig. 8.5-1(b).

The reactant mixture enters the exchanger system at some specified temperature T_{c0} and is heated to a temperature T_0 which is equal to the inlet temperature to the reactor. Because no catalyst is present in the exchanger, no conversion takes place. Subsequently, the heated reactants enter the catalyst section wherein conversion takes place and exothermic heat of reaction is given off. The heat released manifests itself in the form of sensible heat in the reacting mixture within the reactor section and in the heat exchanger section according to Eqs. 8.5-1 and 8.5-2. The mathematical problem is complicated by the fact that the boundary conditions are split, i.e., one is at $Z = 0$ and the other at $Z = L$. For the reactor and coolant sections the boundary conditions are:

$$\left. \begin{array}{llll} \text{Reactor section:} & Z = 0: & Y_1 = Y_{10}, & T_c = T = T_0 \\ \text{Coolant section:} & Z = L: & Y_1 = Y_{10}, & T_c = T_{c0} \end{array} \right\} \quad (8.5\text{-}3)$$

There is no way to start numerical integration of the equations.

This difficulty was obviated by van Heerden[*] using the following method. Assume a value of T_0. Then Eqs. 8.4-1, 8.5-1, and 8.5-2 can be integrated to calculate T_{c0} and T_f at $Z = L$ for various choices of T_0. These results[†] are shown in Fig. 8.5-2 where the temperature difference, $T_0 - T_{c0}$, is plotted versus T_0. The values of $\bar{\mathscr{R}}$ in Eq. 8.5-1 were computed from the rate expression for ammonia synthesis.[‡] The parameter γ on these curves is easily developed from Eq. 8.5-2 which, when rearranged, becomes

$$\frac{dT_c}{d\eta} + \gamma(T - T_c) = 0, \qquad (8.5\text{-}4)$$

where $\eta \equiv Z/L$, $\gamma \equiv U_h a_c L/G_{0c}\bar{C}_c$, and $L = $ length of the reactor. Note also that for this kind of reactor-exchanger system

$$\frac{U a_c L}{G_{0c}\bar{C}_c} = \frac{U a_R L}{G_0 \bar{C}} \qquad (8.5\text{-}5)$$

* C. van Heerden, *Ind. Eng. Chem.* **45**, 1242 (1953).

† These results are based upon a reactor height and diameter of 12 and 0.7 meters, respectively. The feed contains 1.5% NH_3 and has a 3:1 H_2-to-N_2 ratio. The total pressure in the reactor is 300 atmospheres.

‡ M. Temkin and V. Pyzhev, *Acta Physicochim.* URSS **12**, 327 (1940).

because the mass flow rate in the exchanger and reactor sections must be identical.

The shape of the $T_0 - T_{c0}$ versus T_0 curves agrees qualitatively with its expected behavior at large and small values of T_0. If T_0 is small, the reaction rate is slow and very little heat release and heat transfer takes place. At large values of T_0, the equilibrium shifts to smaller ammonia concentrations, and in this case the extent of reaction approaches zero. Figure 8.5-2 is based upon a feed having an equilibrium temperature T_e of 1080°C.

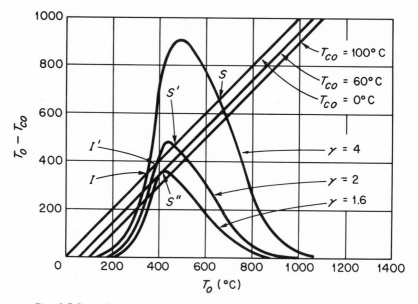

Fig. 8.5-2. Relationship between $T_o - T_{co}$ and T_o as a function of the heat transfer properties of the exchanger. [Redrawn from C. van Heerden, *Ind. Eng. Chem.*, **45**, 1242 (1953).]

The straight lines on Fig. 8.5-2 are simply a statement which satisfies the boundary condition specifying the inlet temperature $T_c = T_{c0}$ at $Z = L$.

The solutions satisfying Eqs. 8.4-1, 8.5-1, and 8.5-2 and the boundary conditions are on the intersection of the curves and the straight lines. These intersections are labeled I and S on Fig. 8.5-2 and correspond to values of $T_{c0} = 0°C$ and $\gamma = 4$. The solution I is unstable and S is stable. This can be easily shown by a qualitative argument. The quantity $T_0 - T_{c0}$ is a measure of the heat transferred between the reactor and the exchanger. If the system operating at the steady-state I were upset in such a way as to increase the value of T_0, then more heat transfer would occur and raise the value of T_0. In fact, T_0 would continue to rise until the point S is reached, in which case a similar argument verifies this as the stable operating steady-state. Another stable solution located below I exists mathematically, but is physically unrealizable owing to the importance of even small heat losses.

The unstable solution I may be looked upon alternately as an ignition condition. As γ decreases, keeping T_{c0} constant, the corresponding points I' and S' approach the same value. In Fig. 8.5-2, for $T_{c0} = 60°C$ and $\gamma = 1.6$, I'' and S'' have collapsed to the same value. At these conditions a minor fluctuation in the inlet stream to decrease T_{c0} below $60°C$ would quench the reaction.

These simple diagrams give a powerful insight into the behavior of such systems. As an example of their utility, van Heerden shows from the shapes of the conversion and temperature profiles the desirability of operating a reactor close to the stability limit (S'' of Fig. 8.5-2). However, as the catalyst ages and its activity declines, the curves of $T_0 - T_{c0}$ versus T_0 shift downward and eventually the system will be quenched. To continue operation, then, more heat exchange capacity (a greater value of γ) must be added to the system with the result that the temperature level in the reactor rises along with a corresponding decrease in conversion. The necessity of operating in this way is easily understood from diagrams like Fig. 8.5-2.

The second example illustrates the operating characteristics of a reactor-exchanger system of the type shown on Fig. 8.5-1(c). In contrast to the preceding example, heat exchange occurs between the reacting fluid and an independent cooling fluid, and an examination of the physical situation reveals that the flow rates and inlet temperatures of each stream can be varied independently. These additional degrees of freedom lead to a system behavior entirely different from that of the previous example. We shall not try to show this behavior of a general case, but rather bring out some of the salient features by analyzing an idealized case—that of constant heat generation rate in one of the streams.

In such a system we anticipate the possibility of temperature maxima in the reacting fluid and the cooling fluid. These are illustrated by Fig. 8.5-3 which shows the usual temperature profiles which may result when one of the streams contains a heat source. From the figure it becomes clear that heat transfer from the reacting mixture to the coolant takes place in one section of the unit whereas in the other section the reverse is true. In essence, a portion of the heat released is prevented from leaving the system until a high temperature level is established within the system. The extent to which energy is contained in the system by this mechanism depends upon the conditions of operation.

In this idealized case we immediately eliminate Eq. 8.4-1 from the system and substitute for the term $-\Delta H\mathscr{R}$ in Eq. 8.5-1 a term J, a constant rate of heat regeneration per unit volume. Carrying out this substitution and making

Eqs. 8.5-1 and 8.5-2 dimensionless we obtain

$$\frac{d\Theta}{d\eta} + \alpha(\Theta - \Theta_c) = 1 \tag{8.5-6}$$

$$\frac{d\Theta_c}{d\eta} + \alpha\beta(\Theta - \Theta_c) = 0, \tag{8.5-7}$$

where $\Theta \equiv (T - T_0)\delta$, $\qquad \Theta_c \equiv (T_c - T_0)\delta$, $\qquad \eta \equiv Z/L$,

$$\left.\alpha \equiv \frac{Ua_R L}{G_0 \bar{C}}, \qquad \beta \equiv \frac{G_0 \bar{C} a_c}{G_{0c} \bar{C}_c a_R}, \qquad \delta \equiv \frac{G_0 \bar{C}}{JL}, \quad \text{and} \right\} \tag{8.5-8}$$

$J \equiv$ heat generation per unit volume per unit time.

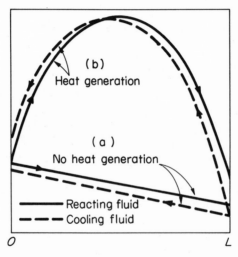

Fig. 8.5-3. Temperature profiles within the reactor—exchanger system of Fig. 8.5-1(c). [Redrawn from E. A. Grens and R. A. McKean, *Chem. Eng. Sci.*, **18**, 291 (1963).]

Equations 8.5-6 and 8.5-7 are subject to the boundary conditions

$$\left.\begin{array}{ll} \eta = 0, & \Theta = 0 \\ \eta = 1, & \Theta_c = \Theta_{c0} \end{array}\right\} \tag{8.5-9}$$

The mathematical problem is easily solved by eliminating one of the equations by multiplying Eq. 8.5-6 by β and subtracting Eq. 8.5-7 to obtain Θ_c as a function of Θ. The remaining equation is a first-order linear inhomogeneous equation in Θ. From the solution to these equations* we obtain the temperature profiles within the system.

* See E. A. Grens II and R. A. McKean, *op. cit.*

As explained earlier, we are interested in the maximum temperature in the system as a function of the parameters of the system. Although this information is expressible in terms of known functions, the results are perhaps more easily displayed in graphical form. Two graphs are needed to describe the system. The first shows the value of β, β_c corresponding to the maximum temperature rise for each value of α. That such a maximum exists can be shown qualitatively from limiting values of β. Certainly as β goes to zero, no maximum can build up because the heat generated in the system is so rapidly

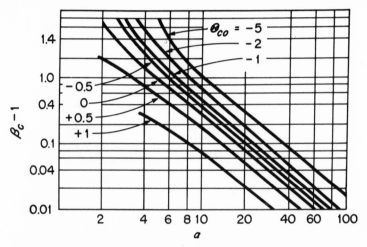

Fig. 8.5-4. Values of the critical flowrates in an exchanger reactor to obtain the maximum temperature rise. [Redrawn from E. A. Grens and R. A. McKean, *Chem. Eng. Sci.*, **18**, 291 (1963).]

flushed out that it cannot be transferred back to the stream in which the heat is generated. As β gets larger, in fact approaches unity, the opportunity exists for feedback of energy. As β becomes much larger and approaches infinity there is again no opportunity for feedback of energy. Thus intermediate values of β give maximum temperatures.

To be somewhat more quantitative, as $\beta \to \infty$, we get essentially adiabatic operation because $\Theta - \Theta_c$ goes to zero and $\Theta_c = \eta$. Alternatively, if $\beta \to 0$, $\Theta_c = \text{const}$ and Eqs. 8.5-6 and 8.5-7 are directly integrable. The latter limiting case corresponds to a special case of the problem considered in Section 8.4. The critical value β_c must lie somewhere between 0 and ∞. However, one easily analyzed case is that for which $\beta = 1$. The maximum temperature rise occurs in this system for $\alpha \to \infty$, and we find that the β_c for this system is greater than unity. Figure 8.5-4 shows a plot of the relationship between β_c, Θ_{c0} and α. Figure 8.5-5 shows the magnitude of the corresponding maximum temperature at β_c. Notice that large values of α

correspond to high heat transfer rates and the energy builds up in the system to give a large temperature maximum.

We can expect a similar behavior when the heat source is a result of an exothermic chemical reaction. For this more general case, it can be shown

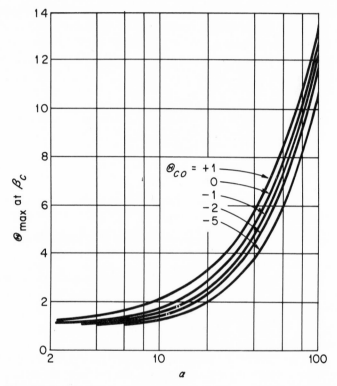

Fig. 8.5-5. Maximum temperatures in an exchanger reactor. [Redrawn from E. A. Grens and R. A. McKean, *Chem. Eng. Sci.*, **18**, 291 (1963).]

that as $\alpha \to \infty$, the critical value of β is unity, and at the critical value the maximum temperature becomes unbounded. These results show that, when heat transfer is efficient, α is large and an unexpectedly large temperature maximum will result if the ratio of the mass flow rates of the reactant and coolant fluids is close to unity.

8.6 Axial dispersion in one-dimensional reactors

In the earlier sections of this chapter, we have not considered the possibility of fluxes arising from diffusion-like mechanisms which tend to transport mass in the axial direction in a reactor. Chemical engineers have spent much effort studying the nature of these transport mechanisms as well as determining the numerical magnitude of the axial eddy diffusivity. As a result of the information available from such studies it is possible to assess the importance of axial mass transport in chemical reactors.

We can make a general statement at this point to the effect that axial transport is *rarely* an important consideration in fixed-bed reactors. This statement is more in the nature of a rule of thumb and although it is a good one, we should feel uneasy about it because there is no way of knowing when it will fail.

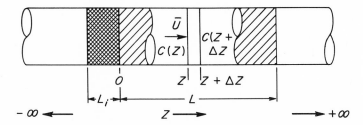

Fig. 8.6-1. Diagram of a one-dimensional fixed-bed reactor.

The purpose of this section is to consider a simple one-dimensional reactor in which a term for axial transport is included and to determine from an analysis of the system when the axial dispersion term must be included in the conservation equations. In essence, we shall develop a criterion whereby this question can be resolved rationally.

Although the particular system considered concerns an isothermal system in which a first-order reaction occurs, the method employed is by no means restricted to this simple case, and it can be generalized to more complex situations in much the same way as the simple Thiele problem was generalized in Chapter 4. We shall not generalize the method here because, as stated earlier, we rarely need to consider axial dispersion in fixed-bed reactors. Axial dispersion will be discussed further in Chapter 10 which concerns moving bed reactors.

The reactor configuration is shown in Fig. 8.6-1. The space in the region $0 \leq Z \leq L$ is filled with catalyst and a catalytic reaction occurs therein. Moreover, in this same region, reactants and products are transported by flow and diffusive mechanisms. The steady state conservation equation for the general element between Z and $Z + \Delta Z$ is

$$E_{DA}\left(\frac{d^2C}{dZ^2}\right) - \bar{U}\left(\frac{dC}{dZ}\right) - kC = 0, \tag{8.6-1}$$

where C = reactant concentration,

Z = axial coordinate,

E_{DA} = axial dispersion coefficient within the packed section of length L,

$\bar{U}$ = average velocity of the reaction mixture in the packed section, and

k = first-order rate constant.

Equation 8.6-1 is subject to the boundary conditions* at $Z = 0$:

$$\bar{U}C(0_-) = \bar{U}C(0_+) - E_{DA}\left(\frac{dC}{dZ}\right)_{Z=0_+}.$$

The symbol 0_- means that we approach $Z = 0$ from the negative values of Z. Analogously, the symbol L_+ used later means approach to the value of $Z = L$ from values of Z greater than L. Therefore:

$$C(0_+) = C(0_-) + \frac{E_{DA}}{\bar{U}}\left(\frac{dC}{dZ}\right)_{Z=0_+}. \tag{8.6-2}$$

At $Z = L$:

$$\bar{U}C(L_-) - E_{DA}\left(\frac{dC}{dZ}\right)_{Z=L} = \bar{U}C(L_+).$$

But $C(L_-)$ is equal to $C(L_+)$ because no further reaction can occur beyond L. Thus, the second boundary condition is

$$\left(\frac{dC}{dZ}\right)_{Z=L_-} = 0. \tag{8.6-3}$$

Note that these boundary conditions remain unchanged even when a length of inert packing is placed in front of the catalyst or after the catalyst. For a complete discussion of these boundary conditions, the reader should consult the article of Wehner and Wilhelm.

For purposes of analysis, it is convenient to make Eq. 8.6-1 dimensionless by the transformations

$$\mathscr{z} \equiv \frac{kZ}{\bar{U}}; \qquad \psi \equiv \frac{C}{C(0_-)}; \qquad \alpha^2 \equiv \frac{kE_{DA}}{\bar{U}^2} \tag{8.6-4}$$

to give

$$\alpha^2\left(\frac{d^2\psi}{d\mathscr{z}^2}\right) - \frac{d\psi}{d\mathscr{z}} - \psi = 0. \tag{8.6-5}$$

In dimensionless form the boundary conditions are:

At $\mathscr{z} = 0$; $\qquad\qquad \psi = 1 + \alpha^2\left(\frac{d\psi}{d\mathscr{z}}\right)$

At $\mathscr{z} = Z(L)$; $\qquad\qquad \dfrac{d\psi}{d\mathscr{z}} = 0$

$$\left.\begin{array}{c}\\[2em]\end{array}\right\} \tag{8.6-6}$$

* J. F. Wehner and R. H. Wilhelm, *Chem. Eng. Sci.* **6**, 89 (1956).

Equations 8.6-5 and 8.6-6 are a complete description of the system. A solution satisfying these equations will yield the conversion as a function of the dimensionless length $\mathscr{y}$ and a parameter α. However, it is more convenient to represent the solution in a different, but equivalent, way. We shall compute the ratio of the length of reactor L_P required to obtain a given conversion with no axial dispersion to the length of a reactor L_M required to obtain the same conversion with axial dispersion. We shall call this factor *the dispersion factor* $\mathscr{F}$. The subscripts P and M refer respectively to the unmixed or piston-flow reactor and the axially mixed reactor. In equation form,

$$\mathscr{F} \equiv \frac{L_P}{L_M}. \tag{8.6-7}$$

Knowing L_P and $\mathscr{F}$, it becomes a simple matter to compute L_M.

First, let us determine L_P. Clearly, when $E_{DA} = 0$, $\alpha^2 = 0$, and Eq. 8.6-5 becomes

$$\frac{d\psi}{d\mathscr{y}} + \psi = 0,$$

whereupon

$$\psi = e^{-\mathscr{y}}, \tag{8.6-8}$$

which satisfies the boundary condition at $x = 0$. By means of Eq. 8.6-8, L_P and ψ are related, $\mathscr{y}_P$ being equal to kL_P/t.

To obtain L_M is not quite so simple. We could, of course, solve Eq. 8.6-5 directly by standard methods for linear equations; however, it was stated earlier that a method would be used which was not restricted to linear equations. To do this, we again make use of asymptotic methods.

We already have the asymptotic solutions as $\alpha^2 \to 0$. It is

$$\mathscr{F} = 1.$$

Let us find the solution as $\alpha \to \infty$. A transformation of Eq. 8.6-5 is made using an independent variable ξ, which is defined as

$$\xi \equiv \frac{\mathscr{y}}{\alpha}. \tag{8.6-9}$$

Substitution of this variable into Eq. 8.6-5 gives

$$\frac{d^2\psi}{d\xi^2} - \frac{1}{\alpha}\frac{d\psi}{d\xi} - \psi = 0. \tag{8.6-10}$$

where evidently as $\alpha \to \infty$, the second term from the left drops out provided $d\psi/d\xi$ does not become infinite.

But now, we must be careful to understand what happens physically when $\alpha \to \infty$. From its definition in Eq. 8.6-4, α can become infinite either by $E_{DA} \to \infty$ or by $k \to \infty$,* and it is important to designate which because the boundary conditions are different for each of the cases. Let us consider first the case where $k \to \infty$.

The basic differential equation is

$$\frac{d^2\psi}{d\xi^2} - \psi = 0, \tag{8.6-11}$$

and because the new variable

$$\xi = \frac{\mathcal{Z}}{\alpha} = \frac{kZ}{\bar{U}}\sqrt{\frac{\bar{U}^2}{E_{DA}k}} = Z\sqrt{\frac{k}{E_{DA}}}, \tag{8.6-12}$$

the new boundary conditions as $k \to \infty$ are:

$$\left.\begin{array}{ll} \xi = 0; & \psi = 1 + \alpha\left(\dfrac{d\psi}{d\xi}\right) \\[2mm] \xi \to \infty; & \dfrac{d\psi}{d\xi} = 0, \quad \psi = 0 \end{array}\right\} \tag{8.6-13}$$

The asymptotic solution† to Eq. 8.6-11 which satisfies the boundary conditions of Eq. 8.6-13 is

$$\psi = \frac{e^{-\mathcal{Z}/\alpha}}{1 + \alpha}. \tag{8.6-14}$$

By means of Eq. 8.6-14, L_M is related to ψ and an expression for $\mathscr{F}$ follows from Eqs. 8.6-7, 8.6-8, and 8.6-14. This relationship is

$$\mathscr{F} = \frac{1}{\alpha} + \frac{\ln(1 + \alpha)}{\alpha^2\, \text{Pe}}, \tag{8.6-15}$$

where $\text{Pe} = \bar{U}L_M/E_{DA}$.

Since Pe remains bounded, it becomes clear that the second term on the right-hand side of Eq. 8.6-15 drops out as $\alpha \to \infty$.

The asymptotic solutions for $\alpha \to 0$ and $\alpha \to \infty$ (for $k \to \infty$) are shown on Fig. 8.6-2. The important conclusion from this figure is that the dispersion factor $\mathscr{F}$ is close to unity for values of $\alpha < 1$. This becomes the important case because the value of Pe for packed beds has been shown to be about 2,‡ based upon the pellet diameter. Here of course L_M is the length of the reactor; therefore Pe above is much larger in general than 2.

The other case, $\alpha \to \infty$ because $E_{DA} \to \infty$, will be taken up here. Although it does not apply to this kind of reactor, we will make some use of this result in Chapter 10. Equation 8.6-11 again applies, but in this case,

---

* The case where $\bar{U} \to 0$ is the same as for $k \to \infty$.

† The solution is obtained using the same method as given in Chapter 4.

‡ See Section 9.3.

as $E_{DA} \to \infty$ the concentration ψ approaches a constant value because the reactor approaches a stirred tank. Integrating Eq. 8.6-11 for constant ψ yields

$$\left(\frac{d\psi}{d\xi}\right)_{\xi=\xi_L} - \left(\frac{d\psi}{d\xi}\right)_{\xi=0} = \psi\xi_L. \tag{8.6-16}$$

The boundary conditions are:

$$\left.\begin{array}{ll} \text{at } \xi = 0; & \psi = 1 + \alpha\left(\dfrac{d\psi}{d\xi}\right) \\[2em] \text{at } \xi = \xi_L; & \dfrac{d\psi}{d\xi} = 0 \end{array}\right\} \tag{8.6-17}$$

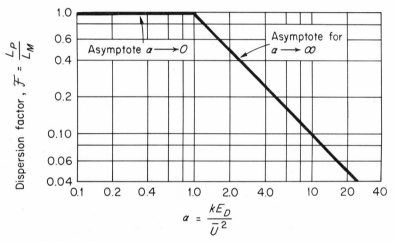

Fig. 8.6-2. Asymptotic behavior of the dispersion function for a first-order reaction.

Note that $\xi_L = \mathscr{Y}_M/\alpha$ and approaches zero as $\alpha \to \infty$. Accordingly, from Eq. 8.6-16,

$$\alpha\left(\frac{d\psi}{d\xi}\right)_{\xi=0} = -\psi\mathscr{Y}_M, \tag{8.6-18}$$

which from the first boundary condition of Eq. 8.6-17 gives

$$\psi = \frac{1}{1 + \mathscr{Y}_M}. \tag{8.6-19}$$

Equation 8.6-19 is the well-known form for a stirred-tank reactor.

The expression for $\mathscr{F}$ for the case of large diffusivity is

$$\mathscr{F} = \frac{\ln(1 + \mathscr{Y}_M)}{\mathscr{Y}_M}. \tag{8.6-20}$$

In summary, axial diffusion in packed-bed reactors does not appreciably influence the steady state conversion when the parameter α is small. However, in other kinds of reactors when the axial Pe $\to 0$, the reactor performance is materially changed.

8.7 Stability of adiabatic packed-bed reactors

A general discussion of the stability of packed-bed reactors is beyond the scope of this section. We shall confine the discussion to a qualitative description of one cause of instability in packed beds which arises naturally from our discussion of multiple steady state on a single catalytic pellet. This essentially follows the work of Wicke and Vortmeyer* and Liu and Amundson.† The reader should also refer to the numerical study of packed-bed reactors by Barkelew.‡

In Section 6.5 we discussed the conditions under which single pellets exhibited multiple steady-state behavior. This behavior arises from the sigmoid shape of the curve for the rate of energy release versus pellet temperature. That is, at low temperatures the over-all rate is essentially reaction-rate controlled which in turn increases as an exponential function of surface temperature. At high temperatures, the rate is limited by the transport of reactants to the surface. The corresponding heat transfer equation is a linear function of the difference between the catalyst surface temperature and the bulk fluid phase temperature. The points of intersection of these two curves can give as many as three steady-state operating points.

In a packed-bed reactor, each pellet may be exposed to different environmental conditions, and the particular steady-state operation point of each particle may depend upon the method of startup. Or large fluctuations in the entrance conditions may change the performance of such a reactor from one stable steady-state reaction rate to another, even though the initial operation is stable to small fluctuations in operating conditions.

We can show this qualitatively without using an unsteady-state analysis by extending slightly the discussion in Sections 6.4 and 6.5. To focus attention on the physical phenomenon, the discussion will be restricted to a simple system—that of a first-order irreversible reaction of the form

$$A_1 \to A_2. \tag{8.7-1}$$

The same methods will apply to more complex reactions; however, a more general treatment would be burdened with mathematical complications.

  * E. Wicke, *Chem. Ing. Tech.* **29,** 305 (1957); E. Wicke and D. Vortmeyer, *Z. Elektrochem.* **63,** 145 (1959); E. Wicke, *ibid.* **65,** 267 (1961).

  † Shean-Lin Liu and N. R. Amundson, *Ind. Eng. Chem. Fund.* **1,** 200 (1962) and *Ind. Eng. Chem. Fund.* **2,** 183 (1963).

  ‡ C. Barkelew, *Chem. Eng. Progr. Symp. Ser.* **55,** No. 25, 37 (1959).

Since we are already familiar with the multiple steady-state solutions for a first-order reaction on a single catalyst pellet, we need only modify our previous results so that they will apply to a packed-bed reactor. Again, we can effect a considerable simplification by selecting a one-dimensional adiabatic packed-bed reactor. Using this system as an example we shall qualitatively explain one cause of instability in packed-bed reactors.

Equations 6.4-3 and 6.4-4, when applied to the reaction system described above, become

$$(C_\infty - C_0)\beta_m = \mathscr{R}_x \tag{8.7-2}$$

$$(T_\infty - T_0)\beta_h = -(-\Delta H_R)\mathscr{R}_x, \tag{8.7-3}$$

where C_0 = concentration of component 1 at the pellet surface,

C_∞ = concentration of component 1 in the bulk fluid phase,

T_0 = temperature of the pellet surface,

T_∞ = temperature of the bulk fluid phase,

β_m = mass transfer coefficient,

β_h = heat transfer coefficient, and

$$\mathscr{R}_x = A_1 e^{-\Delta E/R_g T_0} C_0. \tag{8.7-4}$$

The reaction rate $\mathscr{R}_x$ is the specific rate per unit external surface are of the pellet. If we substitute Eq. 8.7-4 into Eq. 8.7-2 and solve it for C_0, we obtain

$$C_0 = C_\infty \left(\frac{1}{1 + \delta} \right), \tag{8.7-5}$$

where

$$\delta = \frac{A_1 e^{-\Delta E/R_g T_0}}{\beta_m}. \tag{8.7-6}$$

If, furthermore, Eq. 8.7-2 is multiplied by $-\Delta H_R$ and added to Eq. 8.7-3, the result is

$$C_\infty - C_0 = \frac{\beta_h}{\beta_m(-\Delta H_R)} (T_0 - T_\infty) \tag{8.7-7}$$

But

$$\frac{C_\infty - C_0}{C_\infty} = 1 - \left(\frac{1}{1 + \delta} \right) \tag{8.7-8}$$

$$= \frac{\delta}{1 + \delta} \tag{8.7-9}$$

to give from Eqs. 8.7-7 and 8.7-9,

$$\frac{\delta}{1 + \delta} = \frac{\beta_h}{\beta_m(-\Delta H_R)} \left(\frac{T_0 - T_\infty}{C_\infty} \right). \tag{8.7-10}$$

Equation 8.7-10 should be familiar. The left-hand side of this equation when plotted versus T_0 gives the sigmoid curve whereas the right-hand side gives a linear curve. The steady-state solutions must lie on the intersections of these curves. Therefore Eq. 8.7-10 is a relationship which must be satisfied locally at each point within the reactor.

The local conditions of temperature and concentration T_∞ and C_∞ vary with position in the reactor. We need expressions which will allow their prediction in terms of their inlet values. Let us call the inlet temperature and concentration of the fluid $T_{\infty 0}$ and $C_{\infty 0}$, respectively. Now, from Eq. 8.3-5 for an adiabatic reactor, T_∞ and C_∞ are related by the equation

$$T_\infty - T_{\infty 0} = \frac{(-\Delta H_R)}{\bar{C}} [C_{\infty 0} - C_\infty], \tag{8.7-11}$$

which upon rearrangement gives

$$C_\infty = C_{\infty 0} - \frac{\bar{C}}{(-\Delta H_R)} [T_\infty - T_{\infty 0}]. \tag{8.7-12}$$

It follows from Eq. 8.7-12 that the maximum temperature of the fluid in the bulk phase, $T_{\infty,\max}$, corresponds to $C_\infty = 0$. That is,

$$0 = C_{\infty 0} - \frac{\bar{C}}{(-\Delta H_R)} [T_{\infty,\max} - T_{\infty 0}]. \tag{8.7-13}$$

If Eqs. 8.7-13 is subtracted from Eq. 8.7-12, we get

$$C_\infty = \frac{\bar{C}}{(-\Delta H_R)} [T_{\infty,\max} - T_\infty]. \tag{8.7-14}$$

This is the relationship between T_∞ and C_∞ sought. Note that had we assumed a nonisothermal instead of an adiabatic reactor, no such simple relationship would have been obtained. Equation 8.7-14 is now substituted into Eq. 8.7-10 and the result is

$$\frac{\delta}{1 + \delta} = \frac{\beta_h \bar{C}}{\beta_m} \left[\frac{T_0 - T_\infty}{T_{\infty,\max} - T_\infty} \right]. \tag{8.7-15}$$

We can best interpret Eq. 8.7-15 graphically. The left-hand side of this equation is shown on Fig. 8.7-1, and it has the sigmoid shape. The right-hand side is shown by the lines L_i. Clearly, when $T_\infty = T_{\infty,\max}$, the slope of the line $L_{\max}$ is infinite. Note also that when $T_0 = T_{\infty,\max}$, the right side of Eq. 8.7-15 has the same value, regardless of the magnitude of T_∞. Thus all lines L_i go through the common point 0. Finally, when $T_0 = T_\infty$, the right-hand side of Eq. 8.7-15 is zero. The lines L_i therefore are as shown on Fig. 8.7-1.

This means that any line going through the point 0 and having a slope greater than L_0 is a permissible operating line. If, as do L_0 and L_i, the line L_i intersects the sigmoid curve more than once, the particle exposed to these environmental conditions can operate at more than one steady-state. And, although in general such steady-states are stable to small fluctuations in environmental conditions, large fluctuations can cause operation to change. Moreover, the particular steady-state operation of the reactor depends upon the startup conditions.

The objective of this discussion has been accomplished. We have carried an analysis to the point where it is clear that more than one steady state in a packed-bed reactor is a possibility. To find out what steady-state is reached

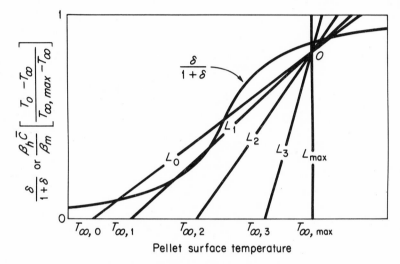

Fig. 8.7-1. Graphical illustration of possible steady states of pellets in a packed-bed reactor. [Redrawn from Shu-lin Liu and N. R. Amundson, *Ind. Eng. Chem. Fund.*, **1**, 200 (1962).]

as a result of particular startup conditions, a transient analysis must be employed.

The results of a transient analysis depend strongly upon the initial and operating conditions. No general result can be given except that such analyses verify the prediction of multiple steady-state operation of fixed-bed adiabatic reactors.*

8.8 The nonisothermal two-dimensional reactor

All fixed-bed reactors in which heat is exchanged with the surroundings are at least two-dimensional. Since they constitute an important class of reactors, we shall look at them in detail. However, only certain simple cases will be treated. The reason for this is that a major difficulty arises in

* Shu-lin Liu and N. R. Amundson, *op. cit.*

analyzing the performance of these reactors because the set of partial differential equations describing the system are all highly nonlinear and coupled. This forces us to seek numerical methods of solution in most cases. We shall illustrate the methods using simple reactions, and the reader should recognize that more complex situations can be handled by the same techniques with little or no additional complexity save that of labor in obtaining the solution.

For a steady-state fixed-bed reactor in which a simple reaction of Eq. 8.2-5 occurs, the conservation equations may be written in the form:

$$-\overline{\text{div}\,(\vec{U}C_i)} + a_i\bar{\mathscr{R}}(C_1, C_2, \ldots, C_n, T) = 0 \qquad (i = 1, 2, \ldots, n) \quad (8.8\text{-}1)$$

$$-\overline{\text{div}\,(\rho\bar{C}\vec{U}T)} + (-\Delta H_R)\bar{\mathscr{R}}(C_1, C_2, \ldots, C_n, T) = 0$$
$$(i = 1, 2, \ldots, n), \quad (8.8\text{-}2)$$

where $\vec{U}$ is the vector velocity in the packed bed, and the bar over the first term in Eqs. 8.8-1 and 8.8-2 refers to the space averaging of these quantities. All other symbols have their previously defined meanings. In Section 9.2, the physical meaning of the space-averaged quantities and their equivalent mathematical form are treated. Readers unfamiliar with these ideas should study Section 9.2 before proceeding with the remainder of this section. Substituting Eqs. 9.2-2 and 9.2-12 into Eq. 8.8-1 we obtain

$$\frac{-\rho_0\bar{U}_0}{\bar{M}}\,\text{div}\,Y_i + \text{div}\left(\frac{\rho_0\,d_p\bar{U}_0}{N\bar{M}}\,\text{grad}_R\,Y_i\right) + a_i\,\bar{\mathscr{R}}(Y_1, Y_2, \ldots, Y_n, T) = 0,$$
$$(8.8\text{-}3)$$

where Y_i = number of moles of the ith species in a mass of fluid equal numerically to the average molecular weight of the feed stream,
$N = (\rho_0/\rho)$ Pe,
Pe $= d_p\bar{U}_0/E$,
$\bar{U}_0$ = average velocity at the entrance of the fixed bed,
E = radial eddy diffusivity,
d_p = catalyst pellet diameter,
ρ_0 = initial fluid density,
ρ = fluid density as a function of position in the reactor, and
$\bar{M}$ = average molecular weight of the feed stream to the reactor.

A similar equation can be written for Eq. 8.8-2. If we restrict the discussion to a reactor of cylindrical cross section normal to the direction of $\bar{U}_0$ shown on Fig. 8.8-1, then Eq. 8.8-3 becomes

$$\frac{-\rho_0\bar{U}_0}{\bar{M}}\frac{\partial Y_i}{\partial Z} + \frac{1}{r}\frac{r}{\partial r}\left(\frac{r\rho_0\,d_p\bar{U}_0}{N\bar{M}}\frac{\partial Y_i}{\partial r}\right) + a_i\bar{\mathscr{R}} = 0 \qquad (i = 1, 2, \ldots, n). \quad (8.8\text{-}4)$$

The first term of Eq. 8.8-3 has only one term because the radial and angular components of $\bar{U}_0$ are zero. The second term is resolved to a single term because axial fluctuations leading to an axial diffusion term are neglected (see Section 8.6), and as will be shown below, the boundary conditions are assumed symmetric about the angle θ. By analogy, Eq. 8.8-2 is

$$-\rho_0 \bar{U}_0 \frac{\partial T}{\partial Z} + \frac{1}{r} \frac{\partial}{\partial r} \left(\frac{r \rho_0 d_p \bar{U}_0 \bar{C}}{N} \frac{\partial T}{\partial r} \right) + (-\Delta H_R) \bar{\mathscr{R}} = 0. \qquad (8.8\text{-}5)$$

The boundary conditions on Eqs. 8.8-4 and 8.8-5 are

at $Z = 0$; $T = T_0$, $Y_i = Y_{i0}$ for all r,

at $r = r_0$; $-E_{HR} \dfrac{\partial T}{\partial r} = h_T[T(r_0) - T_w]$, $\dfrac{\partial Y_i}{\partial r} = 0$ for all Z,

    where h_T = heat transfer coefficient accounting for the heat transfer resistance between the wall and the fixed bed (see Section 9.4),

at $r = 0$; $\dfrac{\partial T}{\partial r} = \dfrac{\partial Y_i}{\partial r} = 0$ for all Z

$(8.8\text{-}6)$

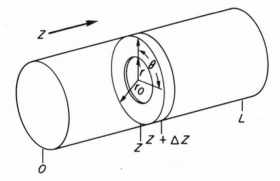

Fig. 8.8-I. Two-dimensional, nonisothermal, fixed-bed reactor of cylindrical shape.

The boundary conditions bring to light two points about the behavior of the equations describing the system. The first is that the coefficients of the radial diffusion term and longitudinal flow term in the conservation equation for each species are identical and the boundary conditions are identical. As a consequence we shall be able to eliminate all but one of these conservation equations. The second point is that the boundary conditions for the conservation equation of energy differ from those of conservation of each species, and as a consequence we shall *not* be able to eliminate it as a dependent equation.

To show the dependence of $n - 1$ of the conservation equations of Eq. 8.8-4 we shall rearrange the latter equation to the following form:

$$-\frac{1}{a_i \bar{M}} \frac{\partial Y_i}{\partial Z} + \frac{d_p}{a_i \bar{M} N} \frac{1}{r} \frac{\partial}{\partial r} \left(r \frac{\partial Y_i}{\partial r} \right) + \frac{\bar{\mathscr{R}}}{\rho_0 \bar{U}_0} = 0, \qquad (8.8\text{-}7)$$

where N has been assumed independent of r. A similar equation can be written for the jth component and subtracted from Eq. 8.8-7 to give upon rearrangement:

$$-\frac{\partial \phi}{\partial Z} + \frac{d_p}{N}\frac{1}{r}\frac{\partial}{\partial r}\left(r\frac{\partial \phi}{\partial r}\right) = 0, \qquad (8.8\text{-}8)$$

where

$$\phi = Y_i - \frac{a_i}{a_j}Y_j.$$

The boundary conditions are

at $Z = 0$; $\phi = \phi_0$

at $r = r_0$; $\dfrac{d\phi}{dr} = 0$ $\qquad\qquad$ (8.8-9)

at $r = 0$; $\dfrac{d\phi}{dr} = 0$

The solution satisfying this equation and the boundary condition is:

$$\phi = \phi_0, \qquad (8.8\text{-}10)$$

or substituting back,

$$Y_{i0} - Y_i = \frac{a_i}{a_j}(Y_{j0} - Y_j). \qquad (8.8\text{-}11)$$

In this way we show that the composition of the mixture with respect to each of the $n-1$ species can be calculated in terms of a single species. This species will be identified by the symbol Y without a subscript. The choice of the species to follow in the equations is arbitrary, but it must be remembered that from a physical argument no value of Y_i in the mixture can become negative. Generally then, the choice of Y is that species present stoichiometrically in least amount in the reaction mixture.

The equations describing the system are reduced to two coupled equations: Eq. 8.8-5 and one member of the set of Eqs. 8.8-4. Equation 8.8-11 is carried along as an auxiliary equation to compute those mass fractions which enter into the rate expression $\mathcal{R}$ and to compute the composition of the mixture leaving the reactor.

As mentioned earlier, these partial differential equations are highly nonlinear and do not lend themselves to analytical methods of solution. Numerical methods for solving these equations have been the subject of numerous investigations and some of the experience with numerical methods for their solution has been made available in the open literature. The methods employed are all based upon the finite difference methods, the one most

familiar to chemical engineers being the one first suggested by Schmidt.*
This is a graphical method based upon finite difference methods. We shall
develop the finite difference equations in a form such that the integrations
may be easily programmed for high-speed digital computers.

The method is based upon satisfying the equations for values of the
dependent variables at discrete points in the reactor. To show what is meant
by this refer to Fig. 8.8-2. This figure is constructed upon a surface generated

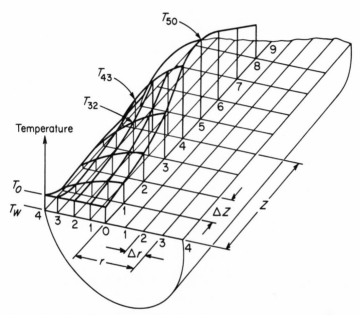

Fig. 8.8-2. Diagram showing the position of the doubly subscripted
$T_{n,m}$ in a tubular reactor.

by cutting the cylindrical reactor in half. A grid system is superimposed
upon this surface by dividing the radial space into increments of Δr and the
longitudinal space into increments of ΔZ. The dependent variables are
specified only at the intersections of the grid lines, the so-called mesh points.
Furthermore, the magnitude of the dependent variables at each mesh point
is indicated by the height above the grid line, i.e., by constructing a line of
length proportional to the magnitude of the dependent variable through each
mesh point perpendicular to the plane of the grid. Figure 8.8-2 represents
the temperature field in a two-dimensional reactor in which an exothermic
reaction takes place. Each temperature T is given two subscripts, n and m,

* E. Schmidt, *Beitr. Tech. Mech. u. tech. Phys.*, A. Fopple Festschrift, 179 (1924).
See also M. Jacob, *Heat Transfer*, Vol. I, p. 383, John Wiley & Sons, Inc., New York,
1949.

corresponding respectively to the number of ΔZ increments from the entrance and the number of Δr increments from the axis of the cylinder. The solution to the partial differential equation in the temperature is approximated by the continuous surface going through each of these temperatures. Note that the hot-spot temperature $T_{\max}$ is located on the axis of the reactor between the fourth and fifth ΔZ increments in length.

Our next task is to develop a method whereby the magnitudes of the dependent variables can be evaluated at each mesh point. This is accomplished by noting that the partial derivatives can be approximated in terms of the temperatures at discrete mesh points in the neighborhood of $T_{n,m}$ by the following expressions.

$$\left.\left(\frac{\partial T}{\partial Z}\right)_{n,m} = \frac{T_{n+1,m} - T_{n,m}}{\Delta Z}\right.$$

$$\left.\left(\frac{\partial T}{\partial r}\right)_{n,m} = \frac{T_{n,m+1} - T_{n,m}}{\Delta r}\right\} \quad (8.8\text{-}12)$$

$$\left.\left(\frac{\partial^2 T}{\partial r^2}\right)_{n,m} = \frac{T_{n,m+1} - 2T_{n,m} + T_{n,m-1}}{(\Delta r)^2}\right.$$

These approximations become more accurate as the distances between mesh points is made smaller. In the limit as the distances between mesh points becomes arbitrarily small the expressions are exact. Analogous expressions may be written for the derivatives in mass fractions.

If approximations like those of Eq. 8.8-12* are substituted into Eq. 8.8-4, then upon rearrangement, this partial differential equation is transformed into a set of algebraic equations. One member of this set valid at the position $n \Delta Z$ and $m \Delta r$ is:

$$Y_{n+1,m} = \Delta_{1m} Y_{n,m+1} + \Delta_2 Y_{n,m} + \Delta_{3m} Y_{n,m-1} + \Delta_4 \bar{\mathscr{R}}'_{n,m} \quad (8.8\text{-}13)$$

where $\Delta_{1m} = \beta(1 + 1/2m); \quad m \neq 0, \quad \beta = \dfrac{d_p}{N} \dfrac{\Delta Z}{(\Delta r)^2}$

$\Delta_2 = (1 - 2\beta),$

$\Delta_{3m} = \beta(1 - 1/2m); \quad \begin{matrix} m \neq 0 \\ m \neq s \end{matrix}, \quad \bar{\mathscr{R}}'_{n,m} = \bar{\mathscr{R}}'(Y_{n,m}, T),$

$\Delta_4 = (\Delta Z) a \bar{M}/\rho_0 \bar{U}_0, \quad \bar{\mathscr{R}}'(Y_{n,m}, T) = \bar{\mathscr{R}}(Y_1, Y_2, \ldots, Y_n, T).$

It becomes clear that if the values of the independent variables are known at $Z = 0$ (i.e., $n = 0$), at each of the radial increments from 0 to, say, s (making $s\Delta r = r_0$), then their values at $Z = \Delta Z$ may be predicted from

---

* To develop this expression:

$$\frac{1}{r}\frac{dY}{dr} \approx \frac{1}{m(\Delta r)}\left(\frac{Y_{n,m+1} - Y_{n,m-1}}{2\Delta r}\right).$$

$m = 1$ to $s - 1$ using Eq. 8.8-13. There are a number of ways to obtain the values of Y at $m = 0$ and at $m = s$ where from Eq. 8.8-6, $\partial Y/\partial r = 0$. The one we shall use here is*

$$\left. \begin{array}{l} Y_{n,s} = \tfrac{18}{11}Y_{n,s-1} - \tfrac{9}{11}Y_{n,s-2} + \tfrac{2}{11}Y_{n,s-3} \\[4pt] Y_{n,0} = \tfrac{18}{11}Y_{n,1} - \tfrac{9}{11}Y_{n,2} + \tfrac{2}{11}Y_{n,3} \end{array} \right\} \qquad (8.8\text{-}15)$$

The same formula can be used to obtain $T_{n,0}$, the temperature along the reactor axis. The boundary temperature $T_{n,s}$ can be obtained directly from the boundary condition,

At $r = r_0$; $$-E\frac{\partial T}{\partial r} = h_T[T(t_0) - T_w],$$

which in finite difference form becomes

$$E\left[\frac{T_{n,s-1} - T_{n,s}}{\Delta r}\right] = h_T[T_{n,s} - T_w],$$

and simplifies to

$$T_{n,s} = \frac{T_w + (E/h_T\,\Delta r)T_{n,s-1}}{1 + (E/h_T\,\Delta r)}. \qquad (8.8\text{-}16)$$

We have now succeeded in calculating the magnitudes of all the dependent variables across the radius of the reactor at $Z = \Delta Z$ in terms of the known values at $Z = 0$. The process can be repeated to obtain the values of the dependent variables at $Z = 2\Delta Z$ in terms of those at $Z = \Delta Z$. In this way,

---

* The basis of this formula is outlined here. Expand both the functions Y and $\partial Y/\partial r$ in a Taylor's series about the interval $s - 1$:

$$Y_{n,s} = Y_{n,s-1} + \left(\frac{\partial Y}{\partial r}\right)_{n,s-1}(\Delta r) + \frac{1}{2!}\left(\frac{\partial^2 Y}{\partial r^2}\right)_{n,s-1}(\Delta r)^2 + \frac{1}{3!}\left(\frac{\partial^3 Y}{\partial r^3}\right)_{n,s-1}(\Delta r)^3 \quad (8.8\text{-}a)$$

$$\left(\frac{\partial Y}{\partial r}\right)_{n,s} = \left(\frac{\partial Y}{\partial r}\right)_{n,s-1} + \left(\frac{\partial^2 Y}{\partial r^2}\right)_{n,s-1}(\Delta r) + \frac{1}{2!}\left(\frac{\partial^3 Y}{\partial r^3}\right)(\Delta r)^2 + \ldots = 0. \quad (8.8\text{-}b)$$

Equation 8.8-b is set equal to zero because the boundary condition is

$$\left(\frac{\partial Y}{\partial r}\right)_{n,s} = 0. \qquad (8.8\text{-}c)$$

Solve Eq. 8.8-b for $(\partial Y/\partial r)_{n,s-1}$ and substitute into Eq. 8.8-a to give:

$$Y_{n,s} = Y_{n,s-1} - \frac{1}{2}\left(\frac{\partial^2 Y}{\partial r^2}\right)_{n,s-1}(\Delta r)^2 - \frac{1}{3}\left(\frac{\partial^3 Y}{\partial r^3}\right)(\Delta r)^3 + \ldots \qquad (8.8\text{-}d)$$

Now using finite difference approximations of the partial derivative in Eqs. 8.8-d,

$$Y_{n,s} = Y_{n,s-1} - \tfrac{1}{2}(Y_{n,s} - 2Y_{n,s-1} + Y_{n,s-2}) - \tfrac{1}{3}[Y_{n,s} - 3Y_{n,s-1} + 3Y_{n,s-2} - Y_{n,s-3}].$$
$$(8.8\text{-}e)$$

Solving Eq. 8.8-e for $Y_{n,s}$ gives Eq. 8.8-15 above.

it is possible to compute to obtain the conversion of the reactor at a prescribed length Z, or alternatively to predict the length of reactor which would
be required to give a prescribed conversion.

In using the finite difference equations, the choices of the value of the
mesh ratios, $\Delta Z/(\Delta r)^2$, and the absolute magnitude of one of the increments
(usually the number of radial increments, s) determine how satisfactorily the
solution to the difference equation will agree with the solution to the corresponding partial differential equations. The apparent freedom which a
designer has in choosing these parameters is severely restricted by the
recognition of the two kinds of errors resulting therefrom. The first, and
more obvious, is known as the truncation error. This error results when the
partial differential equations are replaced by finite difference equations, and
the latter are satisfied only at discrete mesh points. The agreement between
the solutions to the above sets of equations depends upon the number of
mesh points selected—as the number of mesh points in a given interval
increases, the closer the correspondence between the solutions.

The second error is known as the round-off error. In numerical work,
numbers must be carried with a finite number of digits and regardless of the
number of significant figures carried the last is always rounded off to the
nearest integer. The choice of the mesh ratio determines whether the error
made in rounding off grows larger or smaller with successive iterations in the
numerical computation. If the magnitude of mesh ratio is too large, the
amplitude of the errors propagating along with the solution will grow with
the result that, if the integration is carried too far, the errors will completely
mask the form of the stable solution sought. Unfortunately for nonlinear
equations there is no method for evaluating the largest numerical value of
the mesh ratio which will insure stability. Such a method does in fact exist
for the corresponding linear equation. Although the method is not explicitly
applicable here, the results based upon it are useful guides in the selection
of mesh ratios for nonlinear systems. The method, attributable to von
Neuman,* focuses attention on the error growth in a corresponding linear
equation, known as Fick's second law,†

$$Y_{n+1,m} - Y_{n,m} = \frac{d_p}{N}\frac{\Delta Z}{(\Delta r)^2}[Y_{n,m+1} - 2Y_{n,m} + Y_{n,m-1}], \qquad (8.8\text{-}17)$$

and shows that for

$$\beta \equiv \frac{d_p}{N}\frac{\Delta Z}{(\Delta r)^2} \leq \frac{1}{2} \qquad (8.8\text{-}18)$$

* See for example, G. G. O'Brien, M. A. Hyman, S. Kaplan, *J. Math. Phys.* **29,** 223 (1951).

† See for example, J. Crank, *The Mathematics of Diffusion*, p. 3, Oxford University Press, New York, 1956.

random errors do not grow. It can also be demonstrated that the corresponding finite difference form which was suggested by Richardson,*

$$Y_{n+1,m} - Y_{n-1,m} = \frac{2d_p}{N} \frac{\Delta Z}{(\Delta r)^2} [Y_{n,m+1} - 2Y_{n,m} + Y_{n,m-1}], \quad (8.8\text{-}19)\dagger$$

which is appealing from the standpoint of reducing the truncation error, is inherently unstable, i.e., unstable for any finite value of β.

The results of the stability analysis of Eq. 8.8-17 show that the amplitude of errors propagating through the system grow exponentially when $\beta > \frac{1}{2}$.‡ This serves as a guide to selection of the proper value of β for the nonlinear system which should be a value somewhat below this critical value as a measure of safety.

The result of an upper limit on the value of β leads to the more pragmatic result that if we investigate the truncation error at constant β by, say, halving the magnitude of Δr, the number of ΔZ increments will quadruple and the amount of labor in obtaining the solution to a given value of Z increases by about eight-fold.

The use of implicit forms of the finite difference equations allows somewhat more control of the size of ΔZ because analysis of the corresponding linear systems shows these forms to be stable with respect to error growth for all values of β. Briefly, an implicit form of the finite difference equation corresponding to Eq. 8.8-17 is:

$$Y_{n+1,m} - Y_{n,m} = \beta[Y_{n+1,m+1} - 2Y_{n+1,m} + Y_{n+1,m-1}]. \quad (8.8\text{-}20)$$

The form of Eq. 8.8-20 shows that all values of Y are unknown except $Y_{n,m}$. However, when the entire set of equations for $m = 0$ to s§ are written, it will be observed that there are $s + 1$ equations in $s + 1$ unknowns and for the linear case the solution of the set for $Y_{n+1,m}$ $(m = 0, 1, 2, \ldots, s)$ can be handled by standard methods. For the chemical reaction case a set of implicit finite difference equations in Y will be obtained similar to Eq. 8.8-13 of the form

$$Y_{n+1,m} = \Delta_{1m} Y_{n+1,m+1} + \Delta_2 Y_{n+1,m} + \Delta_3 Y_{n+1,m-1} + \Delta_4 \bar{\mathscr{R}}'_{n,m} \quad (8.8\text{-}21)$$

* L. F. Richardson, *Phil. Trans. Roy. Soc.* (London), **A210,** 307 (1910).

† $(Y_{n+1,m} - Y_{n-1,m}/2\Delta Z)$ is a better approximation of $(\partial Y/\partial Z)_{n,m}$ than is $Y_{n+1,m} - Y_{n,m}/\Delta Z$ of Eq. 8.8-17.

‡ It is perhaps of interest to note here that in the method as originally developed by Schmidt (*op. cit.*), the choice of $\beta = \frac{1}{2}$ was prompted by the ease with which this value allows Eq. 8.8-17 to be graphically satisfied. That this choice also turns out to be the stability limit is purely fortuitous. This critical value of β for linear equations casts some doubt as to the advisability of using $\beta = \frac{1}{2}$ in a method such as Baron's [T. Baron, *Chem. Eng. Progr.* **4,** 118 (1952)] for highly nonlinear systems.

§ Here we can make use of Eq. 8.8-15 in order to obtain equations for $m = 0$ and $m = s$.

Note that direct inversion of this set is not possible unless the $\bar{\mathscr{R}}'$ term is based upon $Y_{n,m}$ instead of $Y_{n+1,m}$. If the latter are used, some iterative method must be developed.

Common practice is to use mixed implicit and explicit formulae. So long as the weighting of the implicit formula is at least $\frac{1}{2}$, the resulting system will be stable for all values of β. The equation below illustrates the mixed formula that is weighted $\frac{1}{2}$ implicit and $\frac{1}{2}$ explicit.

$$Y_{n+1,m} - Y_{n,m}$$
$$= \beta \left(\frac{Y_{n+1,m+1} - 2Y_{n+1,m} + Y_{n+1,m-1}}{2} + \frac{Y_{n,m+1} - 2Y_{n,m} + Y_{n,m-1}}{2} \right).$$

$$(8.8\text{-}22)$$

For a further discussion of integration of Eqs. 8.8-4 and 8.8-5 the reader should consult the work of Kjaer* and Beek.†

Deans and Lapidus‡ have developed an alternate method for numerically computing the performance of two-dimensional, nonisothermal, fixed-bed reactors. Their method is based upon the supposition that the fixed bed may be replaced by a system of interconnected mixing cells. The interstitial space formed among pellets of a fixed bed is complex to describe geometrically, but it is characterized by enlarged regions interconnected by constricted channels. In the model of Deans and Lapidus, the enlarged regions correspond to the mixing cells. The complex flow patterns which occur among adjacent cells and the mixing processes which take place in the cells give rise to transport processes which resemble diffusion and convection. Thus, in a natural way, it accounts for radial and axial eddy diffusion as well as axial and net radial convective flows. The cell model offers a computational advantage over the method described earlier in this section if the decision is made to include the axial diffusion term because the method eliminates the trial and error methods necessary to meet the boundary conditions at points where the reactants enter and leave the reactor. In summary, by means of the cell model the processes occurring within a fixed bed can be described more accurately than any other model especially when treating reacting systems.

For the steady-state system, the Deans and Lapidus method leads to a set of algebraic equations similar to Eq. 8.8-13. However, we shall not develop them for two reasons. The first is that as a generality we have shown that axial diffusion rarely needs to be taken into account in the fixed-bed reactors. Under these conditions, the integration of Eqs. 8.8-4 and 8.8-5 by

* Jorgen Kjaer, *Measurement and Calculation of Temperature and Conversion in Fixed-Bed Catalytic Reactors*, Jul. Gjellerups Forlag, Copenhagen, 1958.
† John Beek, "Design of Packed Catalytic Reactors," *Advan. Chem. Eng.* **3**, 204 (1962).
‡ H. A. Deans and L. Lapidus, *A.I.Ch.E. Journal* **6**, 656 (1960).

the methods outlined in this section can be carried out using increments larger than the individual pellet dimension required by the method of Deans and Lapidus. The time required to compute individual cases is thereby substantially decreased. The second reason is that the conceptual difficulties in the continuum model which are so easily obviated by cell models rarely lead to differences in predicted performance greater than the inherent errors in kinetic data. For these reasons we shall view the cell model as an alternate method for handling fixed-bed nonisothermal reactors.

NOTATION FOR CHAPTER 8

a_i stoichiometric coefficient in a general simple reaction; $a < 0$ is a reactant, $a_i > 0$ is a product

a_{ij} stoichiometric coefficient in a general complex reaction

a heat transfer area per unit volume of reactor

a_R heat transfer area per unit volume of reactor

a_c heat transfer area per unit volume of cooling section

A_i ith species in a reaction mixture

C_i concentration of the ith species

$\bar{C}$ mean heat capacity of reaction mixture

d_p catalyst pellet diameter

ΔE activation energy

E_{DA} eddy axial diffusivity

E_{HR} eddy radial thermal diffusivity

E_{DR} eddy radial diffusivity

F volumetric flow rate

G_0 $\rho_T \bar{U}$, the mass velocity

h_T heat transfer coefficient (see Eq. 8.4-2)

$\bar{H}_i$ enthalpy per mole of the ith species in the mixture

ΔH_R enthalpy of reaction

$\tilde{H}$ partial molal enthapy of the ith species in the reaction mixture

ΔH_i defined by Eq. 8.3-10

J heat generated per unit volume of reactor per unit time

k first-order rate constant

k_0 pre-exponential factor

L	reactor length
L_P	length of piston-flow reactor
L_M	length of reactor with axial mixing
$\bar{M}$	average molecular weight of the feed
N	(ρ_0/ρ_r) Pe
P_i	production rate of the ith species in a complex reaction system
Pe	Peclet number, $d\rho\bar{U}_0/E$
r	radial coordinate
R_g	gas constant
T	fluid temperature
T_f	effluent fluid temperature
T_0	initial fluid temperature
$T_{\max}$	hot-spot temperature
$T_{\min}$	cold-spot temperature
T_w	wall temperature
$\bar{U}$	average velocity in a fixed bed
$\vec{U}$	vector velocity in a fixed bed
$\bar{U}_0$	initial average velocity in a fixed bed
U_h	over-all heat transfer coefficient
V	volume occupied by reaction mixture in a fixed bed
Y_i	moles of A_i per mass of fluid numerically equal to the average molecular weight of the feed
Z	coordinate along the axis of a cylindrical reactor

GREEK LETTERS

α	$\bar{U}a_R L/G_0\bar{C}$
α	$\sqrt{\dfrac{kE_{DA}}{\bar{U}^2}}$
β	$h_T a/G_0\bar{C}$ (see Eq. 8.4-7)
β	defined by Eq. 8.8-18
β	$G_0\bar{C}a_c/G_{0c}\bar{C}_c a_R$ (see Eq. 8.5-8)
β_m	mass transfer coefficient
β_h	heat transfer coefficient
γ_{gi}	a coefficient defined by Eqs. 2.3-13 and 2.3-14

γ $\quad$ $U_h a_c L / G_{0c} \bar{C}_c$

δ $\quad$ $\dfrac{A_1 e^{-\Delta E/R_g T_0}}{\beta_m}$ $\quad$ (see Eq. 8.7-6)

δ $\quad$ $\dfrac{G_0 \bar{C}}{JL}$

ξ $\quad$ $\mathscr{Y}/\alpha$

η $\quad$ Z/L

ρ_T, ρ $\quad$ fluid density

ρ_0 $\quad$ initial fluid density

ψ $\quad$ $C/C(0_-)$

Θ $\quad$ $(T - T_0)\left(\dfrac{G_0 \bar{C}}{JL}\right)$

Θ_c $\quad$ $(T_c - T_0)\left(\dfrac{G_0 \bar{C}}{JL}\right)$

Δ_i $\quad$ coefficients in Eq. 8.8-13

SCRIPT

$\mathscr{f}_1, \mathscr{f}_2$ $\quad$ defined by Eq. 8.2-7

$\mathscr{F}$ $\quad$ L_P/L_M

$\imath_1, \imath_2$ $\quad$ defined by Eq. 8.2-6

$\bar{\mathscr{R}}$ $\quad$ pseudo-homogeneous rate expression

$\mathscr{R}_x$ $\quad$ specific reaction rate per unit of external surface of the pellet

$\mathscr{Y}$ $\quad$ $kZ/\bar{U}$

Phenomenological Parameters of Fixed-bed Reactors

9

> I like a bit of a mongrel myself,
> whether it's a man or a dog: they're
> best for everyday.
>
> GEORGE BERNARD SHAW

9.1 Introduction

In the previous chapter we have found that the conversion and performance characteristics of fixed-bed reactors depend upon the numerical values of certain parameters. While some of the quantities making up these parameters are well defined physically, certain others are not. Parameters of the latter group largely characterize the macroscopic heat and mass transfer processes which occur within fixed beds and the heat transfer process between the fixed bed and the reactor wall or a coolant outside the wall. A more detailed discussion of these macroscopic quantities is taken up in this chapter primarily for two reasons: to provide information on their numerical magnitude, and to give some insight as to their nature.

Radial eddy transport relates directly to the two-dimensional reactors of Section 8.8, and is discussed first.

9.2 Radial eddy transport

Convection is an important process in all flow reactors and terms are included in the design equations to account for the transport of the relevant scalar quantities by this mechanism throughout the reactor. However, because the vector velocity fluctuates from point to point within a fixed bed,

216

the convection term separates into two parts, one which is the usual flow flux and another which more closely resembles a diffusion process. This so called eddy transport process, although a macroscopic phenomenon, takes a form somewhat similar to molecular transport processes and is generally, although not always, sufficiently large to mask the corresponding molecular processes. To arrive at suitable mathematical expression to account for this means of transport, investigators have made use of early work in arriving at Reynolds stress equations for momentum and energy transport in turbulent fields* and the well known Einstein development of the diffusion equation. An analysis of this type is not necessarily limited to fixed beds, but the following discussion will be so restricted for two reasons: Experimental data are available to test the model and the correspondence between the experiments and the model for packed beds leave little doubt as to the usefulness of the approach.

In writing an equation for, say, the conservation of a particular species i, a convective term of the form $-\mathrm{div}\,(UC_i)$ will appear, which accounts for the accumulation of the ith species within the control differential volume due to convective flow through the area enclosing the volume. This control volume element is a macroscopic volume in the sense that it contains a statistical number of particles, and the true velocity vector U will be a space fluctuating quantity as the fluid is forced to pass around the particles. Paralleling Reynolds original idea, we replace the vector velocity and the concentration by an average and a spatially fluctuating component, and take the space average over the macroscopic volume element of the four resulting terms.

Let
$$U = \bar{U} + u \qquad\qquad (9.2\text{-}1)$$
$$C_i = \bar{C}_i + c_i$$

then
$$\overline{-\mathrm{div}\,(UC_i)} = -\mathrm{div}\,\overline{(\bar{U}\bar{C}_i + u\bar{C}_i + c_i\bar{U} + uc_i)}, \qquad (9.2\text{-}2)$$

where the line above each expression is to remind us that a space average of these quantities is necessary. Since by definition

$$U = \frac{1}{V}\iiint_V U\,dV = \frac{1}{V}\iiint_V \bar{U}\,d\bar{v} + \frac{1}{V}\iiint_V u\,dv, \qquad (9.2\text{-}3)$$

where V is the macroscopic volume chosen earlier which includes enough particles to represent statistically the bed but small enough so as not to include variations of $\bar{U}$ in the field. It follows from this definition that the space average of the fluctuating velocity u and concentration c_i are zero. Hence the second and third terms of the right side of Equation 9.2-2 are

* See for example, H. Schlicting, *Boundary Layer Theory*, p. 371, McGraw-Hill Book Company, New York, 1955.

identically zero. The first term is the usual convective term which we have already considered. The last term $-\text{div}\,(uc_i)$ is the one which gives rise to radial transport. If u and c_i are not correlated, this term would also be zero. However, they are correlated and the following qualitative argument may be used to illustrate the reasonableness of the close correlation between u and c_i. Suppose that we have a concentration gradient within the fixed bed and that owing to a fluctuating velocity field, macroscopic packets of fluid arrive at some point labeled r on Fig. 9.2-1 from positions adjacent to r

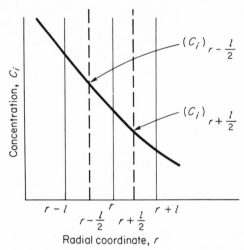

Fig. 9.2-1. Concentration profile in a fixed bed.

labeled $r - l/2$ and $r + l/2$. Since we have postulated the existence of a concentration gradient $\bar{C}_i$ in the r direction, it follows that packets arriving from the position $r - l/2$ owing to a velocity in the $+r$ direction will have on the average a greater concentration than at the point r and packets arriving from the position $r + l/2$ will have on the average a lower concentration than at r. It is clear then that positive values of the fluctuation c_i will be associated with positive values of u at the point x and, of course, $-c_i$ with $-u$. In this way, the correlation between u and c_i is physically realistic.

To develop this model more quantitatively, we modify the Einstein treatment of the diffusion process so that the results apply to the conditions characteristic of a packed bed. The fluid passing through a packed bed is forced to flow in the interstitial space formed among particles. This complex flow pattern may be characterized for our purposes in the following way: the fluid stream in a channel formed at a certain level in the bed has its path generally obstructed by a particle in the next layer downstream. The fluid is forced to go around this particle resulting in elements of the impinging stream being directed to each of several channels surrounding the given particle. In neighboring channels, at the same level as the original, the fluids are similarly separated. In this way elements from different channels combine to form new streams which are repeatedly separated. The process results in a net transport of material if a concentration gradient exists in the system. The degree to which the streams are mixed depends upon the Reynolds and the Schmidt numbers. However, even at relatively low values of Re_p, say greater than 100, the streams appear to be well mixed.

Before anything quantitative can be done in the way of a model, we need to characterize the velocity within a packed bed. The flow of a non-reacting fluid through a packed bed results in a radial distribution of velocity.* However, for our purpose, we shall assume that a non-reacting fluid will flow around the particles in such a way that equal average velocities $\bar{U}$ are found throughout the bed. If the fluid flowing is a mixture which reacts according to the stoichiometric equation $\sum_{i=1}^{n} a_i A_i = 0$, where $\sum_{i=1}^{n} a_i \neq 0$, the average velocity at various points within the packed bed will vary with extent of conversion. This difficulty stems from the fact that mass is conserved in chemical reactions; hence $\rho \bar{U}$ or G_0 is an invariant with conversion. However, even with an idealized packed bed, $\rho \bar{U}$ is not constant everywhere in the system because the conversion can vary with radial position, which in turn sets up radial pressure gradients. Then secondary flows occur to relieve these gradients. Despite this inconsistency, we will assume that $\rho \bar{U}$ is a constant throughout the bed for two reasons: First, a more realistic analysis results in untenable complications; and second, the assumption of constant $\rho \bar{U}$ is better in most cases than constant $\bar{U}$.

Cognizant of the inherent limitations in the model above, we shall attempt of obtain a semi-quantitative description of the eddy transport process in the direction normal to the bulk flow. With respect to an observer moving through the bed with a velocity $\bar{U}$, the fluid elements are forced to go from one mixing cell to another as they flow round particles of packing. The distance the elements move radially on the average is designated as l the mean free path. After each "jump," a part of the fluid elements flowing in adjacent streams are mixed, resulting in mass transfer in the presence of a concentration gradient.

If u_l is the magnitude of the lateral velocity fluctuations, then the net flux of material moving laterally at r is

$$\tfrac{1}{2}[(u_r \bar{C}_i)_{r-(l/2)} - (u_r \bar{C}_i)_{r+(l/2)}] = -\frac{l}{2} \operatorname{grad}_r (u_r \bar{C}_i) \qquad (9.2\text{-}4)$$

where the factor of $\tfrac{1}{2}$ is brought in to account for the fact that u_l of a given

* V. P. Dorweiler and R. W. Fahien, *A.I.Ch.E. Jour.* **5**, 139 (1959); M. Morales, C. W. Spinn and J. M. Smith, *Ind. Eng. Chem.* **43**, 225 (1951); C. E. Swartz and J. M. Smith, *Ind. Eng. Chem.* **45**, 1209 (1953).

sign operates through only half of the area. If each of the quantities on the left-hand side of Eq. 9.2-4 is expanded in a Taylor's series, and subtracted, we obtain the right-hand side. Now, if we assume that u_l is proportional to $\bar{U}$ and $\rho\bar{U}$ is conserved, then ρu_r is also conserved and

$$-\tfrac{1}{2}\,\mathrm{grad}_r\,(u_rC_i) = -\frac{l}{2}\,\mathrm{grad}_r\left[\frac{\rho u_r}{\bar{M}}\left(\frac{\bar{M}C_i}{\rho}\right)\right] \qquad (9.2\text{-}5)$$

$$= -\frac{l\rho u_r}{2\bar{M}}\,\mathrm{grad}_r\,Y_i, \qquad (9.2\text{-}6)$$

where Y_i = the number of moles of the component i in the mixture per mass
　　　　of fluid numerically equal to $\bar{M}$,
　　$\bar{M}$ = the average molecular weight of the feed mixture,
But　　$u_r = l/\theta_l$ where θ_l is the time for a jump to occur. From the Einstein equation, the diffusivity E_{DR} is given by

$$E_{DR} = \frac{l^2}{2\theta_l}. \qquad (9.2\text{-}7)$$

Therefore, the net flux in the lateral direction is of the form

$$-\frac{\rho}{\bar{M}}\,E_{DR}\,\mathrm{grad}_r\,Y_i. \qquad (9.2\text{-}8)$$

Following Baron* and Ranz,† it is possible to determine the order of magnitude of E_{DR} in terms of relevant bed parameters. The quantity l of Eq. 9.2-6 is of the order to $d_p/2$, the catalytic pellet radius, and θ_l is of the order of $d_p/\bar{U}$. Substituting these quantities into Eq. 9.2-7 and remembering that $\rho\bar{U}$ is conserved we obtain

$$E_{DR} = \frac{l^2}{2\theta_l} = \frac{d_p^2\rho_0\bar{U}}{8d_p\rho} = \frac{d_p\bar{U}\rho_0}{8\rho}, \qquad (9.2\text{-}9)$$

whereupon

$$\rho E_{DR} = \frac{d_p\bar{U}\rho_0}{8}. \qquad (9.2\text{-}10)$$

More generally for packed beds

$$\rho E_{DR} = \frac{d_p\bar{U}\rho_0}{N}, \qquad (9.2\text{-}11)$$

where N is a number of the order of 8. The term $\overline{-\mathrm{div}\,(uC_i)}$ in Eq. 9.2-2 can be replaced by

$$\overline{-\mathrm{div}\,(uC_i)} = -\mathrm{div}\left[\frac{-\rho_0\,d_p\,\bar{U}}{N\bar{M}}\,\mathrm{grad}_r\,Y_i\right]. \qquad (9.2\text{-}12)$$

* T. Baron, *Chem. Eng. Prog.* **48**, 118 (1952).
† W. Ranz, *Chem. Eng. Prog.* **48**, 247 (1952).

It would be unwise to use a value of $N = 8$ in reactor design calculations based upon the eddy diffusion model developed above. It is preferable to use experimental values of N. Unfortunately, very little if any data are available for reacting systems. Experimental values of N are, however, available for non-reacting systems. Note that $\rho_0 \cong \rho$ and N is equal to the Peclet number Pe.

$$N = \text{Pe} \equiv \frac{d_p \bar{U}}{E_{DR}}. \tag{9.2-13}$$

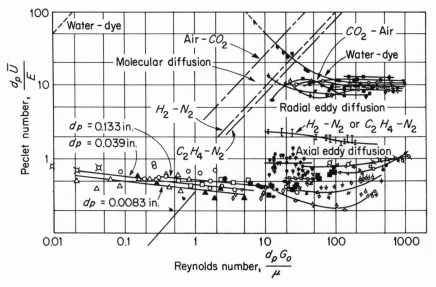

Fig. 9.2-2. Compilation of data for axial and radial dispersion among particles, liquids, and gases. [Adapted from R. H. Wilhelm, *Pure and Applied Chemistry*, **5**, 403 (1962), by permission of International Union of Pure and Applied Chemistry and Butterworth's Scientific Publications.]

The experimental results of a number of workers[*] are shown on Fig. 9.2-2, which was originally prepared by Wilhelm.[†] On this figure

$$\text{Pe} = \frac{d_p \bar{U}}{E_{DA}} \quad \text{and} \quad \text{Re} = \frac{d_p G_0}{\mu},$$

* V. G. Bakhurov and G. U. Boreskov, *J. Appl. Chem.* (USSR) **20**, 721 (1947); R. A. Bernard and R. H. Wilhelm, *C.E.P.* **46**, 233 (1950); G. A. Latimen, *Ph.D. Dissertation*, Department of Chemical Engineering, Princeton University, New Jersey; R. W. Fahien and J. M. Smith, *A.I.Ch.E. Jour.* **1**, 28 (1955); D. A. Plautz and H. F. Johnston, *Ibid.* **1**, 292 (1955).

† R. H. Wilhelm, *Pure Appl. Chem.* **5**, 403 (1962).

where $\bar{U}$ = average velocity in the fixed bed,

$\quad d_p$ = diameter of pellets making up the fixed bed,

$\quad E_{DA}$ = axial eddy diffusivity,

$\quad G_0$ = mass velocity,

$\quad \mu$ = viscosity.

Focusing attention on the upper right-hand corner of the figure, we note that the experimental values of Pe lay between 5 and 15 for all values of Re greater than about 50.

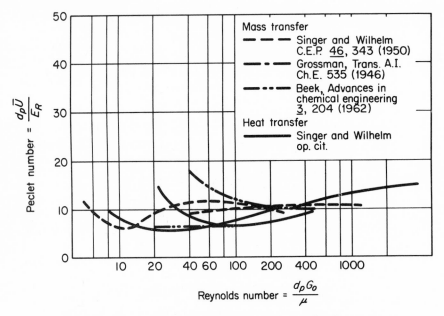

Fig. 9.2-3. Radial diffusivity versus Reynolds number for gases in a packed bed. Adapted from E. Singer and R. H. Wilhelm, *C.E.P.* **46**, 343 (1950).

Figure 9.2-3 shows some data eddy thermal diffusivities. While this figure appears to justify a value of about 10 for the Peclet number of radial heat transfer, it should be recognized that parallel mechanisms of radial transport by radiation and conduction through the solids alter the analogy. Above Reynolds numbers of about 100 the effect of the latter is generally small.

On Fig. 9.2-2, a comparison is made between the Pe for radial eddy transport and transport by molecular processes. Also shown are experimental values of Pe for axial eddy transport, a subject discussed in the following section.

9.3 Axial eddy diffusivity

In the discussion of axial dispersion in one-dimensional reactors of Section 8.6, we anticipated the result of this section in order to establish the criterion that if the parameter α, defined for the first-order reactions in Eq. 8.6-4 as

$$\alpha = \sqrt{\frac{kE_{DA}}{\bar{U}}} \tag{9.3-1}$$

is small, the effect of axial dispersion is small provided that the numerical value of the Peclet number does not approach zero.

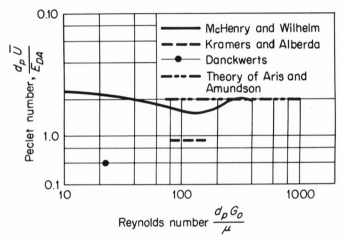

Fig. 9.3-1. Axial dispersion for gases.

In this section, we shall summarize some of the work on the axial diffusivity in packed beds to report its numerical values as obtained from experimental and theoretical investigations, and to establish the nonisotropy of the eddy transport processes in packed beds.

Experimental numerical values of the axial Peclet number for gases is presented on Fig. 9.3-1 as a function of the Reynolds number. The upper solid line summarizes the experimental findings for gas phase mixing of McHenry and Wilhelm* which were obtained using a frequency response technique. The fixed beds used in these experiments were composed of randomly packed spherical glass pellets of uniform size. Their results substantiate the numerical magnitude of the axial Peclet number of about 2 over a range of Reynolds numbers from 10 to 400. This is in agreement

* K. W. McHenry, Jr. and R. H. Wilhelm, *A.I.Ch.E. Jour.* **3**, 83 (1957).

with the theoretical results of Aris and Amundson* which predicts the same value of the Peclet number for large Reynolds numbers. This latter model as well as the model of Kramers and Alberda† formed in part the basis for the mixing cell model of a fixed bed discussed at the end of Chapter 8 in connection with the model of Deans and Lapidus.

The experimental results of Kramers and Alberda and Danckwerts‡ are also shown. These experimentors used Raschig rings for the packing material and the pellet-to-tube ratio of 0.13 and 0.20, respectively. These rather high values suggest that by-passing might account for the layer value of E_{DA} found from these experiments.

On Fig. 9.2-2, the results of Ebach and White§ on the dispersion of liquids, of Carberry and Bretton,‖ of Strang and Geankoplis¶, Hennico, Jacques and Vermeulen,** and Cairns and Prausnitz†† are shown which

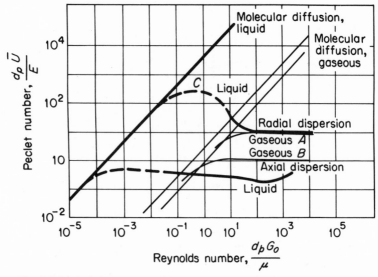

Fig. 9.3-2. Axial and radial dispersion, interlocking hydrodynamic regions. [Adapted from R. H. Wilhelm, *Pure and Applied Chemistry*, **5**, 403 (1962), by permission of International Union of Pure and Applied Chemistry and Butterworth's Scientific Publications.]

* R. Aris and N. R. Amundson, *A.I.Ch.E. Jour.* **3**, 280 (1957).

† H. Kramers and G. Alberda, *Chem. Eng. Sci.* **2**, 173 (1953).

‡ P. V. Danckwerts, *Chem. Eng. Sci.* **2**, 1 (1953).

§ E. A. Ebach and R. R. White, *A.I.Ch.E. Jour.* **4**, 161 (1958).

‖ J. J. Carberry and R. H. Bretton, *A.I.Ch.E. Jour.* **4**, 367 (1958).

¶ D. A. Strang and C. J. Geankoplis, *Ind. Eng. Chem.* **50**, 1305 (1958).

** A. Hennico, G. Jacques and T. Vermeulen, University of California, Lawrence Radiation Laboratory Report UCRL 10696 (1963).

†† E. J. Cairns and J. M. Prausnitz, *Chem. Eng. Sci.* **12**, 20 (1960).

demonstrate that the Peclet number for liquids is smaller than gases at low Reynolds numbers.

The results shown on Fig. 9.2-2 are sufficient to substantiate our earlier statement that the magnitude of the parameter α serves to determine whether axial dispersion is important in fixed-bed reactors, because the axial Peclet is of the order of unity, not zero. This figure also shows us that the eddy diffusive processes in fixed beds are nonisotropic: the numerical values of the radial and axial diffusivities in the fully developed region vary by an order of magnitude.

Recommended values of the axial and radial eddy diffusivities and their comparison with molecular transport processes are shown in Fig. 9.3-2.

9.4 Heat transfer coefficients

In Section 8.8, we used the heat transfer coefficient h_T in the boundary condition of Eq. 8.8-6. The coefficient h_T accounted for the resistance to heat transfer between the wall of the reactor and the fixed bed. This is a

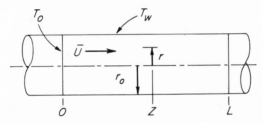

Fig. 9.4-1. Diagram of system in which heat is transferred from the fluid in a packed bed to the region near a wall where a finite heat transfer coefficient is observed.

difficult quantity to measure because in essence it requires a knowledge of the temperature of the fixed bed adjacent to the heat transfer surface. This temperature is generally obtained by extrapolating the temperature profile within the fixed bed to the heat transfer surface. Because h_T is difficult to measure accurately, there are wide discrepancies between the data of various investigators. However, perhaps the most important information to the designer of reactors is to get some insight as to how important it really is to have accurate values of h_T.

We shall do this by considering a system in which heat transfer takes place in the absence of chemical reaction. We are led to the standard problem of piston-flow of a hot fluid through a fixed bed where the cylindrical boundaries of the tube are held at some constant temperature smaller than the input fluid temperature shown in Fig. 9.4-1. The flow of heat in the axial direction results from a convective flux and in the radial direction, from radial eddy diffusion. In dimensionless form the equation describing the system is

$$\frac{\partial \Theta}{\partial \mathscr{z}} = \frac{1}{\xi} \frac{\partial}{\partial \xi} \left(\xi \frac{\partial \Theta}{\partial \xi} \right),$$ (9.4-1)

where

$$\Theta = \frac{T - T_w}{T_0 - T_w},$$

$$\xi = \frac{r}{r_0},$$

$$\mathscr{z} = \frac{E_{HR} Z}{U R_0^2}.$$

E_{HR} = eddy thermal diffusivity in the radial direction and where all of the other quantities have their standard meanings or are shown on Fig. 9.4-1. The boundary conditions for this problem are:

$$
\left.
\begin{array}{lll}
\text{At} & \mathscr{z} = 0, & \Theta = 1 \\[2mm]
\text{at} & \xi = 1, & \dfrac{\partial \Theta}{\partial \xi} = \sigma \Theta \\[2mm]
\text{and at} & \xi = 0, & \dfrac{\partial \Theta}{\partial \xi} = 0
\end{array}
\right\}
$$ (9.4-2)

where

$$\sigma = \frac{h_T r_0}{\rho \bar{C} E_{HR}}.$$ (9.4-3)

The solution to Eqs. 9.4-1 and 9.4-2 is available in standard references;* however, the important point is that as the parameter σ becomes large, say numerically greater than 10, essentially all of the heat transfer resistance is in the fixed bed and there is very little resistance to heat transfer between the fixed bed and the wall at $R = R_0$. Thus, if

$$\frac{h_T r_0}{\rho C E_{HR}} > 10,$$ (9.4-4)

we can change one of the boundary conditions of Eq. 9.4-2 to at $\xi = 1$, $\Theta = 0$. We know from Fig. 9.2-2 that

$$\frac{d_p \bar{U}}{E_{HR}} = 10, \quad \text{Re} > 50.$$ (9.4-5)

* See for example, H. S. Carslaw and J. C. Jaeger, "Conduction of Heat in Solids," 2nd ed., p. 201, Oxford University Press, Inc., 1959.

Therefore, substitution of Eq. 9.4-5 into 9.4-4 yields:

$$\frac{h_T r_0 10}{\rho \bar{C} \bar{U} d_p} > 10. \qquad (9.4\text{-}6)$$

Normally $r_0/d_p \approx 10$, whereupon Eq. 9.4-6 becomes

$$\frac{h_T}{\rho \bar{C} \bar{U}} > 0.1. \qquad (9.4\text{-}7)$$

Equation 9.4-7 is a rough criterion which, if satisfied, tells us we need not consider h_T in the analysis. It is not a rigorous criterion because the analysis upon which it is based did not include a term for a chemical reaction heat source.

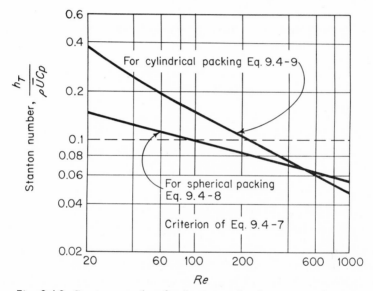

Fig. 9.4-2. Stanton number for heat transfer from a gas flowing through a fixed bed reactor to the reactor wall.

Beek* suggests the following empirical formula for fixed beds of spherical pellets:

$$\frac{h_T}{\rho \bar{C} \bar{U}} = \frac{0.203}{\mathrm{Re}^{2/3} \mathrm{Pr}^{2/3}} + \frac{0.220}{\mathrm{Re}^{0.2} \mathrm{Pr}^{0.6}}, \qquad (9.4\text{-}8)$$

and for fixed beds of cylindrical pellets:

$$\frac{h_T}{\rho \bar{C} \bar{U}} = \frac{2.58}{\mathrm{Re}^{2/3} \mathrm{Pr}^{2/3}} + \frac{0.094}{\mathrm{Re}^{0.2} \mathrm{Pr}^{0.6}}. \qquad (9.4\text{-}9)$$

These two equations are plotted on Fig. 9.4-2 for gases ($\mathrm{Pr} = 0.7$). From the position of the criterion with respect to the empirical formulæ, it appears

* J. Beek, *Adv. Chem. Eng.* **3**, 204 (1962).

that the heat transfer coefficient is large enough in fixed beds so that appreciable resistance to heat transfer at the wall does not greatly influence the behavior of such reactors. An alternate but equivalent statement is that the amount of heat transferred is not sensitive to the precise value of the heat transfer coefficient, which is perhaps the reason why h_T is so difficult to measure with precision.

It is more difficult to treat the other heat transfer coefficient h_T and the over-all heat transfer coefficient U_h discussed in Sections 8.4 and 8.5. The numerical values of these parameters depend upon the nature of the chemical reaction occurring within the reactor in much the same way as in homogeneous reactors.* By analogy with the latter reactions we know that the magnitude of these heat transfer coefficients can be several fold larger than in the absence of chemical reaction. Therefore, it behooves a designer to be aware of this fact and to anticipate at least qualitatively the consequences of larger values of U_h.

NOTATION FOR CHAPTER 9

a_i stoichiometric coefficient

A_i species of a reaction mixture

C_i spacially fluctuating concentration of ith species

$\bar{C}_i$ average concentration of ith species

c_i fluctuating component of concentration of ith species

$\bar{C}$ mean heat capacity of fluid

d_p diameter of pellets making up the fixed bed

E_{DR} radial eddy diffusivity

E_{DA} axial eddy diffusivity

E_{HR} radial eddy diffusivity of heat

G_0 mass velocity

h_T heat transfer coefficient between fixed bed and wall of reactor

l mean free path

$\bar{M}$ average molecular weight of the feed mixture

N defined by Eq. 9.2-11

* See for example: Stephan S. T. Fan and D. M. Mason, Jr. *J. Chem. Eng. Data* **7**, 183 (1962); W. Schotte, *Ind. Eng. Chem.* **50**, 683 (1958); D. Secrest and J. O. Hirshfelder, *Phys. Fluids* **4**, 61 (1961); J. O. Hirshfelder, *Heat Conductivity in Polyatomic, Electronically Excited or Chemically Reacting Mixtures*, III, p. 351, Reinhold Publishing Co., New York (1957).

r radial coordinate

r_0 radius of cylindrical reactor

U vector velocity in a packed bed

$\bar{U}$ mean velocity in a packed bed

u fluctuating component of velocity; see Eq. 9.2-1

V volume

Y_i number of moles of the ith species in a mixture per mass of fluid numerically equal to $\bar{M}$

GREEK LETTERS

α defined by Eq. 9.3-1; see also Eq. 8.6-4

ξ r/r_0, dimensionless radial coordinate

ρ fluid density

ρ_0 initial fluid density

θ_l characteristic time; see Eq. 9.2-7

Θ dimensionless temperature

μ viscosity

σ defined by Eq. 9.4-3

SCRIPT

$\mathscr{z}$ $\dfrac{h_T r_0}{\rho \bar{C} E_{HR}}$, dimensionless axial coordinate

Moving-bed Reactors   10

"Oh, anywhere! Forward! 'Tis all the same, Colonel:
You'll find lovely fighting all along the whole line!"

EDMUND STEDMAN

10.1 Introduction

Resort to moving-bed catalytic reactors* is in general necessary when as a result of reaction or owing to impurities in the reaction mixture, rapid deactivation of the catalyst occurs. In this type of reactor, catalyst is withdrawn from the reactor continuously and is treated for reactivation in some unit external to the reactor. At the same time freshly reactivated catalyst is continuously returned in order to keep the inventory of catalyst in the reactor constant. Obviously, this recirculation of the catalyst complicates the analysis of the reactor system, because the inventory contains catalyst particles in various stages of deactivation. Thus in order to design reactors of this type, we need in addition to the "point"† values of concentrations and temperature, the distribution of catalyst activities. Since activity is directly related to the intrinsic rate constant, the local pseudo-homogeneous rate expression may be characterized by some local mean activity. Therefore, methods must be developed for determining the local activity distribution at points throughout the reactor. The local pseudo-homogeneous rate expression also depends upon local values of the catalyst density, i.e., the mass of catalyst per unit volume of reactor at operating conditions.

* The terminology "moving-bed reactor" as used here is intended to include all reactor systems in which catalyst is continuously circulated to and from the reactor. The term is customarily more restrictive in its meaning.

† "Point" in this case refers to a volume element containing a statistical number of catalyst particles.

230

Certain kinds of moving-bed reactors are similar to packed beds. The catalyst pellets are large and move through the units in rather well defined paths and may be thought of as slowly moving packed beds. The design of such reactors may be approached in principle in a manner similar to that discussed in the preceding chapter for packed-bed reactors with, of course, some adjustment in the local pseudo-homogeneous rate expression to account for local variations in activity.

Fluidized reactors present a different problem. For example, in dense fluidized beds, i.e., fluidized systems having a high concentration of solid, violent agitation results from the interactions among catalyst particles and reacting fluids. Backmixing, recirculation, and other rapid transport mechanisms, which appear to account for the motion of the solid and fluid phases, call for design methods quite unlike those used for fixed-bed reactors. A further complication in dense-bed fluidized reactors is that a fraction of the fluid phase appears to "by-pass" the solid phase owing to "bubble"* formation.

In dilute fluidized reactors, i.e., fluidized systems having a low concentration of solids, hydrodynamic considerations are important in determining the catalyst distribution, the velocity distribution of each phase and, of course, the slip velocities between phases. Although the design of this type of reactor is complicated by some of the same difficulties in describing the fluxes of energy and material that are found in dense-bed fluidized reactors, in some ways it yields to analysis more readily.

From this brief introduction, it should be clear that methods for the analysis of packed-bed reactors are not necessarily applicable to moving-bed reactors because of conceptual difficulties in describing the mechanisms of transport phenomena. In fact, Wilhelm† states that fluidized beds, like flames and jets, ". . . are beyond immediate *a priori* design objectives because of incomplete theory . . . ." The hydrodynamic flow patterns of the mixture of phases give rise to transport fluxes, the functional forms of which are as yet unknown. Hence we cannot use approaches analogous to those successfully applied to packed beds in the preceding chapter because we are unable to write a conservation equation for each phase which describes functionally the local processes occurring pointwise throughout the reactor volume.

Accordingly, the topics on moving-bed reactors will be taken up from two points of view: First, certain cases of moving-bed reactors are treated by conventional methods in which the limiting forms of the transport properties are assumed. Second, the system is studied operationally with the result that a method is obtained which is useful for interpretation of reactor

* The term "bubble" here refers to localized zones of low catalyst density in a dense fluidized bed. In a gross sense, these zones appear similar to a discontinuous phase immersed in a continuous phase, hence the name "bubble."

† R. H. Wilhelm, *Pure Appl. Chem.* **5**, 403 (1962).

performance rather than for *a priori* design. The latter approach will be taken up first because the general characteristics of these reactor types are brought out more clearly and because it suggests a means whereby a more detailed understanding of the transport mechanisms may be obtained experimentally. These methods are based upon a statistical description of the time required for tagged elements to appear at various points in the prototype system as obtained by tracer techniques. The amount of information which may be obtained and the rigor with which deductions follow depend upon the kind of tracer used, how it is introduced, and the manner in which the signal is followed in the system. The oldest and simplest of these techniques will be discussed first. It makes use of the residence-time distribution function which may be looked upon as the probability that an element will remain in the system less than a specified residence time. This early technique requires only a small amount of information to determine its form experimentally, and of course is correspondingly limited in its application to the design of moving-bed reactors. These ideas will then be extended to include techniques which, although of more general applicability, still fall short of providing all the information that is needed for analysis and design of reactors. There follows a comparison of the performance characteristics of certain limiting types of moving-bed reactors.

10.2 The residence-time distribution function

The residence-time distribution function $T(t)$ is defined as the fraction of the elements, all entering at $t = 0$, which have a residence time in a system equal to or less than t. If more than one phase enters a unit, it is possible to obtain a set of residence-time distribution functions, one for each phase, which in general may differ from each other. A number of techniques have been devised for obtaining $T(t)$, but they are all based upon the observation of the change in a tracer signal as it passes through a particular system. The derivative of $T(t)$, $T'(t)\,dt$, is a statement of the probability that an element will reside in the system for a time between t and $t + dt$. It is important to recognize at this point that, given $T(t)$, no statement can be made as to the detailed mechanism giving rise to it, or even as to how elements of a certain age are distributed within the system. Another way of saying this is that several mechanisms can give rise to the same function $T(t)$. Therefore, it follows that a knowledge of $T(t)$, in addition to the detailed form of the rate expression, is generally *not* sufficient information to predict the conversion of a chemical reactor. Nevertheless, there are instances where this function alone leads to a complete description of certain features of reactors. We shall discuss the utility and limitations of the residence-time distribution function later. Meanwhile, we shall assume that this function is important to know about, and concentrate upon methods for its determination as well as some of its characteristics.

Consider now an experimental method for determining $T(t)$. Let us assume that the reactor shown in Fig. 10.2-1 is operating at steady state

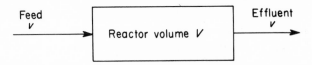

Fig. 10.2-1. Reactor diagram.

with a normal feed which we shall designate as white. Of course, the effluent is entirely white. If, at zero time, the feed is suddenly changed to a tagged variety of material, say red, which is identical to the white in every respect except that it is tagged red, then at some time t

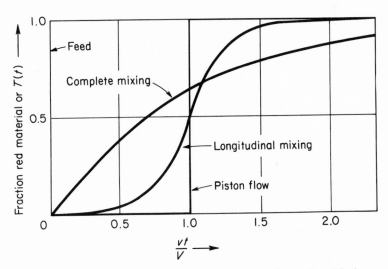

Fig. 10.2-2. Residence-time distribution functions for various kinds of flow types.

later, the effluent can be examined for its fractional content of red material. Because of the way the experiment is conducted, it can be concluded that the red fraction of the effluent stream must have entered the reactor during the time interval t. Thus, this fraction is $T(t)$, the fraction of the effluent having resided a time equal to or less than t. Figure 10.2-2 shows qualitatively the shapes of curves for several different mixing patterns with the reactor.

Certain general relationships can be developed from simple conservation principles. Let $I(t)\,dt$ be the fraction of the material within the reactor having ages between t and $t + dt$, and $T'(t)\,dt$ be the fraction of the material in the effluent stream having resided in the reactor for time between t and $t + dt$.

Referring again to the model of Fig. 10.2-1, the amount of red material having entered the reactor at a time t is vt, where v is a volumetric flow rate, and V is the volume occupied by the fluid in the reactor.* A material balance on the red material is therefore:

$$vt = V\int_0^t I(x)\,dx + v\int_0^t\int_0^x T'(y)\,dy\,dx. \tag{10.2-1}$$

The first term on the right-hand side of Eq. 10.2-1 is the amount of red material still remaining in the reactor whereas the second term accounts for the material having left the reactor during the time interval t. Differentiating Eq. 10.2-1 we get

$$1 - \int_0^t T'(x)\,dx = \frac{V}{v}I(t). \tag{10.2-2}$$

If we now use the definition of $T'(t)$, which is

$$\int_0^t T'(x)\,dx = T(t), \tag{10.2-3}$$

and remember that the functions are normalized, i.e.,

$$\int_0^\infty T'(t)\,dt = 1 \quad\text{and}\quad \int_0^\infty I(t)\,dt = 1, \tag{10.2-4}$$

then the integration of Eq. 10.2-2 leads to

$$\frac{v}{V}\int_0^\infty [1 - T(t)]\,dt = 1. \tag{10.2-5}$$

It will be noted in Fig. 10.2-3 that the sum of the areas labeled $(1 - A_1)$ and A_2 must according to Eq. 10.2-5 be equal to unity; thus $A_1 = A_2$ for any function $T(t)$. We can now proceed to define a useful average residence time of elements in the effluent stream $\bar{t}_E$. By definition:

$$\bar{t}_E = \frac{\displaystyle\int_0^\infty tT'(t)\,dt}{\displaystyle\int_0^\infty T'(t)\,dt} = \int_0^\infty tT'(t)\,dt, \tag{10.2-6}$$

but

$$\frac{dT(t)}{dt} = T'(t). \tag{10.2-7}$$

---

* The terms v and V as used here can apply to any phase in the system. However, later in this chapter they will refer only to the fluid phase. The catalyst feed rate will then be n and the amount of catalyst in the reactor will be N.

Substituting Eq. 10.2-7 into Eq. 10.2-6 and changing limits we get

$$\frac{v\bar{t}_E}{V} = \int_0^1 \left(\frac{vt}{V}\right) dT(t). \tag{10.2-8}$$

where now the definite integral on the right-hand side of Eq. 10.2-8 has the same value as that in Eq. 10.2-5. This becomes obvious from the meaning of each integral on Fig. 10.2-3. Therefore,

$$\frac{v\bar{t}_E}{V} = 1. \tag{10.2-9}$$

We now see the meaning of the abscissa coordinate vt/V which is the time as measured as a fraction or multiple of the average residence time.

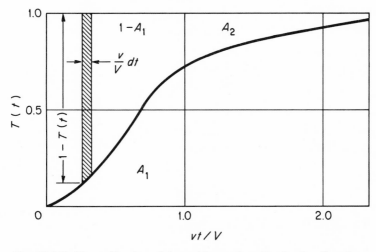

Fig. 10.2-3. Normalization of the residence-time distribution function.

The average age of the particles in the system $\bar{t}_I$ is similarly defined.

$$\bar{t}_I = \frac{\int_0^\infty tI(t)\, dt}{\int_0^\infty I(t)\, dt} = \int_0^\infty tI(t)\, dt. \tag{10.2-10}$$

Using Eq. 10.2-2 and integrating by parts,

$$t_I = \frac{v}{2V} \int_0^1 t^2\, dT(t). \tag{10.2-11}$$

In the framework of the preceding analysis, we can define two characteristics of a particular system: holdback and macroscopic segregation. Although these characteristics are quantitatively defined, they are more useful to characterize a system qualitatively. Holdback is the fraction of material having a residence time greater than the nominal value $\bar{t}_E$. This, of course, corresponds to the area A_2 of Fig. 10.2-3. For piston-flow, the holdback is zero. Hence, holdback is a comparison between the real system and the idealized system in which all elements reside an equal time in the reactor.

The other quantity, the macroscopic segregation, is a comparison of the characteristics of the real system with a completely mixed system. Here it is

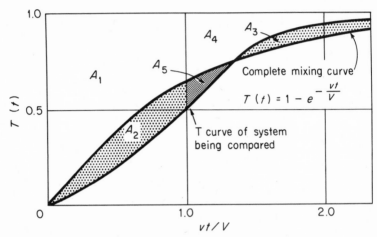

Fig. 10.2-4. Segregation in flow systems.

necessary to distinguish between macroscopic and microscopic segregation.[*] The magnitude of macroscopic segregation is determined by the area A_3 of Fig. 10.2-4. It is easily shown from the previous relationships for each $T(t)$ curve that

$$A_3 = A_2 + A_5. \tag{10.2-12}$$

In terms of a hypothetical tracer experiment with a step function input, we have shown how a $T(t)$ versus vt/V curve is obtained for a particular system. By means of a similar experiment using impulse or delta-function input of tracer material, an analogous measurement of the $T'(t)$ versus vt/V can be obtained. This is shown in Fig. 10.2-5 for several types of mixing processes. If a quantity Q of tracer is injected at $t = 0$, the concentration of tracer in the effluent stream $\mathbf{C}(t)$ follows from the following argument.

$$Q = \int_0^\infty v\mathbf{C}(t)\, dt \tag{10.2-13}$$

or

$$\int_0^\infty \frac{V\mathbf{C}(t)}{Q}\, d\frac{vt}{V} = 1. \tag{10.2-14}$$

* P. V. Danckwerts, *Chem. Eng. Sci.* **7**, 116 (1958).

A material balance on the tracer material yields

$$1 - \int_0^t \frac{v\mathbf{C}(x)\,dx}{Q} = \frac{V}{v}I(t),\qquad (10.2\text{-}15)$$

where the second term on the left-hand side of Eq. 10.2-15 is the fraction of the tracer material which has left the reactor. One minus this quantity is the fraction remaining in the reactor which, of course, is the physical meaning

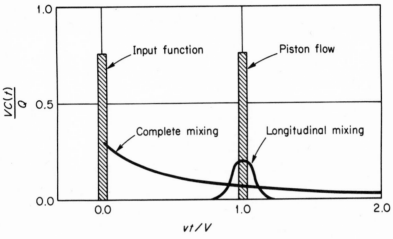

Fig. 10.2-5. Response of system to delta-function input.

of the right-hand side of the equation. A comparison of Eqs. 10.2-15 and 10.2-2 yields

$$T'(t) = \frac{v}{Q}\,\mathbf{C}(t).\qquad (10.2\text{-}16)$$

As would be expected, the same information is obtained from the step-function and the delta-function inputs.

Having described the residence-time distribution function and some of the methods for measuring it experimentally, we shall give some examples of its use.

EXAMPLE 10.2-1 FIRST-ORDER REACTION ON THE SURFACE OF A UNIFORMLY DISTRIBUTED AND COMPLETELY MIXED CATALYST

The function $T'(t)$ is sufficient information for the design of only a very restricted class of moving-bed reactors. In this system, the probability that a molecule of fluid will react depends solely upon its time of residence within the unit. The residence-time distribution function supplies us with precisely this information. Therefore, if the average activity per unit volume is given by a first-order, pseudo-homogeneous rate constant $\bar{k}$, the fraction of the molecules remaining in an element of fluid contacting the catalyst for a time t is

$$\frac{C(t)}{C(0)} = e^{-\bar{k}t}, \tag{10.2-17}$$

where $C(0)$ is the concentration in the element at $t = 0$. However, each of the fluid elements resides in the reactor according to the residence-time distribution function $T'(t)$, and the fraction of the molecules converted in such a reactor is

$$1 - f = \int_0^\infty e^{-\bar{k}t} T'(t) \, dt. \tag{10.2-18}$$

This system yields to elementary analysis because in postulating a uniformly distributed and completely mixed catalyst, an element of reacting fluid is exposed to the same environment regardless of its location in the reactor. It is immaterial, then, where each element is at a particular time. More important, however, it is immaterial where it has been at previous times—its history in the reactor does not alter its present probability of reaction. It follows then that this example is indeed a very special case and one cannot generalize this method to include more complex systems.

EXAMPLE 10.2-2 RESIDENCE-TIME DISTRIBUTION OF CATALYST IN COMMERCIAL FLUIDIZED REGENERATORS

Despite its limitations, the use of the residence time distribution function has provided valuable qualitative information on the behavior of equipment. In particular, the results of tracer tests on prototype regenerators are available. Singer, Todd, and Guinn* report the residence time characteristics of the catalyst phase in three different catalytic cracking units. Some of their results are shown on Fig. 10.2-6 in which the mixing characteristics of the solid phase in regenerators is compared with that of an ideal mixer. As shown on the figure, the curves for Unit I appear to approximate rather closely that for complete mixing for the cases of both high and low catalyst inventory. The curves for Units II and III deviate more from the ideal mixer, the latter showing the greater deviation from a completely mixed stage. Although not subject to unique interpretation, these curves give considerable insight as to the nature of the mixing processes occurring within the respective units.

* E. Singer, D. B. Todd, and V. P. Guinn, *Ind. Eng. Chem.* **49,** 11 (1957).

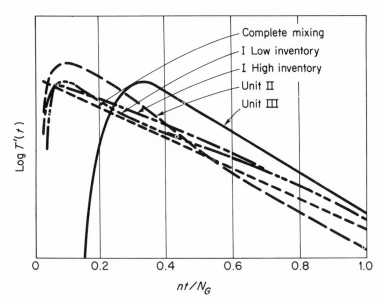

Fig. 10.2-6. $T'(t)$ distributions in three commercial regenerators compared with a completely mixed stage. [Adapted from Singer *et al, Ind. Eng. Chem.* **49**, 11, (1957).]

EXAMPLE 10.2-3 RESIDENCE-TIME DISTRIBUTION OF THE FLUID PHASE IN COMMERCIAL FLUIDIZED REGENERATORS

Mixing processes occurring in the gas phase were reported in studies by Danckwerts, Jenkins, and Place* and Handlos, Kunstman, and Schissler.† In the former study, a helium tracer signal was introduced into the regenerator air supply line and the corresponding tracer signal was followed in the flue of the regenerator, as shown schematically in Fig. 10.2-7. Unfortunately, the nominal residence times in the dense phase (between points B and C of Fig. 10.2-7) and dilute phase (between points C and D) fluidized beds were 10.9 and 21.1 seconds, respectively, so that the experiments probably reflect the characteristics in the dilute phase more than in the dense phase. It is in the latter phase that most of the regeneration takes place. Primarily on the basis of a lag in the tracer signal of about 11 seconds, Danckwerts and his coworkers concluded that the gases pass through the regenerator very nearly in piston flow.

Handlos and his group were able to obtain samples within a regenerator itself (corresponding to point C on Fig. 10.2-7) and as a result, their data

* P. V. Danckwerts, J. W. Jenkins and G. Place, *Chem. Eng. Sci.* **2**, 1 (1953).
† A. E. Handlos, R. W. Kunstman and D. O. Schissler, *Ind. Eng. Chem.* **49**, 25 (1957).

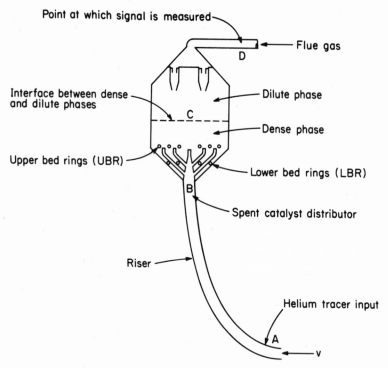

Fig. 10.2-7. Diagram of fluidized regenerator.

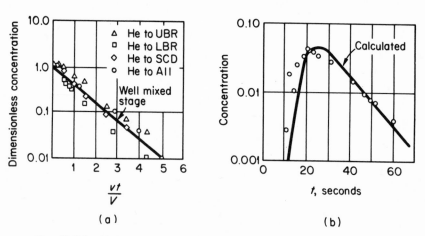

Fig. 10.2-8. (*a*) Dilute phase samples in unsteady state. (*b*) Flue samples from regenerator. [Adapted from Handlos *et al.*, *Ind. Eng. Chem.* **49**, 25 (1957).]

probably reflect more closely the processes which occur in the dense-phase fluidized bed. Their unsteady-state experiments show that the behavior of the dense phase approximates that of a well-mixed stage. This is shown on Fig. 10.2-8. On this figure, the concentration of the tracer signal immediately above the dense bed is plotted versus the time of injection of a tracer at various positions within the regenerator air distributors. These curves all tend to fall off exponentially with time and therefore support the contention that the dense phase is a well-mixed stage.

In further support of this model, Handlos reinterpreted the data of Danckwerts using the well-mixed stage model of the dense bed. They assumed that the dilute phase can be represented by a one-dimensional flow with axial dispersion superimposed. If the numerical value of the eddy diffusivity is chosen to have a magnitude intermediate between that found in the dense phase and in an empty tube, i.e., 1 ft²/sec, the result is the solid curve on Fig. 10.2-8. This curve is a reasonable representation of the data of Danckwerts *et al.* shown by the open circles. This interpretation accounts for the peak signal at about 22 seconds better than does the piston-flow model.

From the manner in which the residence-time distribution function is defined, it follows that it is rigorously applicable to systems in which the only dependent variable is time. Although this restriction greatly limits its application in reactor design, there are certain features of reactors which may be analyzed by the use of this function. We have already discussed examples of the utility of the residence-time distribution function in gaining some insight as to how the solid and gas phases pass through a fluidized regenerator.

There are other properties which appear to depend only upon time as a reasonably good approximation—in particular, catalyst deactivation. This topic is developed in the next section.

10.3 Activity distribution

The type of information needed to obtain the activity distribution depends upon the nature of the deactivation process. In a general case the activity may depend upon the catalyst pellet's history; its inlet condition as well as its detailed reaction path since entering the system. Under such conditions the activity equation is coupled with the energy and concentration equations at every point in the system. Data on this kind of system are virtually nonexistent. Another type of deactivation may be postulated in which the extent of deactivation depends upon the time of residence in the reactor and in the regenerator. This postulate, when applicable, leads to a decoupling of the activity equation from the energy and concentration equations and greatly simplifies the analysis. In attempting to describe the properties of deactivating systems quantitatively, in the literature various workers have either explicitly or implicitly made the latter postulate.

A number of systems appear to deactivate approximately as a unique function of time. For example, catalysts often change structurally upon exposure to high temperatures owing to such processes as sintering or migration of active metal films upon the catalyst support. These changes are, by and large, irreversible* and will be referred to as permanent deactivation. Other types of deactivation result from strongly adsorbed impurity or product molecules which react slowly on the catalyst surface. These adsorbed species

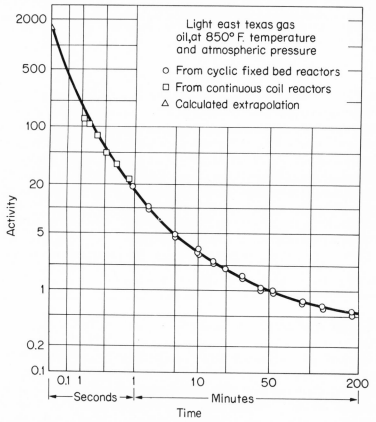

Fig. 10.3-1. Activity as a function of age for fresh natural clay catalyst. [Adapted from F. H. Blanding, *Ind. Eng. Chem.*, **45**, 1186, (1953).]

---

* Metals on surfaces can in many instances be redistributed by reprocessing, but these will still be classified here as permanent.

effectively remove active centers from the system, and the activity declines with the passage of time as fewer active centers remain available to the reactants. This type of deactivation is readily reversed in an impurity-free or different environment and will be referred to as temporary deactivation. Although the discussion that follows is concerned primarily with temporarily deactivated systems wherein the catalyst activity is uniquely determined by the time of residence at specified conditions, the methods apply equally well to permanently deactivated systems.

It is of interest at this point to present an experimental deactivation process. Blanding's* data for natural clay catalyst cracking a light East Texas gas-oil at 850°F at atmospheric pressure are presented on Fig. 10.3-1. Values of the instantaneous activity are shown as a function of catalyst age under the above reactor conditions. Note that the ordinate scale is logarithmic, whereas the abscissa scale is proportional to the fourth root of the age. This choice of scales, although empirical, permits an extrapolation to obtain the activity at zero time.

All catalyst particles which enter a reactor at a given instant do not in general leave at the same time. Various dispersive and mixing processes act on the particles to give rise to a distribution of residence times. Nonuniform velocity profiles, circulation phenomena and diffusion-like processes are examples of the dispersive mechanisms. The extent to which it is necessary to have an intimate familiarity with the detailed mechanisms giving rise to the distribution of residence times depends upon the particular characteristic of the system under examination. This point is illustrated in the following examples.

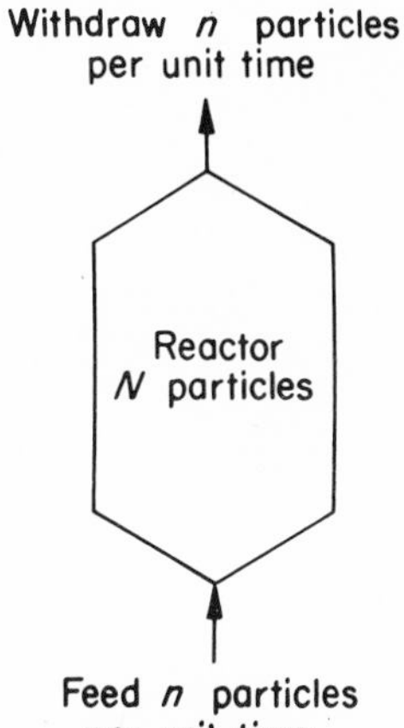

EXAMPLE 10.3-1 AVERAGE ACTIVITY IN A REACTOR BEING FED WITH CATALYST OF UNIT ACTIVITY

Suppose we wish to know the average activity of catalyst in a reactor into which fresh catalyst (unit activity) is continuously fed at a prescribed rate. Spent catalyst is, of course, continuously removed at the same rate, thereby maintaining a constant inventory. Figure 10.3-2 shows the system. If the activity of the catalyst depends only upon its residence time within the reactor, the average activity can be obtained from the residence-time distribution function and the activity decline curve. The analysis is readily carried out as follows.

Fig. 10.3-2. Schematic diagram of a fluidized reactor.

* F. H. Blanding, *Ind. Eng. Chem.* **45**, 1186 (1953).

Let $T'_R(t_R) \, dt_R$ = fraction of the particles fed to the reactor which reside therein for times between t_R and $t_R + dt_R$,

$R(t_R)$ = relative activity of catalyst after residing for a time t_R in the reactor. By definition, then, $R(0) = 1$,

t_R = residence time in the reactor,

n = number of particles fed to and removed from the reactor per unit time,

N = number of particles residing in the reactor at any time.

The continuity equation is satisfied by the statement of the problem.

The fraction of the particles residing in the reactor having ages between t_R and $t_R + dt_R$ is $I(t_R) \, dt_R$, and from Eq. 10.2-2,

$$I(t_R) = \frac{n}{N}\left[1 - \int_0^{t_R} T'(x) \, dx \right]. \tag{10.3-1}$$

The average activity inside the reactor is:

$$\bar{R}_I = \int_0^\infty I(t_R) R(t_R) \, dt_R. \tag{10.3-2}$$

Attention should be called to two points: First, Eq. 10.3-1 can be used because the feed stream has unit activity; and second, $\bar{R}_I$ as given by Eq. 10.3-2 represents an average based upon the entire reactor volume and does not indicate local values of activity at various positions within the reactor. From the latter point it follows that Eq. 10.3-2 is useful in the design of reactors only in cases where local activity can be inferred from over-all average activity. Two cases of this type are: completely mixed catalyst phase, which uniquely determines the form of $T'_R(t_R)$, and completely mixed reactant phase, which places no restriction on the form of $T'_R(t_R)$.

The above example, then, further supports the statement that the residence time distribution alone has only limited utility in reactor design.

EXAMPLE 10.3-2 AVERAGE ACTIVITY OF A REACTOR BEING FED CATALYST HAVING A DISTRIBUTION OF ACTIVITIES

The feed stream to a reactor frequently is not of uniform activity but contains catalyst with a distribution of ages. This more general problem offers only a slight complication in that it makes it necessary to characterize the feed stream. To do this we need an activity distribution function, i.e., the fraction of the particles in the feed stream F having an activity R. However, since R can be related to the catalyst's age, or its residence time in the environment of the reactor, we shall say that F is a function of θ. Thus F is defined as

$F(\theta) \, d\theta$ = fraction of the catalyst particles in the inlet stream to the reactor having ages between θ and $\theta + d\theta$

Furthermore, if we make the reasonable assumption that each of the elements making up the feed stream are, in a statistical sense, subject to the same residence-time distribution in the reactor, the average activity of the reactor effluent stream $\bar{R}_E$ can be calculated by the expression

$$\bar{R}_E = \int_0^\infty \int_0^\infty F(\theta)R(\theta + t_R)T_R'(t_R)\, dt_R\, d\theta. \tag{10.3-3}$$

The meaning of this equation is readily apparent. The fraction of the feed $F(\theta)\, d\theta$ having ages between θ and $\theta + d\theta$ enters the reactor with an activity $R(\theta)$. Since all elements entering the reactor are subject to the age distribution function $T_R'(t_R)$, the quantity $F(\theta)T_R'(t_R)\, dt_R\, d\theta$ is the fraction of the entering feed having ages between θ and $\theta + d\theta$ which leaves at the time t_R. Upon leaving this fraction has an activity $R(\theta + t_R)$, because its age has been increased by t_R. To get the average age of the effluent stream, this function must be integrated over the limits of 0 and ∞ for t_R and θ.*

A similar expression for the average activity of the catalyst in the reactor is

$$\bar{R}_I = \frac{n}{N_R}\int_0^\infty \int_0^\infty F(\theta)R(\theta + t_R)\left[1 - \int_0^{t_R} T_R'(x)\, dx\right] dt_R\, d\theta \tag{10.3-4}$$

which is a more general form of Eq. 10.3-2. The quantity N_R is the number of catalyst particles in the reactor.

The age distribution in the catalyst stream leaving the reactor $P(\xi)$, where $\xi \equiv \theta + t_R$, can be obtained directly. Note that there are many ways, according to this model, for a particle to attain a specified age, ξ. Two limiting cases are: It can come in with an age ξ and reside zero time and leave, or it can come in with zero age and reside for a time ξ. Therefore, to have an age ξ when leaving, a particle must enter the reactor with an age equal to or less than ξ. All of the possibilities for obtaining an age ξ are included in the mathematical expression

$$P(\xi) = \int_0^\xi F(\theta)T_R'(\xi - \theta)\, d\theta. \tag{10.3-5}$$

Accordingly, an alternate representation of the mean activity in the catalyst stream leaving the reactor is

$$\bar{R}_E = \int_0^\infty R(\xi)P(\xi)\, d\xi. \tag{10.3-6}$$

Substituting Eq. 10.3-5 into the above equation yields:

$$\bar{R}_E = \int_0^\infty R(\theta)\int_0^\xi F(\theta)T_R'(\xi - \theta)\, d\theta\, d\xi, \tag{10.3-7}$$

* The functions $T'(t_R:)$ and $F(\theta)$ are normalized; therefore the expression

$$\int_0^\infty \int_0^\infty F(\theta)T'(t_R)\, dt_R\, d\theta = 1.$$

which is equivalent to Eq. 10.3-3. Equation 10.3-5 is a useful representation for the analysis of a more general problem—that of the reactor-regenerator combination.

Such a system is shown in Fig. 10.3-3. Deactivated catalyst is continuously withdrawn from the reactor at a rate of n particles per unit time and fed into the regenerator wherein activation occurs. Reactivated catalyst is withdrawn from the regenerator at an equal rate and fed to the reactor. In such a system, we would like to know the magnitude of the mean activity level in

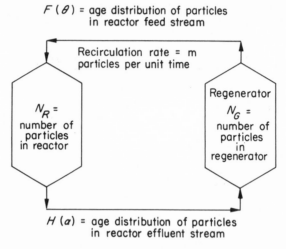

Fig. 10.3-3. Schematic diagram of a fluidized reactor and fluidized regenerator.

the reactor as a function of the operating variables, such as the recirculation rate, the size of the units, and the deactivation and activation functions. Even making the assumption that the activation and deactivation functions are dependent only on the time of residence within the respective units, an analysis of the general problem of this type is complex. As a final example of the utility of the residence-time distribution function, we shall outline the approach to the general problem and solve it for a particularly simple limiting case.

EXAMPLE 10.3-3 THE AVERAGE CATALYST ACTIVITY IN A REACTOR FOR A SYSTEM COMPOSED OF A REACTOR AND A REGENERATOR

The mean activity depends upon the specific nature of the deactivation and activation functions. Such a set of functions is shown on Fig. 10.3-4. The meaning of these hypothetical curves and the assumptions implicit in their formulation are best demonstrated by following a particle through the system. Suppose we place a fresh particle of catalyst in the reactor feed stream and follow its path through the system for a cycle or two. Being fresh, its relative activity is unity and its corresponding age θ is zero as shown by point A. In its first cycle around the system, suppose this particle spends a time t_R' in the reactor. According to Fig. 10.3-4, it will leave the reactor with a relative activity of $R(\theta')$ corresponding to point B, whereupon it will enter the regenerator with the same relative activity $G(\alpha')$ and have an age corresponding to α' in the regenerator (point C). Upon residing for a time t_G' in

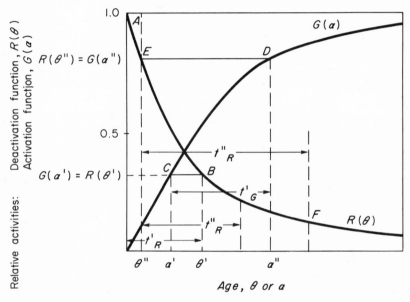

Fig. 10.3-4. Deactivation and activation functions in the reactor and regenerator.

the regenerator, its activity will have been increased to $G(\alpha'')$ corresponding to an age of α'', given by point D. It re-enters the reactor at the same activity, point E. The activity of this particle upon leaving the reactor depends upon the time t_R'' spent therein, and so forth. The problem is mathematically fixed because, after a large number of cycles through the system, the residence times in each of the units must conform to the residence-time distribution function.

Starting the problem in this way, the average activity of the effluent stream from the reactor can be represented by Eq. 10.3-6 or in terms of the age distribution in the reactor effluent $H(\alpha)$ shown on Fig. 10.3-3 and the $G(\alpha)$ function, i.e.,

$$\bar{R}_E = \int_0^\infty H(\alpha)G(\alpha)\, d\alpha. \tag{10.3-8}$$

Moreover, in a similar way the mean activity in the reactor feed stream, $\bar{R}_F$, is given by

$$\bar{R}_F = \int_0^\infty F(\theta)R(\theta)\,d\theta. \tag{10.3-9}$$

Alternatively, $\bar{R}_F$ can be expressed in terms of a function $Q(\eta)$, where $\eta \equiv \alpha + t_G$, and t_G is the residence time within the regenerator. An equation for $Q(\eta)$, analogous to Eq. 10.3-5, is

$$Q(\eta) = \int_0^\eta H(\alpha)T'_G(\eta - \alpha)\,d\alpha, \tag{10.3-10}$$

where $T'_G(t_G) =$ derivative of the residence time distribution function in the regenerator. Thus, an alternate form of the equation for $\bar{R}_F$ is

$$\bar{R}_F = \int_0^\infty Q(\eta)G(\eta)\,d\eta. \tag{10.3-11}$$

From these relationships it is possible to obtain an integral equation in $F(\theta)$ which in general must be solved numerically in terms of the known functions $R(\theta)$, $G(\alpha)$, $T'_R(t_R)$ and $T'_G(t_G)$. As the calculation is available elsewhere* we shall not repeat it here. Let us rather look at a case for which a solution is readily obtained. If the deactivation and activation curves can be represented by exponential functions of the form

$$R(\theta) = e^{-k_R\theta} \tag{10.3-12}$$

and

$$G(\alpha) = 1 - e^{-k_G\alpha}, \tag{10.3-13}$$

the problem is greatly simplified. To show this, substitute Eq. 10.3-12 into Eq. 10.3-3, which gives

$$\bar{R}_E = \int_0^\infty F(\theta)e^{-k_R\theta}\,d\theta \int_0^\infty e^{-k_R t_R}\,T'_R(t_R)\,dt_R. \tag{10.3-14}$$

But from Eq. 10.3-9,

$$\bar{R}_F = \int_0^\infty F(\theta)e^{-k_R\theta}\,d\theta. \tag{10.3-15}$$

Hence Eq. 10.3-14 becomes

$$\bar{R}_E = \bar{R}_F \int_0^\infty e^{-k_R t_R}\,T'_R(t_R)\,dt_R. \tag{10.3-16}$$

By considerations analogous to the development of Eq. 10.3-3, we can start with

$$\bar{R}_F = \int_0^\infty \int_0^\infty H(\alpha)G(\alpha + t_G)T'_G(t_G)\,dt_G\,d\alpha \tag{10.3-17}$$

* E. E. Petersen, *A.I.Ch.E. Journal* **6**, 488 (1960).

and substitute Eq. 10.3-13 for $G(\alpha)$ to get

$$\bar{R}_F = \int_0^\infty H(\alpha)\, d\alpha \int_0^\infty T'_G(t_G)\, dt_G - \int_0^\infty H(\alpha) e^{-k_G \alpha}\, d\alpha \int_0^\infty e^{-k_G t_G}\, T'_G(t_G)\, dt_G,$$

(10.3-18)

which from Eq. 10.3-8 is

$$\bar{R}_F = 1 - (1 - \bar{R}_E) \int_0^\infty e^{-k_G t_G}\, T'_G(t_G)\, dt_G.$$ (10.3-19)

Solving Eq. 10.3-16 and 10.3-19 simultaneously gives

$$\bar{R}_F = \frac{1 - f_G(k_G)}{1 - f_G(k_g) f_R(k_R)},$$ (10.3-20)

where

and

$$\left. \begin{array}{l} f_G(k_G) \equiv \displaystyle\int_0^\infty e^{-k_G t_G}\, T'(t_G)\, dt_G \\[1em] f_R(k_R) \equiv \displaystyle\int_0^\infty e^{-k_R t_R}\, T'(t_R)\, dt_R \end{array} \right\}$$ (10.3-21)

Finally, Eqs. 10.3-4, 10.3-9, and 10.3-12 yield:

$$\bar{R}_I = \frac{n\bar{R}_F}{N_R} \int_0^\infty e^{-k_R t_R} \left[1 - \int_0^{t_R} T'_R(x)\, dx \right] dt_R,$$ (10.3-22)

which is the desired expression for the mean activity in the reactor.

The mean activity $\bar{R}_I$ from Eq. 10.3-22 is plotted on Figs. 10.3-5 and 10.3-6 for $k_G = k_R$ and for $k_G = 5k_R$ as a function of the parameter $k_R N_R/n$. In each case $N_G = N_R$. On the figures two limiting cases are compared: complete mixing and piston flow of solids. As would be expected, a higher mean activity is obtained for piston flow than for complete mixing. Note also that even at infinite circulation rate, the highest mean activity depends upon the ratio k_R/k_G. When $k_R N_R/n$ is zero by letting k_R become identically zero, the mean activity in the reactor is unity.

These examples illustrate the utility of the residence-time distribution function. The mean activity follows directly from the residence-time distribution function. Note that we do not know where the activity is located because the residence-time distribution function does not contain any information about point conditions of age within the reactor. In the particular cases presented on Figs. 10.3-5 and 10.3-6, however, we have specified more than the residence-time distribution function; we have in fact specified how the activity is disturbed by assuming either piston flow or complete mixing leading to point values of the activity.

We shall now extend the methods used to get the residence-time distribution function for the purpose of learning more about the local conditions in a reactor.

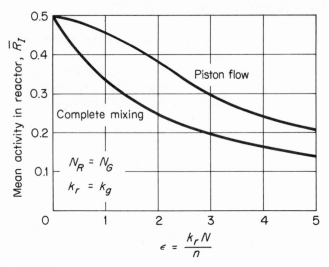

Fig. 10.3-5. Mean activity within reactor for the case of temporary deactivation. (Adapted from E. E. Petersen, *J.A.I.Ch.E.*, **6**, 488, (1960).)

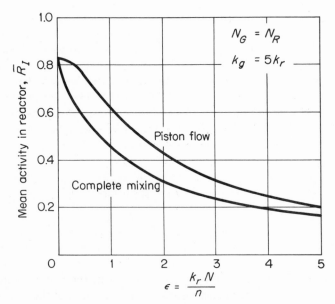

Fig. 10.3-6. Mean activity within reactor for the case of temporary deactivation. (Adapted from E. E. Petersen, *J.A.I.Ch.E.*, **6**, 488, (1960).)

10.4 The spatial-age distribution function

The spatial-age distribution function $\mathscr{S}$ is defined as the fraction of the elements of either the fluid phase or the solid phase at a "point," having resided for times between t and $t + dt$ in the reactor. Thus the fraction $\mathscr{S}'(r, \phi, z, t)\, dt$* depends upon position within the reactor. From their definitions, these functions are normalized, and each has the property that

$$\int_0^\infty \mathscr{S}'(r, \phi, z, t)\, dt = 1. \tag{10.4-1}$$

The $\mathscr{S}'$ function is related to a function $\mathscr{S}$ by

$$\int_0^t \mathscr{S}'(r, \phi, z, t)\, dt = \mathscr{S}(r, \phi, z, t). \tag{10.4-2}$$

The function $\mathscr{S}$ may be measured by an experiment similar to that described in Section 10.2 to measure $T(t)$, with the exception that a probe designed to measure the fraction of red material as a function of time is located within the reactor at some spatial position designated by the cylindrical coordinates r, ϕ, and z. Clearly, to obtain the dependence of the function $\mathscr{S}$ on position the experiment must either be repeated many times or several probes must be used simultaneously.

The following experiment illustrates a possible means of determining the function $\mathscr{S}$ for the solid in a reactor. A reactor is at steady state with an all-white feed as shown in Fig. 10.2-1. At some time designated as zero time, the feed is changed to an all-red feed every property of which is identical with that of the original white feed except that it may be identified as being red. By means of the various probes, samples are taken periodically at the various positions and analyzed for their fraction of red material. These fractions correspond to the values of $\mathscr{S}$ at each of the probe locations. The function $\mathscr{S}'$ could be obtained in a similar way using a delta-function input of red material.

From the way in which the $\mathscr{S}'$ function is defined, it is related to $I(t)$ discussed in Section 10.2. The latter is simply the integral of $\mathscr{S}'(t)$ throughout the reactor space, i.e.:

$$I(t) = \frac{1}{\pi r_0^2 L} \int_0^L \int_0^{2\pi} \int_0^{r_0} \mathscr{S}'(r, \phi, z, t)\, r\, dr\, d\phi\, dz, \tag{10.4-3}$$

where $r_0 =$ radius of the reactor, and $L =$ length of the reactor. Equation 10.4-3 is of little value except as a rather insensitive check of the consistency

---

* Here the prime indicates differentiation of the function $\mathscr{S}(r, \varphi, z, t)$ with respect to t. Note also that cylindrical coordinates are indicated because this is a commonly used geometry. Other geometries could, of course, be used.

of the experimental measurements. The function $\mathscr{S}'$ contains more information than $I(t)$ and cannot be obtained from the latter any more than the age distribution function of a collection of catalyst particles can be obtained from a single determination of their collective average age.

Having some appreciation of the nature of the $\mathscr{S}$ function and its experimental determination, we can now look briefly at a means of analytically describing its variation throughout a reactor. We expect the $\mathscr{S}$ function to obey certain conservation equations because it is determined directly from tracer experiments, and, of course, the tracer material is a conserved quantity in the system. The catalyst particles are distributed by various transport mechanisms which are operative in a particular reactor. Without specifying these in detail, we can write conservation equations in terms of $\rho_B\mathscr{S}$ and ρ_B, where ρ_B is the mass of total particles irrespective of their color per unit volume. Their respective fluxes by the ith mechanism are represented by $[\text{flux}_i(\rho_B\mathscr{S})]$ and $[\text{flux}_i(\rho_B)]$. Conservation equations for ρ_B and $\rho_B\mathscr{S}$ in symbolic form similar to Eqs. 7.2-8 and 7.2-6 are:

$$- \operatorname{div}\left[\sum_{i=1}^{n}\text{flux}_i\,(\rho_B)\right] = 0 \tag{10.4-4}$$

and

$$- \operatorname{div}\left[\sum_{i=1}^{n}\text{flux}_i\,(\rho_B\mathscr{S})\right] = \frac{\partial(\rho_B\mathscr{S})}{\partial t}. \tag{10.4-5}$$

Equations 10.4-4 and 10.4-5 with their appropriate boundary conditions are really not useful because very little is known about the functional forms of the transport mechanisms within moving bed reactors. If the transport mechansims were known, then it would be possible to calculate the function $\mathscr{S}$ without resort to experiments. We thus find ourselves in the unenviable position of having a solution to a differential equation (presuming that it has been measured experimentally) of unknown functional form and the problem is to determine the forms of the flux terms in the equation from the solution. This, of course, is not a uniquely defined problem. We conclude that rigorous methods for the design of moving-bed reactors are not available, and we must await the results of future work to elucidate the mechanisms of transport as the first step in the development of such design methods.

The $\mathscr{S}$ function, however, has some direct utility. If the catalyst deactivates as a unique function of time, then a knowledge of the functions ρ_B and $\mathscr{S}$ is sufficient to account for the role of the catalyst in the system. To show this, we repeat Eq. 4.1-1:

$$\bar{\mathscr{R}}_i = \rho_p S(1 - \epsilon)\mathscr{R}_i(C_{10}, C_{20}, \ldots, C_{n0}, T_0), \tag{10.4-6}$$

where $\bar{\mathscr{R}}_i$ is the rate of reaction of the ith species per unit volume of reactor, $\mathscr{R}_i$ is the rate of reaction of the ith species per unit of surface area of catalyst, and S is the surface area of the catalyst at $\theta = 0$. Recall that we have assumed unity values for the transport and effectiveness factors, $\mathscr{T}$ and $\mathscr{E}$ in this equation. To modify Eq. 10.4-6 to make it useful in the present discussion we replace the quantity $\rho_p S(1 - \epsilon)$ by its equivalent ρ_B and multiply the right-hand side by $R(\theta)$, the relative activity of the catalyst as a function of its age. Equation 10.4-6 therefore becomes:

$$\bar{\mathscr{R}}_i = \rho_B S R(\theta) \mathscr{R}_i (C_{10}, C_{20}, \ldots, C_{n0}, T_0)$$

or simply

$$\bar{\mathscr{R}}_i = \rho_B S R(\theta) \mathscr{R}_i. \tag{10.4-7}$$

Now $\bar{\mathscr{R}}_i$ has the meaning of a rate of reaction of the ith species per unit volume of particles all having an age θ. Since we are considering a case where there is an age distribution, at some point, r, ϕ, z, the average activity

$$\overline{\bar{\mathscr{R}}_i(r, \phi, z)} = \rho_B S \bar{\mathscr{R}}_i \int_0^\infty R(\theta) \mathscr{S}'(r, \phi, z, \theta)\, d\theta. \tag{10.4-8}$$

When $\mathscr{T}$ and $\mathscr{E}$ are not unity, they each depend upon $R(\theta)$; hence analogous to Eq. 10.4-8, Eq. 4.1-2 becomes

$$\overline{\bar{\mathscr{R}}_i(r, \phi, z)} = \rho_B S \bar{\mathscr{R}}_i \int_0^\infty R(\theta) \mathscr{T}[R(\theta)] \mathscr{E}[R(\theta)] \mathscr{S}'(r, \phi, z, \theta)\, d\theta \tag{10.4-9}$$

Another use of the $\mathscr{S}$ function, or more directly of the $\mathscr{S}'$ function, is to give some indication of the flow pattern of each of the phases through the system. For example, if the dependence of $\mathscr{S}$ on time for a phase is the same everywhere in the system, this evidence strongly supports a model of complete mixing of that phase in the system. Similarly, a sharp peak in the $\mathscr{S}'$ function progressing at constant velocity through the system is evidence for piston flow. The suggestion here is to use the $\mathscr{S}$ function data as a guide to a model of the system. On the basis of the model, the functional forms of Eqs. 10.4-4 and 10.4-5 can be established which when integrated, give a calculated $\mathscr{S}$ distribution which matches the measured value. This model may be used as a basis for the design, although again it should be stressed that this procedure will not necessarily be correct. In the next section we shall consider how the phases flow through the system, using cases based upon simple models.

10.5 Idealized cases of moving-bed reactors

Of the many possible configurations for moving-bed reactors, we shall consider four cases in this section: (1) solid and fluid phases both well mixed; (2) solid and fluid phases both in piston flow; (3) solid phase well-mixed fluid phase in piston flow; and (4) solid phase in piston-flow–fluid phase well mixed. A schematic diagram of these systems is shown on Fig. 10.5-1. All of the design equations corresponding to these cases will be based upon three assumptions: the deactivation of catalyst is a function only of time within the reactor environment; the mass of catalyst per unit volume of reactor space is constant; and the contacting of phases locally is complete. Because in selecting the above cases we have assumed the transport mechanisms acting within the reactors, the first of these restrictions can be relaxed provided data on the deactivation mechanism is available in more detail.

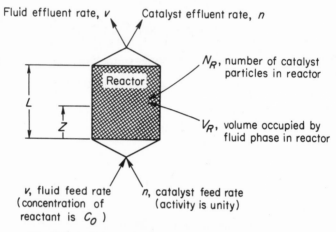

Fig. 10.5-1. Schematic diagram of a fluidized reactor.

The second restriction can be relaxed if data on the solids distribution are available.* Relaxing the third restriction involves a complication which we shall not consider here.

EXAMPLE 10.5-1 SOLID AND FLUID PHASES EACH WELL MIXED IN REACTOR

As shown in Section 10.2, case (1) appears to be a reasonably good approximation for a dense-bed fluidized reactor. In a reactor of this type the conditions everywhere are the same, so that the relative activity from Eq. 10.4-8 is

$$\bar{\bar{\mathscr{R}}}_i = \rho_B S \bar{\mathscr{R}}_i \int_0^\infty R(\theta)\left(\frac{n}{N_R}\right) e^{-n\theta/N_R}\, d\theta, \qquad (10.5\text{-}1)$$

where

$$\mathscr{S}'(\theta) = \frac{n}{N_R} e^{-n/N_R\theta}$$

* See for example F. A. Zenz and D. F. Othmer, *Fluidization and Fluid-Particle Systems*, Reinhold Publishing Corp., New York, 1960.

for a well-mixed vessel* and where we have assumed that $\mathscr{T}$ and $\mathscr{E}$ are unity to avoid distracting mathematical complexities. Thus, $\overline{\overline{\mathscr{R}}}_i$ is the rate of reaction of the ith species per unit volume of reactor space. If for simplicity we consider the case of an isothermal first-order reaction, then

$$\overline{\mathscr{R}}_i = kC_i = kC_0\psi_i, \tag{10.5-2}$$

where $\psi_i = C_i/C_0$ and C_0 is the feed concentration of the ith reactant. When Eq. 10.5-2 is substituted into Eq. 10.5-1, we get:

$$\overline{\overline{\mathscr{R}}}_i = KC_0\psi_i, \tag{10.5-3}$$

where

$$K = \rho_B Sk \int_0^\infty R(\theta)\, \frac{n}{N}\, e^{-n\theta/N} d\theta. \tag{10.5-4}$$

From a material balance of the ith species in the fluid phase of the reactor, we get

$$v(C_0 - C_i) = V_R K C_i = V\overline{\overline{\mathscr{R}}}_i, \tag{10.5-5}$$

where $v =$ volumetric feed rate to the reactor, and
$V_R =$ volume occupied by the fluid phase in the reactor.

Rearranging Eq. 10.5-5 gives

$$\psi_i = \frac{1}{1 + \mathscr{Y}_M}, \tag{10.5-6}$$

where $\mathscr{Y}_M = \dfrac{V_R}{Kv}$.

The form of Eq. 10.5-6 is the same as Eq. 8.6-19 if we identify V/v as $Z/\bar{U}$ and K as k, where V is the volume of the reactor between the entrance and the position Z.

EXAMPLE 10.5-2 SOLID AND FLUID PHASES EACH FLOWING CONCURRENTLY IN PISTON FLOW THROUGH THE REACTOR

We consider case (2) in very much the same way. Again the catalyst phase is analyzed in order to specify the average activity at various positions within the reactor. In a piston-flow reactor, all of the catalyst particles entering at a time zero remain together until they leave; therefore all of the particles in a given location have the same age.

Reference to Fig. 10.5-1 quickly establishes the age, in terms of the coordinate Z, as

$$\theta = \frac{N_R Z}{nL}, \tag{10.5-7}$$

whereupon

$$\overline{\mathscr{R}_i(Z)} = \rho_B S\, \overline{\mathscr{R}}_i\!\left(\frac{N_R Z}{nL}\right). \tag{10.5-8}$$

---

* For a well-mixed vessel $\mathscr{S}'$ is the same function of time everywhere in the system. From Eq. 10.4-3, it is identical with $I(t)$ which has the above form for a well-mixed vessel.

A material balance equation for the ith species in the fluid phase in a piston-flow tubular reactor, for no change in total moles with reaction, is

$$\bar{U}\frac{dC_i}{dZ} = -\overline{\mathscr{R}_i(Z)}, \tag{10.5-9}$$

where Z is the distance coordinate along the axis of the reactor and $\bar{U}$ is the average velocity. Thus, for this example $\bar{U}/Z$ is equal to v/V. Substitution of Eqs. 10.5-2 and 10.5-8 into Eq. 10.5-9 and subsequent integration yields:

$$\ln \psi_i = -\frac{\rho_B S k}{\bar{U}}\int_0^L R\left(\frac{N_R Z}{nL}\right) dZ. \tag{10.5-10}$$

Equation 10.5-10 gives the outlet concentration of the ith reaction for a reactor corresponding to case (2) whereas Eq. 10.5-6 gives the outlet concentration from a reactor corresponding to case (1).

It should be clear from the development above that solutions to cases (3) and (4) can be synthesized from Eqs. 10.5-1 and 10.5-9, and Eqs. 10.5-5 and 10.5-8, respectively. Furthermore, there is nothing in the development above which prevents its application to more complex kinetic cases as well as to nonisothermal conditions. The key assumptions (and limitations) concern the way the phases mix in the reactor. By the initial statements of various cases, we have implicitly assumed the nature of the transport fluxes operating on each of the phases in the reactor. The correctness of the predicted values of the reactant concentration leaving the reactor hinges upon the correctness of these initial assumptions.

We learn from the analysis of the first two cases how the mixing processes influence the conversion in moving-bed reactors.

EXAMPLE 10.5-3 COMPARISON OF THE CONVERSIONS FROM THE REACTORS OF EXAMPLES 10.5-1 AND 10.5-2 UNDER THE SAME OPERATING CONDITIONS

Let us take as an example the effluent reactant concentrations from two reactors of the same size and operating under identical conditions but, as in cases (1) and (2), differ in their mixing properties. In order to make the comparison, the form of $R(\theta)$ must be assumed. As before, let

$$R(\theta) = e^{-k_R \theta}. \tag{10.5-11}$$

Using Eqs. 10.5-4 and 10.5-11, the variable $\mathscr{Y}_M$ of Eq. 10.5-6 becomes

which upon integration is:

$$\left.\begin{array}{l} \mathscr{Y}_M = \dfrac{\rho_B S k V n}{v N_R}\displaystyle\int_0^\infty e^{-k_R \theta} e^{-n\theta/N_R}\, d\theta, \\[16pt] \mathscr{Y}_M = \left(\dfrac{\rho_B S k V}{v}\right)\left(\dfrac{n/k_R N_R}{1 + n/k_R N_R}\right). \end{array}\right\} \tag{10.5-12}$$

The effluent concentration ψ_1 from the reactor having the completely mixed phases of case (1), from Eq. 10.5-6, is:

$$\psi_1 = \frac{1}{1 + \mathscr{Y}_M}, \tag{10.5-13}$$

where $\mathscr{Y}_M$ is given by Eq. 10.5-12. The concentration of reactant at the outlet for case (1) is ψ_1.

Similarly, from Eq. 10.5-10, the effluent concentration ψ_2 from a reactor having the piston-flow characteristics of case (2) is:

$$\psi_2 = \exp\left\{-\frac{\rho_B SkV}{v}\int_0^1 R\left(\frac{NZ_1}{n}\right)dZ_1\right\}, \tag{10.5-14}$$

where $Z_1 \equiv Z/L$ and ψ_2 is the output concentration from the reactor. Substituting the functional form of R from Eq. 10.5-11, we obtain:

$$\psi_2 = \exp\left\{-\left(\frac{\rho_B SkV}{v}\right)\left(\frac{n}{k_R N_R}\right)\left(1 - \exp\left[-\frac{k_R N_R}{n}\right]\right)\right\}. \tag{10.5-15}$$

The solutions for ψ from Eqs. 10.5-13 and 10.5-15 are shown on Fig. 10.5-2 for various values of the parameters $\rho_B Sk/v$ and $n/k_R N_R$. The most

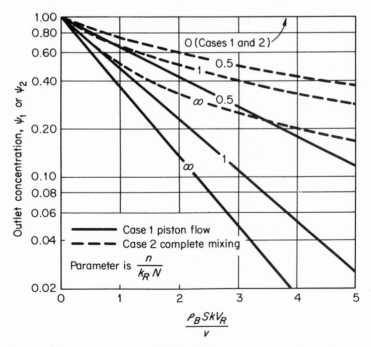

Fig. 10.5-2. Comparison of piston flow and completely mixed reactors for isothermal first-order reaction.

striking result of this figure is that the decided conversion advantage of piston flow over complete mixing in reactive systems wherein no deactivation occurs quickly disappears when the deactivation constant k_R becomes large with respect to n/N_R. Physically this results because the catalyst is deactivating so rapidly that the reactant does not have time to react appreciably before it is out of the zone of high activity. This greatly reduces the advantage of the piston-flow reactor.

This particular comparison, although a greatly simplified kinetic situation, has some application in the understanding of the differences between riser and dense-phase fluidized catalytic cracking units used in the petroleum industry, these units corresponding approximately to cases (2) and (1), respectively. While much more complex to analyze, it is interesting to speculate that in order to take advantage of the piston-flow characteristic of the riser, the catalyst circulation rate must be maintained at a high level.

10.6 Summary

In this chapter we have discussed an area of reaction analysis and design which is not completely understood from a fundamental viewpoint. We were unable to develop methods for analyzing and designing moving-bed reactors of rigor corresponding to those for fixed-bed reactors. Nevertheless, moving-bed reactors are important industrially and cannot be completely ignored simply because the transport properties are poorly understood. We have therefore discussed tracer methods whereby information about these systems can, with difficulty and expense, be obtained on the prototype units. This information, while incomplete, offers a means of gaining considerable insight into the transport mechanisms of the fluid and catalyst phases in moving-bed reactors.

Finally, the prognostication as to how the tracer information might be utilized as an interim "solution" to the design problem is perhaps worthy of remention here, viz., construct a model which will give the same distribution of tracer material as that given by the $\mathscr{S}$ function, and use this model to design the reactor in conjunction with the known kinetic behavior. This result should always be compared with those of limiting behavior such as described in Section 10.5. These latter calculations may show that the design is not sensitive to the mixing properties in the range of interest. May you have the good fortune to find this the case.

NOTATION FOR CHAPTER 10

C_i	concentration of ith species
C_0	initial concentration

$C(t)$	concentration of tracer leaving in the stream of the system
$f_G(k_G), f_R(k_R)$	defined by Eq. 10.3-21
f	fraction of converted molecules leaving in the effluent stream
$F(\theta)\,d\theta$	fraction of catalyst particles in the inlet stream to the reactor having ages between θ and $\theta + d\theta$
$G(\alpha)$	relative activity of catalyst having an age α. See Fig. 10.3-3
$H(\alpha)\,d\alpha$	fraction of catalyst particles in the inlet stream to the regenerator having ages between α and $\alpha + d\alpha$
$I(t)\,dt$	fraction of the elements within a system having resided for the interval between time t and $t + dt$
k	first-order rate constant
k_G	regenerator activation constant. See Eq. 10.3-13
k_R	reactor deactivation constant. See Eq. 10.3-12
n	number of catalyst particles fed to system per unit time
N	number of catalyst particles in the system
N_R, N_G	number of catalyst particles in the reactor and regenerator, respectively
$P(\xi)$	fraction of catalyst particles in effluent stream from reactor having age equal to or less than ξ
Q	quantity of trace material introduced at $t = 0$
$Q(\eta)$	fraction of catalyst particles in effluent stream from regenerator having age equal to or less than η
$R(t_R)$	relative activity of catalyst after residing for a time t_R in the reactor. $R(0)$, therefore, is unity
$\bar{R}_I$	average activity of catalyst particles in the reactor
$\bar{R}_E$	average activity of catalyst particles in effluent stream from a reactor
$\bar{R}_F$	average activity of catalyst particles in feed to reactor
S	surface area per unit mass of catalyst
t_G	residence time in regenerator
t_R	residence time in reactor
t	time
$\bar{t}_E$	average residence time of elements leaving in effluent stream
$\bar{t}_I$	average residence time of elements in the system

$T(t)$	residence-time distribution function. The fraction of elements entering a system at $t = 0$ which leave during the time interval 0 to t
$T'(t)$	derivative of $T(t)$ with respect to t
$T_R(t_R)$	residence-time distribution function in reactor
$T_G(t_G)$	residence-time distribution function in regenerator
$\bar{U}$	average fluid velocity within reactor
v	volumetric feed rate of fluid phase
V_R	volume occupied by fluid phase in a reactor
Z	length of cylindrical reactor

GREEK LETTERS

α	age of particles in regenerator. See Fig. 10.3-3
ξ	age of catalyst particles leaving in effluent stream of a reactor
K	defined by Eq. 10.5-4
η	age of catalyst particles leaving in effluent stream of a regenerator
θ	age of catalyst particle as determined by its activity
ρ_B	mass of catalyst per unit volume of reactor space
ϕ	cylindrical coordinate
ψ	dimensionless concentration

SCRIPT LETTERS

$\mathscr{E}$	effectiveness factor
$\bar{\bar{\mathscr{R}}}_i$	defined by Eq. 10.4-8
$\bar{\mathscr{R}}_i$	pseudo-homogeneous rate expression defined by Eq. 10.4-6
$\mathscr{R}_i$	heterogeneous rate of reaction
$\mathscr{S}(r, \phi, z, t)$	spatial age distribution function. Fraction of elements at the point r, ϕ, z having ages equal to or less than t
$\mathscr{S}'$	derivative of $\mathscr{S}$ with respect to t
$\mathscr{T}$	transport factor
$\mathscr{Y}_M$	$V_R K / v$

Appendix I

General Coordinate Systems

and Vector Operators

The divergence operator appears repeatedly in the conservation equations used to analyze reactions and design reactors. The choice of the coordinate system in which the conservation equations are set up is strongly influenced by the boundary conditions and as a result several coordinate systems are commonly encountered. Since the form of the divergence operator varies with the coordinate system used, a brief discussion of the generalized coordinate systems and the form of the divergence operator might prove to be a convenience for some readers. It may also serve as a ready source of the forms of the divergence operator for the common coordinate systems. The discussion is rather brief, and those desiring a more advanced treatment of this topic should consult the references given below.[*]

We shall first look at some of the properties of coordinate systems. Let us represent three coordinates by ξ_1, ξ_2, and ξ_3. These coordinates are needed in physical problems to locate positions at points in a three-dimensional space relative to some fixed position called the origin. In addition to knowing position, it is frequently necessary to know distances between various points in space in terms of these coordinates. Although in some cases distances in space correspond to differences in the coordinates, in general this is not true. We find it convenient therefore to refer to the distances in the direction of each of the coordinates as s_1, s_2, and s_3. The distance coordinate in differential form ds_i may be thought of as the distance in space represented by allowing the coordinate ξ_i to increase infinitesimally while holding the remaining two coordinates constant, i.e.,

$$ds_i = h_i \, d\xi_i, \tag{I-1}$$

where h_i is a proportionality factor and is, in general, a function of ξ_1, ξ_2, and ξ_3.

[*] A. Aris, *Vectors, Tensors, and the Basic Equations of Fluid Mechanics*, Prentice-Hall Inc., Englewood Cliffs, N.J., 1962; P. M. Morse and H. Feshbach, *Methods of Theoretical Physics*, Vols. I and II, McGraw-Hill Book Company, New York, 1953.

To illustrate the meaning of Eq. I-1 and the nature of the factor h_i, we look at Fig. I-1. On this figure, the position of a point P is located with respect to the origin in terms of the Cartesian coordinates x, y, z. If the coordinate y is increased differentially from y to $y + dy$, while holding x and z constant, we move to a position P'. The distance between P and P', as we all know, is dy; therefore $ds_2 = dy$, and in this case $h_2 = 1$. But the relationship between the distance and position coordinates is not always so simple. To show this, we look at Fig. I-2. Here we have shown the point P located by the cylindrical coordinates r, θ, and z. If we move to a new position P' by increasing from θ to $\theta + d\theta$ while holding r and z constant, the distance between P and P' is

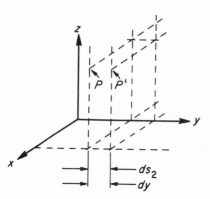

Fig. I-1. Relationship between distance and position coordinates in the Cartesian coordinate system.

$$\left.\begin{aligned} ds_2 &= h_2\, d\xi_2 \\ &= r\, d\theta \end{aligned}\right\} \quad \text{(I-2)}$$

Thus, $h_2 = r$. It is clear from Fig. I-2 that the distance between Q and Q' is different from P and P' even though the change in θ is identical in each case.

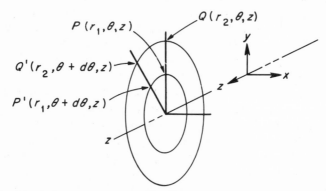

Fig. I-2. Relationship between distance and position coordinates in the cylindrical coordinate system.

The relationship between distance and position coordinates are shown in Table I-1 for the common Cartesian, cylindrical and spherical coordinate systems. Note that the same arguments hold for any orthogonal coordinates, namely those which may be varied independently.

TABLE I-1

RELATIONSHIP BETWEEN DISTANCE AND POSITION COORDINATES
FOR THREE COMMON COORDINATE SYSTEMS

System	ξ_1	ξ_2	ξ_3	ds_1	ds_2	ds_3	h_1	h_2	h_3
Cartesian	x	y	z	dx	dy	dz	1	1	1
Cylindrical	r	θ	z	dr	$r\,d\theta$	dz	1	r	1
Spherical	r	θ	φ	dr	$r\,d\theta$	$r\sin\theta\,d\varphi$	1	r	$r\sin\theta$

More complete tables of coordinate systems are given by Morse and Feshbach.*

With this brief introduction to coordinate systems, we can evaluate the net *influx* of a vector quantity into a differential element expressed in generalized coordinates. For example, in deriving an equation to find temperature profiles within a homogeneous isotropic medium, we must express the flow of energy over the surface enclosing a differential element of the medium. The vector quantity in this case is the product of the Fourier equation and an area

$$\lambda\left(\frac{dT}{d\xi}\right) dA. \tag{I-3}$$

Classically these problems are set up using the divergence theorem.

For our purposes, rather than present a formal proof of the divergence theorem we shall instead derive an expression for the net *influx* of a quantity in generalized coordinates. Consider the flux of some quantity, say B, through the differential volume shown in Fig. I-3. We first evaluate the net rate of flow of B through the areas normal to ξ_1 at the points O and Q, Area O and Area Q, respectively. At the point O, the inward flow is given by the scalar product† of the vector **B** and the unit vector **n** which is normal to Area O and pointing toward the volume. Thus **n** is in the direction ξ_1 at the point O. This product is a contribution to the net inward flux of B into the reference volume. Similar contributions can be shown for the flow through Area Q and the remaining four surfaces enclosing the differential volume. The algebraic sum of all these terms would be equal to the net influx of the quantity into the differential volume and could be represented as:

$$\iint_A \mathbf{B} \cdot \mathbf{n}\, dA. \tag{I-4}$$

An equivalent expression can be written in terms of the three components

* *Op. cit.*

† The scalar or dot product is given by the product of numerical magnitudes of vectors and the cosine of the angle between the vectors, i.e.,

$$\mathbf{B} \cdot \mathbf{n} = B \cos (\mathbf{B}, \mathbf{n}).$$

of the vector, B_{ξ_1}, and the areas. For example, the flow through Area O is

$$B_{\xi_1}\left(\xi_1 - \frac{\Delta\xi_1}{2}, \xi_2, \xi_3\right) ds_2\, ds_3.$$

where B_{ξ_1} is the component of B in the $+\xi_1$ direction. Similarly, the flow through the Area Q is

$$B_{\xi_1}\left(\xi_1 + \frac{\Delta\xi_1}{2}, \xi_2, \xi_3\right) ds_2\, ds_3,$$

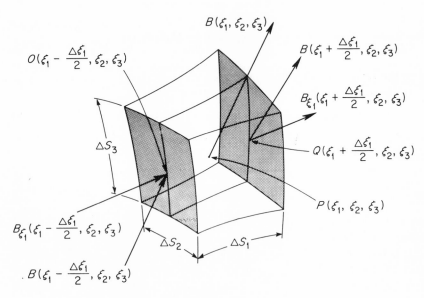

Fig. I-3. A Flux, B, flowing through the surface enclosing a volume element in generalized coordinates.

If each of these functions is expanded in a Taylor series about ξ_1, ξ_2, and ξ_3, and the former subtracted from the latter, the result is the net *inward* flow through the Areas O and Q. This is shown below.

$$+\left\{\beta_{\xi_1}(\xi_1, \xi_2, \xi_3)\, ds_2\, ds_3 - \frac{1}{2}\frac{\partial}{\partial\xi_1}\, [B_{\xi_1}(\xi_1, \xi_2, \xi_3)]\, ds_2\, ds_3\, d\xi_1\right\}$$

influx at Area O

$$-\left\{B_{\xi_1}(\xi_1, \xi_2, \xi_3)\, ds_2\, ds_3 + \frac{1}{2}\frac{\partial}{\partial\xi_1}\, [B_{\xi_1}(\xi_1, \xi_2, \xi_3)]\, ds_2\, ds_3\, d\xi_1\right\}$$

influx at Area Q

$$= -\frac{\partial}{\partial\xi_1}\, [B_{\xi_1}(\xi_1, \xi_2, \xi_3)\, ds_2\, ds_3\, d\xi_1] \quad (\text{I-5})$$

net influx in the ξ_1 direction

In a similar way, account can be taken of the contributions to the net inward flux through the areas normal to the coordinates ξ_2 and ξ_3.

The sum of the terms of the form of Eq. I-5 is the net influx of the quantity.

$$-\frac{\partial}{\partial \xi_1} [B_{\xi_1}(\xi_1, \xi_2, \xi_3) \, ds_2 \, ds_3] \, d\xi_1 - \frac{\partial}{\partial \xi_2} [B_{\xi_2}(\xi_1, \xi_2, \xi_3) \, ds_1, \, ds_3] \, d\xi_2$$

$$-\frac{\partial}{\partial \xi_3} [B_{\xi_3}(\xi_1, \xi_2, \xi_3) \, ds_1 \, ds_2] \, d\xi_3 = \frac{\text{net inward flux into the}}{\text{differential volume}} . \quad \text{(I-6)}$$

Substituting Eq. I-1 into Eq. I-6 and simplifying the result, we get:

$$-\frac{1}{h_1 h_2 h_3} \left\{ \frac{\partial}{\partial \xi_1} [h_2 h_3 B_{\xi_1}] + \frac{\partial}{\partial \xi_2} [h_1 h_3 B_{\xi_2}] + \frac{\partial}{\partial \xi_3} [h_1 h_2 B_{\xi_3}] \right\} = \frac{\text{net inward flux}}{\text{per unit volume}} ,$$

$$\text{(I-7)}$$

using the known relationship that $ds_1 \, ds_2 \, ds_3 = dV$.

In the literature the alternate representations

$$\text{net inward flux per unit volume} = -\text{div } \mathbf{B} = -\nabla \cdot \mathbf{B} \qquad \text{(I-8)}$$

are often used. The *del* operator ∇ is a vector operating on the vector $\mathbf{B}$. It follows from Eqs. I-7 and I-8 that

$$\nabla = \frac{1}{h_1 h_2 h_3} \sum_{i=1}^{3} \frac{\partial}{\partial \xi_i} \left(\frac{h_1 h_2 h_3}{h_i} \right). \qquad \text{(I-9)}$$

Physically the div $\mathbf{B}$ is the net *outward* rate of flow of a quantity per unit volume. Normally, conservation equations are set up on an inward rate of flow, hence $-\text{div}$ is used. If we know the functional form for the flux of a quantity, the negative scalar product of this vector with the del operator gives the net *inward* flow of the quantity into the volume element per unit volume.

In many physical problems, the vector $\mathbf{B}$ is the gradient of some scalar potential. For example, Fourier's law for the flux of heat in the ξ_1 direction is

$$\left. \begin{array}{l} [\text{flux of heat}]_{\xi_i} = -\lambda \dfrac{\partial T}{\partial s_i} \\[2mm] \qquad\qquad = -\dfrac{\lambda}{h_i} \dfrac{\partial T}{\partial \xi_i} \end{array} \right\} \quad \text{(I-10)}$$

where $\lambda =$ thermal conductivity and $T =$ temperature.

If Eq. I-10 is substituted in Eq. I-7 for $\mathbf{B}$, and using Eq. I-8, we obtain:

$$-\text{div} \, (-\lambda \, \text{grad } T) = \frac{1}{h_1 h_2 h_3} \sum_{i=1}^{3} \frac{\partial}{\partial \xi_i} \left(\frac{h_1 h_2 h_3}{h_i^2} \lambda \frac{\partial T}{\partial \xi_i} \right), \qquad \text{(I-11)}$$

where

$$-\lambda \, \text{grad } T = -\lambda \left[\frac{1}{h_1} \frac{\partial T}{\partial \xi_1} + \frac{1}{h_2} \frac{\partial T}{\partial \xi_2} + \frac{1}{h_3} \frac{\partial T}{\partial \xi_3} \right].$$

If λ is constant, an operator is obtained from Eq. I-11 of the form

$$\nabla^2 = \frac{1}{h_1 h_2 h_3} \sum_{i=1}^{3} \frac{\partial}{\partial \xi_i} \left(\frac{h_1 h_2 h_3}{h_i^2} \frac{\partial}{\partial \xi_i} \right) \qquad \text{(I-12)}$$

known as the Laplacean operator, which is useful in describing systems in which the flux vector is the gradient of some scalar potential such as in the transfer of heat and mass by diffusion.

This brief formal discussion of generalized coordinates and the physical meaning of certain vector operators shows that the conservation equations may be set up in general form and subsequently reduced to any coordinate system which most suitably adapts to the boundary conditions of a particular problem. Systematic methods greatly reduce the opportunity for errors in mathematical manipulation. The forms of the divergence, the gradient, and the Laplacean operator for many orthogonal coordinate systems are tabulated in Morse and Feshbach.*

* *Op. cit.*, Vol. I, p. 656.

Appendix II
Matrices and Matrix Operations

Matrix notation as used in this book serves three purposes: to provide a compact, shorthand notation for representing complex systems of equations which is easily generalized; to facilitate manipulation of a system of equations; and sometimes to lead to a formal solution of such a system. The discussion here is only an outline of certain basic operations needed to understand the meaning of the matrix equations appearing in various parts of the book. It is not intended to provide the reader with a complete working knowledge of matrix algebra. For the latter purpose the references listed below should be consulted.*

A matrix is an array of numbers or elements, just as a determinant is an array of numbers or elements. Thus a general n by s matrix is represented by

$$[A_{ns}] = \begin{bmatrix} a_{11} & a_{12} & \cdots & a_{1s} \\ a_{21} & a_{22} & \cdots & a_{2s} \\ \cdot & & & \\ \cdot & & & \\ \cdot & & & \\ a_{n1} & a_{n2} & \cdots & a_{ns} \end{bmatrix}. \tag{II-1}$$

An element of the matrix a_{ij} refers to that member of the array found in the ith row and the jth column.

Given another n by s matrix, $[B_{ns}]$, the meaning of addition and subtraction is defined to give a third n by s matrix, $[C_{ns}]$, whose elements are respectively

$$c_{ij} = a_{ij} \pm b_{ij}. \tag{II-2}$$

That is,

$$[A_{ns}] \pm [B_{ns}] = [C_{ns}], \tag{II-3}$$

where

$$[C_{ns}] = \begin{bmatrix} a_{11} \pm b_{11} & a_{12} \pm b_{12} & & & \\ a_{21} \pm b_{21} & \cdot & & \cdot & \cdot \\ \cdot & & & & \\ \cdot & & & & \\ a_{n1} \pm b_{n1} & & \cdot & & \cdot \end{bmatrix}. \tag{II-4}$$

* For supplementary reading on this topic see for example: A. D. Michal, *Matrix and Tensor Calculus*, John Wiley, New York, 1947; S. Perlis, *Theory of Matrices*, Addison-Wesley, Reading, Mass., 1952; A. Aris, *Vectors, Tensors and the Basic Equations of Fluid Mechanics*, Prentice-Hall, Inc., Englewood Cliffs, N.J., 1962.

The process of addition and subtraction is only defined for matrices each having the same number of rows and the same number of columns.

Multiplication of matrices is illustrated by the product of $[A_{ns}]$ and $[B_{sm}]$ to obtain a product matrix $[C_{nm}]$ which we shall correctly anticipate as an n by m matrix. That is,

$$[A_{ns}][B_{sm}] = [C_{nm}],$$

which when written out completely is

$$
\begin{bmatrix} a_{11} & a_{12} & \cdots & a_{1s} \\ a_{21} & & & \\ \cdot & & & \\ \cdot & & & \\ \cdot & & & \\ a_{n1} & & & a_{ns} \end{bmatrix}
\begin{bmatrix} b_{11} & b_{12} & \cdots & b_{1m} \\ b_{21} & & & \\ \cdot & & & \\ \cdot & & & \\ \cdot & & & \\ b_{s1} & & & b_{sm} \end{bmatrix}
=
\begin{bmatrix} c_{11} & c_{12} & \cdots & c_{1m} \\ c_{21} & & & \\ c_{31} & c_{ij} & & \\ \cdot & & & \\ \cdot & & & \\ c_{n1} & & & c_{nm} \end{bmatrix}
$$

(II-6)

The element c_{ij} is obtained from the elements of the matrices $[A_{ns}]$ and $[B_{sm}]$ by the formula

$$c_{ij} = \sum_{k=1}^{s} a_{ik} b_{kj}, \tag{II-7}$$

which is shorthand notation for

$$c_{11} = a_{11}b_{11} + a_{12}b_{21} + a_{13}b_{31} + \ldots + a_{1s}b_{s1} \qquad (i = j = 1). \tag{II-8}$$

From this definition, we see that the operation of multiplication is defined only when the first matrix, $[A_{ns}]$, has the same number of columns as the second matrix, $[B_{sm}]$, has rows. Also from this definition, it is apparent that the commutative law of multiplication is invalid.

The inverse of a matrix is defined only for a square matrix, i.e., a matrix with an equal number of rows and columns. Consider the square matrix $[M]$. Its inverse will be denoted by $[M]^{-1}$ such that

$$[M][M]^{-1} = [I], \tag{II-9}$$

where

$$
[I] =
\begin{bmatrix} 1 & 0 & 0 & 0 & 0 \\ 0 & 1 & 0 & 0 & 0 \\ 0 & 0 & 1 & 0 & 0 \\ 0 & 0 & 0 & 1 & 0 \\ 0 & 0 & 0 & 0 & 1 \end{bmatrix}. \tag{II-10}
$$

The only non-zero elements in the matrix I are along the diagonal and each has a magnitude of unity. The matrix I is known as the *identity matrix* because when any square matrix of the same size is multiplied by I that matrix is regenerated. Since the inverse matrix is used frequently, one method for finding this matrix is outlined below. This is often referred to as the *method of cofactors.**

Given the square matrix $[A]$ where

$$[A] = \begin{bmatrix} a_{11} & a_{12} & \cdots & a_{1n} \\ a_{21} & a_{22} & & \\ \cdot & & & \\ \cdot & & & \\ \cdot & & & \\ a_{n1} & \cdot & \cdots & a_{nn} \end{bmatrix}. \tag{II-12}$$

To find $[A]^{-1}$ from $[A]$, we first define another matrix, $[A]^{\mathrm{T}}$, *the transpose of* $[A]$, obtained by interchanging the rows and columns of $[A]$. Thus,

$$[A]^{\mathrm{T}} = \begin{bmatrix} a_{11} & a_{21} & \cdots & a_{n1} \\ a_{12} & & & \\ \cdot & & & \\ \cdot & & & \\ \cdot & & & \\ a_{1n} & \cdot & \cdots & a_{nn} \end{bmatrix}. \tag{II-13}$$

We next define the determinant of the matrix $[A]$ as the determinant having elements corresponding to those of the matrix $[A]$, i.e.,

$$\det[A] = (A) = \begin{pmatrix} a_{11} & a_{12} & \cdots & a_{1n} \\ a_{21} & & & \\ \cdot & & & \\ \cdot & & & \\ \cdot & & & \\ a_{n1} & \cdot & \cdots & a_{nn} \end{pmatrix}. \tag{II-14}$$

From these definitions, we can now state the method of cofactors for obtaining the inverse of the matrix $[A]$. The element a'_{ij} of the inverse matrix is computed by the formula

$$a'_{ij} = \frac{(-1)^{i+j} \det[a_{ij}]^{\mathrm{T}}}{\det[A]}, \tag{II-15}$$

where the $\det[a_{ij}]^{\mathrm{T}}$ is the determinant of the matrix obtained by striking out the row i and column j of the matrix $[A]^{\mathrm{T}}$ which contains the element a_{ij}^{T}. Thus $[a_{ij}]^{\mathrm{T}}$ is an $n-1$ by $n-1$ matrix. For the element a_{ij} to exist, $\det[A] \neq 0$. A square matrix $[A]$ having the property that the $\det[A]$ is non-zero is called a *non-singular matrix*. As a corollary, any square matrix which has an inverse is non-singular. In Section 2.8 of the text we make use of these properties to find the largest non-singular matrix of the stoichiometric

---

* For greater detail, see A. D. Michal, *op. cit.*

coefficients of a set of complex reactions. It is necessary to do this because some of the reactions may be linearly dependent upon the others.

Although this nonmathematical discussion of matrix algebra is very brief, hopefully it will serve to acquaint the reader with certain basic manipulations. An example is perhaps appropriate at this point to illustrate most of these operations.

Consider the following set of complex reactions:

$$\left.\begin{array}{ll}
\text{Reaction 1:} & 2A_1 + A_2 + 3A_3 + A_4 + 2A_5 = 0 \\
\text{Reaction 2:} & 3A_1 - A_2 - 2A_3 + 4A_4 = 0 \\
\text{Reaction 3:} & -A_1 + 2A_2 + A_3 - 3A_4 - A_5 = 0 \\
\text{Reaction 4:} & -5A_1 + A_2 - 6A_4 - 2A_5 = 0
\end{array}\right\} \quad \text{(II-16)}$$

If the extent of conversion of these reactions is represented by X_1, X_2, X_3, and X_4, respectively, and if the difference between the initial and final values of the moles of each species present have been measured and found to be 2, 3, 1, and 1, then

$$\left.\begin{array}{l}
2x_1 + 3x_2 - x_3 - 5x_4 = 2 \\
x_1 - x_2 + 2x_3 + x_4 = 3 \\
3x_1 - 2x_2 + x_3 = 1 \\
x_1 + 4x_2 - 3x_3 - 6x_4 = 1
\end{array}\right\} \quad \text{(II-17)}$$

Assuming initially that each of the Eqs. II-17 is linearly independent, the matrix of the coefficients of the first four species should be related to the matrices of the x's and Z's by:

$$[x_1 \ x_2 \ x_3 \ x_4]\begin{bmatrix} 2 & 1 & 3 & 1 \\ 3 & -1 & -2 & 4 \\ -1 & 2 & 1 & -3 \\ -5 & 1 & 0 & -6 \end{bmatrix} = [2 \ 3 \ 1 \ 1], \quad \text{(II-18)}$$

which we shall write more compactly as:

$$[x_4][a_{44}] = [Z_4], \quad \text{(II-19)}$$

where, by comparing Eqs. II-17, II-18, and II-19, $[x_4]$ is the matrix of the unknowns; $[a_{44}]$ is the matrix of the coefficients of the unknowns; and $[Z_4]$ is the matrix of the extent of reaction. Note that by using the rules of multiplication of matrices, we can generate the original equations of Eq. II-17 from Eqs. II-18 and II-16. Multiplying each side of Eq. II-19 times $|a_{44}|$, we obtain upon simplification:

$$[x_4] = [Z_4][a_{44}]^{-1}. \quad \text{(II-20)}$$

But in attempting to obtain $[a_{44}]^{-1}$ from $[a_{44}]$ using Eq. II-15, we find that the $\det[a_{44}] = 0$ and that $[a_{44}]^{-1}$ does not exist. Therefore $[a_{44}]$ is singular, meaning that one or more of Eqs. II-17 are linearly dependent upon the others.

If, now, we choose the matrix of the coefficients of the first three species, then in a similar way we obtain:

$$[x_1 \ x_2 \ x_3]\begin{bmatrix} 2 & 1 & 3 \\ 3 & -1 & -2 \\ -1 & 2 & 1 \end{bmatrix} = [2 \ 3 \ 1], \tag{II-21}$$

whereupon

$$[x_3][a_{33}] = [Z_3]. \tag{II-22}$$

Multiplying each side of Eq. II-22 times $[a_{33}]^{-1}$ and simplifying yields

$$[x_3] = [Z_3][a_{33}]^{-1}. \tag{II-23}$$

This time when we attempt to invert $[a_{33}]$, the $\det[a_{33}] \neq 0$ and $[a_{33}]^{-1}$ exists. The matrix $[a_{33}]$ is therefore the largest nonsingular matrix of the set of Eqs. II-17. Eq. II-22 corresponds to the set

$$\left.\begin{aligned} 2x_1 + 3x_2 - x_3 &= 2 \\ x_1 - x_2 + 2x_3 &= 3 \\ 3x_1 - 2x_2 + x_3 &= 1 \end{aligned}\right\} \tag{II-24}$$

The matrix $[x_3]$ of the unknowns follows directly if $[a_{33}]^{-1}$ is known. Using the method of cofactors for finding inverses, $[a_{33}]^{-1}$ will be found numerically. The transpose of $[a_{33}]$, $[a_{33}]^T$, is

$$[a_{33}]^T = \begin{bmatrix} 2 & 3 & -1 \\ 1 & -1 & 2 \\ 3 & -2 & 1 \end{bmatrix}, \tag{II-25}$$

and the determinant of $[a_{33}]$ is from an expansion:

$$\det[a_{33}] = 6 + 15 - 1 = 20. \tag{II-26}$$

To get a'_{11}, we strike out the first column and row of $[a_{33}]^T$ to obtain $[a_{11}]^T$:

$$[a_{11}]^T = \begin{bmatrix} -1 & 2 \\ -2 & 1 \end{bmatrix}. \tag{II-27}$$

Therefore:

$$\det[a_{11}]^T = 3. \tag{II-28}$$

It follows from Eq. II-15 that

$$a'_{11} = \frac{(-1)^2(3)}{20} = \frac{3}{20}.$$

Similarly,

$$a'_{21} = \frac{(-1)^3(+1)}{20} = -\frac{1}{20},$$

and so forth. The matrix $[a_{33}]^{-1}$ generated by this process is:

$$[a_{33}]^{-1} = \begin{bmatrix} \dfrac{3}{20} & \dfrac{5}{20} & \dfrac{1}{20} \\[2mm] \dfrac{-1}{20} & \dfrac{5}{20} & \dfrac{13}{20} \\[2mm] \dfrac{5}{20} & \dfrac{-5}{20} & \dfrac{-5}{20} \end{bmatrix} \qquad \text{(II-29)}$$

To verify that this is the inverse of $[a_{33}]$, we multiply $[a_{33}]$ times $[a_{33}]^{-1}$ to get the identity matrix I, i.e.,

$$[a_{33}][a_{33}]^{-1} = [I]:$$

$$\begin{bmatrix} 2 & 1 & 3 \\ 3 & -1 & -2 \\ -1 & 2 & 1 \end{bmatrix} \begin{bmatrix} \dfrac{3}{20} & \dfrac{5}{20} & \dfrac{1}{20} \\[2mm] \dfrac{-1}{20} & \dfrac{5}{20} & \dfrac{13}{20} \\[2mm] \dfrac{5}{20} & \dfrac{-5}{20} & \dfrac{-5}{20} \end{bmatrix} = \begin{bmatrix} 1 & 0 & 0 \\ 0 & 1 & 0 \\ 0 & 0 & 1 \end{bmatrix}. \qquad \text{(II-30)}$$

Therefore, from Eq. II-23:

$$[x_1 \ x_2 \ x_3] = [2 \ 3 \ 1] \begin{bmatrix} \dfrac{3}{20} & \dfrac{5}{20} & \dfrac{1}{20} \\[2mm] \dfrac{-1}{20} & \dfrac{5}{20} & \dfrac{13}{20} \\[2mm] \dfrac{5}{20} & \dfrac{-5}{20} & \dfrac{-5}{20} \end{bmatrix}, \qquad \text{(II-31)}$$

whereby

$$\left. \begin{aligned} x_1 &= \tfrac{8}{20} \\ x_2 &= 1 \\ x_3 &= \tfrac{36}{20} \end{aligned} \right\} \qquad \text{(II-32)}$$

These values of x_1, x_2, and x_3 satisfy Eq. II-24.

Index